D1365232

ADVANCES IN GENETICS

VOLUME VII

ADVANCES IN GENETICS

VOLUME VII

Edited by

M. DEMEREC

Carnegie Institution, Cold Spring Harbor, N. Y.

Editorial Board

G. W. BEADLE
WILLIAM C. BOYD
TH. DOBZHANSKY
L. C. DUNN
MERLE T. JENKINS

JAY L. LUSH
ALFRED MIRSKY
J. T. PATTERSON
M. M. RHOADES
CURT STERN

1955

ACADEMIC PRESS INC., PUBLISHERS
NEW YORK, N. Y.
A Subsidiary of Harcourt Brace Jovanovich, Publishers

QH
431
A1
A3
v. 7

COPYRIGHT © 1955, BY ACADEMIC PRESS, INC.
ALL RIGHTS RESERVED.
NO PART OF THIS PUBLICATION MAY BE REPRODUCED OR
TRANSMITTED IN ANY FORM OR BY ANY MEANS, ELECTRONIC
OR MECHANICAL, INCLUDING PHOTOCOPY, RECORDING, OR ANY
INFORMATION STORAGE AND RETRIEVAL SYSTEM, WITHOUT
PERMISSION IN WRITING FROM THE PUBLISHER.

ACADEMIC PRESS, INC.
111 Fifth Avenue, New York, New York 10003

United Kingdom Edition published by
ACADEMIC PRESS, INC. (LONDON) LTD.
24/28 Oval Road, London NW1

LIBRARY OF CONGRESS CATALOG CARD NUMBER: 47-30313

PRINTED IN THE UNITED STATES OF AMERICA

186296
WHEATON COLLEGE LIBRARY
NORTON, MASS. 02766

CONTRIBUTORS TO VOLUME VII

VERNON BRYSON, *Biological Laboratory, Cold Spring Harbor, New York*

ADRIANO A. BUZZATI-TRAVERSO, *Istituto di Genetica, Pavia, Italy, and Scripps Institution of Oceanography, La Jolla, California*

A. BRITO DA CUNHA, *Departamento de Biologia Geral, Faculdade de Filosofia, Ciências e Letras da Universidade de São Paulo, Brasil*

JOHN A. MOORE, *Department of Zoology, Barnard College and Columbia University, New York, New York*

PAUL B. SAWIN, *Roscoe B. Jackson Memorial Laboratory, Hamilton Station, Bar Harbor, Maine*

RENZO E. SCOSSIROLI, *Istituto di Genetica, Pavia, Italy*

WACLAW SZYBALSKI, *Institute of Microbiology, Rutgers University, New Brunswick, New Jersey*

RYUHEI TAKAHASHI, *The Ohara Institute for Agricultural Biology, University of Okayama, Kurashiki, Okayama-ken, Japan*

CONTENTS

Abnormal Combinations of Nuclear and Cytoplasmic Systems in Frogs and Toads

By JOHN A. MOORE, *Department of Zoology, Barnard College and Columbia University, New York, New York*

Recent Genetics of the Domestic Rabbit

By PAUL B. SAWIN, *Roscoe B. Jackson Memorial Laboratory, Hamilton Station, Bar Harbor, Maine*

The Origin and Evolution of Cultivated Barley

By RYUHEI TAKAHASHI, *The Ohara Institute for Agricultural Biology, University of Okayama, Kurashiki, Okayama-ken, Japan*

Microbial Drug Resistance*

VERNON BRYSON AND WACLAW SZYBALSKI†

Biological Laboratory, Cold Spring Harbor, New York, and Institute of Microbiology, Rutgers University, New Brunswick, New Jersey

I. INTRODUCTION

Severe limitations may be imposed on the use of new drugs and antibiotics by the prevalence or development of resistant microorganisms.

* Some of the experiments performed by the authors and cited in this review were supported by grants from the National Tuberculosis Association and the Office of Naval Research.

† The second author was a member of the staff of the Biological Laboratory during the preparation of this article.

1

How do these resistant strains and species arise? The problem has been probed and dissected by bacteriologists, biochemists, physicians, epidemiologists, physical chemists, and cell physiologists. More recently, geneticists have found, in the study of drug resistance, a new source material for the analysis of heredity. Each group of investigators has provided opinions colored by the interests and intellectual limitations acquired in the pursuit of restricted branches of learning. Thus, chemists have been taken to task by geneticists for treating microbial populations as homogeneous reagents. Similarly, geneticists have been accused of minimizing the importance of drug-induced adaptive change in the origin of microbial resistance. Since uncomprising attitudes in science are rarely tenable, and grow less so with advances in knowledge, it should occasion no surprise that categorical denials of extremism are issued with increasing frequency by certain outstanding investigators in the field. We may assume that the trend away from rigid and exclusive views, concerning the origin of microbial drug resistance, arises from an increased awareness of the difficulties involved. Yet there remains an insoluble residue of divergent theory and amorphous literature.

Perhaps it would be allowable to begin with the only two premises agreeable to all: (1) microorganisms vary widely in their resistance to chemical agents, and (2) microbiologists vary widely in their resistance to the evident scientific facts. This at once points up a difficulty. The word "resistance" itself has a number of implications. In the course of investigations, based on a variety of approaches to the subject of resistance and relating to several disciplines, the origin of resistance has become a series of subjects rather than a single subject.

Another difficulty may be attributed to the many ways whereby resistance to chemical agents can develop. Certain drugs have unrelated bacteriostatic and bactericidal modes of action, depending on the concentration. It becomes obvious that a single explanation for resistance may not suffice even in case of a single substance. It is well conceivable that two unrelated strains of bacteria might become resistant to the same agent by means of different pathways. Although this review is concerned with the origin of drug resistance rather than its mechanism, the two are intimately related. An awareness of the multiplicity of mechanisms impels a more careful consideration of origins, with knowledge that the application of simplified generalities to the interpretation of resistance is perhaps convenient or even unavoidable, but certain in due time to be inadequate.

We will now consider whether a compromise can be attained between two opposing points of view, known historically as the theories of *mutation selection* versus *phenotypic adaptation* or, in the terminology of Stanier

(1953), *evolutionary* versus *physiological adaptation*. The potential scope has been limited by considerations of space. Therefore, we shall refer frequently to available reviews, rather than cite extensively the many significant contributions to the subject.

1. *Incidence of Drug Resistance in Microorganisms*

Without presupposing anything about the origin of microbial resistance to drugs, we may divide microorganisms into two groups: those resistant as found in nature, and those generally capable of giving rise to resistant strains from sensitive parent cells, as shown by exposure to toxic agents under appropriate experimental or clinical conditions. While admitting the necessity of dividing microorganisms into categories of resistant and sensitive, it is essential to remember that the terms are relative. If a sensitive strain is defined as one that will not show growth in the presence of drug levels, permitting multiplication of certain derived resistant populations, then one may characterize the usual wild type strains of *Escherichia coli* as sensitive to penicillin (Szybalski and Bryson, 1952a), the exact opposite of the usual clinical classification. As an example of intraspecific variation, pathogenic strains of *Mycobacterium tuberculosis* are inhibited by *p*-aminosalicylic acid (PAS) in concentrations of 0.1–10 μg/ml, yet wild type *Mycobacterium ranae* will grow at once in concentrations of 3000 μg/ml. If *M. ranae* is cultivated serially in increasing concentrations of PAS, it is possible to produce even greater resistance, placing the "resistant" parent in a more intermediate position (Hsie and Bryson, unpublished). Evidently, any species of microorganism occupies a position on a continuous scale of resistance levels, or more properly a range of positions, with limits defined by strains showing the extreme deviations from wild type. Both the range and average position of a microbial species on the resistance scale is presumably subject to change dependent on adaptive capacity of the organism, the ingenuity employed in isolating a complete spectrum of representative individuals, and the nature of the drug. The position occupied on the scale by so-called "wild type" strains may be incidental in its relation to resistance. This is because wild type microorganisms isolated in nature are the ones best fitted for survival in the face of *normal* evolutionary pressures. In Table 1 the range of sensitivity of four representative species of bacteria to several antibacterial agents is given. It is evident that wide variation exists at both the interspecific and intraspecific level. This variation is comparatively large in strains exposed to streptomycin, but very restricted if formaldehyde is used as the test agent. In the presence of certain agents such as furadroxyl, some species (*E. coli*) show a wide range of sensitivity. Other highly sensitive species (*B. megaterium*) may

TABLE 1

Experimental Range in Sensitivity of Four Representative Species of Bacteria to Nine Antibacterial Agents

	Escherichia coli (B/r)			Micrococcus pyogenes var. aureus			Mycobacterium ranae			Bacillus megaterium		
	Derived strains*	Wild type†	Derived strains*	Derived strains*	Wild type†	Derived strains*	Derived strains*	Wild type†	Derived strains*	Derived strains*	Wild type†	Derived strains*
Penicillin	2.5	8	6400	0.15	0.2	600	500	1000	8000	15	20	22
Streptomycin	0.7	1	>10,000	1.5	3	>3000	0.5	0.6	>1000	0.3	0.7	>1000
Chloramphenicol	0.7	1.5	450	1.5	4	320	8	20	>2000	1.3	1.5	3
Chlortetracycline	0.5	1.5	300	0.15	0.3	1.2	0.025	0.05	4	0.25	0.3	6
Bacitracin	500	700	14,000	10	20	2000	100	200	10,000	0.04	0.05	5
Polymyxin B	0.2	20	400	30	60	600	20	25	>375	0.5	1.5	3
Furadroxyl	0.1	4	200	5	5	60		200		3	6	6
Nisin				10	500	1000	750	3000	3000	0.05	0.2	0.8
Formaldehyde	20	20	20	20	20	20	40	40	40	15	20	20

* Figures under the heading of "derived strains" represent the experimental sensitivity limits of strains derived from the wild type. Inhibitory concentrations are expressed in micrograms per milliliter as assayed by the gradient plate method.

† Italicized figures under this heading show sensitivities of the parental wild type strains.

fail to develop resistance to the same agent. The ranges of resistance in Table 1 do not represent the full potential limits (cf. Baron, 1950), but offer the definite advantage of having been obtained with the same bacterial strains by a single technique (gradient plate) and in similar media. Comparisons of resistance levels performed in widely different media have certain obvious sources of error to be considered more fully in section II, 1, c.

Extension of the range of resistances predominantly upward from the original position of the wild type strain may be the result of limitations in prevailing methods of isolation. Strains with greater susceptibility to drugs are difficult to obtain in the absence of "collateral sensitivity," whereby selection for increased resistance (or for some other property) is accompanied by increased sensitivity to unrelated agents (Szybalski and Bryson, 1952a). The polymyxin-sensitive strain of *E. coli* in Table 1 was obtained by this method. Use of a more facile term, "induced sensitivity," has been avoided because the expression carries implications about the mode of origin that may not be applicable.

2. *Brief History*

It has been evident, since the first studies of drug resistance by Kossiakoff (1887), that sensitivity classifications may be no better than temporary statistical guides, if applied to microorganisms which have a wide potential for variation.

The more significant historical events contributing to an understanding of microbial drug resistance have been reviewed by Work and Work (1948) and Abraham (1953). Only a few of the many important contributions can be considered. The earliest experimental study on the development of drug resistance by protozoa was apparently performed in our own laboratory by Davenport and Neal (1895). These workers succeeded in producing strains able to survive in relatively high concentrations of mercuric chloride and quinine. Recognition of the medical import of microbial resistance came from the laboratories of Paul Ehrlich, who was engaged at the turn of the century in establishing the basis for modern chemotherapy. A further development originated in the interesting researches of Jollos (1921), leading to the concept of "Dauermodifikation" (lasting modification), or relatively persistent cytoplasmic changes transmitted by descent from drug-resistant protozoa to their progeny. With the advent of sulfonamides as safe and effective chemotherapeutic agents, microbial drug resistance attained widespread clinical significance. Later, the use of penicillin and streptomycin, with attendant reports of resistance development, served to emphasize the general nature of a problem now recognized as of considerable importance to medicine

(Florey *et al.*, 1949). These developments were paralleled by stimulating researches on the mechanisms of drug action by Woods (1940), and by the contributions of Luria and Delbrück (1943) and Demerec (1945) supporting a genetic basis for microbial drug resistance. Discovery of streptomycin in 1943 (Waksman, 1949) and subsequent isolation of one-step mutants highly resistant or dependent upon this antibiotic (cf. Miller and Bohnhoff, 1950) stimulated great theoretical and practical interest in the problem.

3. *Definitions*

A few definitions are now needed. *Resistance* may be defined as the temporary or permanent capacity of a cell and its progeny to remain viable or multiply under environmental conditions that would destroy or inhibit other cells. All resistance contributing to survival value will be considered as *adaptive*, whether dependent on *genotype* (hereditary constitution) or merely on *phenotype* (sum total of observable physiological and morphological properties). Certain other investigators prefer to confine the term "adaptive" exclusively to nongenetic variations, herein referred to as *phenotypic adaptation*, in contrast to *genotypic adaptation* based on genetic changes. Analogy with higher organisms suggests that genotypic properties are controlled predominantly by structures in the nucleus that replicate at cell division and are either chromosomes or their equivalent. Infrequently, a genetic property may be altered by *mutation*, liberally defined as a sudden heritable change, producing a new genotype. Genetic changes may also depend on rearrangement and reshuffling of the established genetic material. Mutations will be divided into *spontaneous*, or precipitated by unknown events, and *induced*, arising from the action of a specific agent described as a *mutagen*. In very general terms, the average probability that a cell will give rise by mutation to a *mutant* is designated the *mutation rate*, this being the reciprocal of the average size a microbial population must attain before the first resistant mutant appears. The definition of *selection* is self-evident. *Environment* is the total of natural or artificial influences in contact with microorganisms. The environment is rarely uniform, existing more frequently as a number of *microenvironments*. For example, the microenvironment immediately surrounding a bacterial colony on a solid medium often differs from that found at greater distances.

Microorganisms appear to develop some degree of resistance against many toxic agents and drugs, providing the experimental conditions originally imposed are not too rigorous. How does resistance arise, and will knowledge of its mode of origin increase our control over the incidence of resistant strains? Since considerable controversy exists, a purely formal representation of the possible modes of origin is required to provide models for comparison with the evidence.

II. Possible Modes of Origin of Resistance

Most investigators would now agree that the genetic constitution of a cell sets the limits of resistance within a particular environmental situation, and that the genetic endowment of different cells in large microbial populations is sufficiently variable, as a result of mutation, to permit the operation of selective mechanisms in the isolation of resistant strains. As previously observed, this is known as the *mutation selection* hypothesis and implies that resistance arises *before* contact of the cell with the toxic agent. The assumption that drug resistance arises *after* drug contact solely as a result of substrate-induced adaptive modification is called the hypothesis of *phenotypic adaptation*, and in its most restricted form assumes that the reacting cell population and its response to drug action are homogeneous. From an evolutionary standpoint, both modes of origin serve to enhance the probability of survival and must be considered adaptive. Instead of assuming a strongly partisan position on either side of the historical line separating mutation selection and phenotypic adaptation, we shall consider first the origin of *resistant cells* as individuals, and secondly the origin and growth of *resistant populations*. However, genetic terms will be used as needed. This will permit a comprehensive and systematic arrangement of possible alternatives in the development of microbial resistance.

A schematic presentation, published elsewhere (Szybalski and Bryson, 1955) and based in part on figures in the review of Cavalli-Sforza and Lederberg (1953), will aid in an understanding of the origin of resistance at both the primary cell level and the secondary population level. All examples are idealized. We begin with a single cell, representing only one member of a larger population not wholly indicated for lack of space. As a further simplification, it is assumed that (1) sensitive cells cease multiplying at once after addition of the toxic agent, (2) reversion to sensitivity does not occur in the diagramed population (3) changes to resistance are expressed immediately without phenomic lag (with the exception of Fig. 1b), and multiplication of cells is generally synchronous, without selective differences in the survival of sensitive and resistant cells in a drug-free environment (with the exception of Fig. 9a). These assumptions represent an oversimplification of the state of nature, but are necessary as a contribution to clarity and graphic simplicity. In Figs. 1, 2, 3, and 9, the hereditary apparatus or genotype of the cell is represented by letters: S, sensitive, I, inducible (a special case of sensitive, potentially able to undergo a stable or unstable phenotypic adaptation to resistance), and R, resistant. The convenient assumption that these symbols correspond to the genetic properties of bacterial nuclei is supported by some direct evidence and has the advantage of requiring a minimum of special theory. The actual physiological state, or phenotype, of cells in the figures ranges from fully sensitive (white) to fully resistant (black) with intermediate degrees of resistance represented by different intensities of shading. S, R, and I are interconvertible by mutation or other genetic change as indicated by the letter M.

1. *Origin of a Resistant Cell*

The figures illustrate at once a basic dichotomy in the interpretation of resistance. Two principal methods for the origin of resistance are depicted: (1) resistance dependent primarily on a change of genotype (Figs. 1a, 1b, 1c); and (2) resistance not ascribed to genotypic change, but attributed solely to phenotypic adaptation (Figs. 2a and 2b). The process of selection is also shown, but emphasis at present will be placed on the changes leading to the formation of a resistant cell. Superimposition of the diagrams would give rise to numerous composite interpretations, as represented by one example in Fig. 3. This example serves as a model for experiments of Ryan (1952) on lactose fermentation, and may also be of general importance in studies of drug resistance. Attention will now be directed more systematically to the different schematic interpretations.

a. *Resistance Primarily Dependent upon Change of Genotype*. This type of resistance originates through a change in the hereditary properties of the cell, attributable either to mutation or to a sexual exchange of genetic material. The first process is presumably more important because of the rarity of sexual processes in bacteria, a rarity that may be more apparent than real. Undetermined numbers of "mutations" in microorganisms may originate through major chromosomal rearrangements, or delayed segregation processes arising from heterokaryosis and heterozygosis.

(i) *Mutation*. Two kinds of mutation are of significance in the study of drug resistance—spontaneous mutation (i.e. occurring before contact between the microorganism and the drug), and mutation induced by the presence of the toxic drug itself, or indirectly through the action of some environmental agent.

Spontaneous mutation. The classic model of spontaneous mutation followed by selection is illustrated in Figs. 1a and 1b. Only sister cells belonging to a spontaneously formed, resistant clone are able to continue multiplying in the presence of the drug. The majority of careful inquiries into the origin of resistance lead to conclusions compatible with this representation. Figure 1b represents a frequent complication existing in nature and known as phenomic lag. This lag results in a delayed expression of the mutant phenotype, necessitating the intervention of one or more generations between the genetic event and the ability of mutant cells to survive exposure to a selective agent. The illustrated example shows a

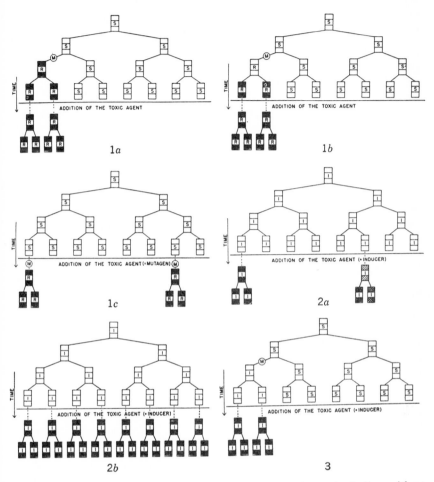

FIG. 1a. Resistance dependent upon spontaneous mutation and selection, with no phenomic lag (from Szybalski and Bryson, 1955).

FIG. 1b. Resistance dependent upon spontaneous mutation and selection, with phenomic lag (from Szybalski and Bryson, 1955).

FIG. 1c. Resistance dependent upon drug-induced mutation and selection (from Szybalski and Bryson, 1955).

FIG. 2a. Resistance dependent upon heterogeneous phenotypic adaptation and selection (from Szybalski and Bryson, 1955).

FIG. 2b. Resistance dependent upon homogeneous phenotypic adaptation (from Szybalski and Bryson, 1955).

FIG. 3. Resistance dependent upon composite changes. Example: spontaneous mutation followed by selection of phenotypically adapted mutants (from Szybalski and Bryson, 1955).

one-generation delay in the expression of resistance, and assumes its appearance in both daughter cells. Resistance of *E. coli* to phages (Demerec and Fano, 1945), to the related colicines (Frédéricq and Betz-Bareau, 1952), and to valine in synthetic media (Manten and Rowley, 1953) arises in a manner generally consistent with the interpretations shown in Figs. 1a or 1b. When lag occurs, the number of generations intervening between mutation and phenotypic expression could be variable, even for different descendents of the same mutated cell.

Induced mutation. It is also possible, at least theoretically, for mutation to be induced by the presence of the toxic drug itself (Fig. 1c). Some degree of specificity may be shown by mutagenic agents (Demerec, 1953), but their usual effect is to cause an acceleration in the production of mutations of all kinds. Perhaps the primary occurrence preceding induced mutation is a general disturbance of cellular metabolism by the mutagen. This is hardly a precise or illuminating observation, but serves to emphasize the randomness of the mutation process. Increase in drug resistance by mutation may, therefore, be only a specific manifestation of a general event. However, the infrequency of most mutations makes it probable that, within any single cell, only one or a few genetic changes will occur as a result of induced mutation. A highly selective mutagenic action, causing the cell to change *only* its resistance to the inducing drug, appears unlikely, although exceptions may exist (Akiba 1955, Szybalski, 1955). Such change would assume two fortuitous simultaneous events in widely separate biochemical systems. First, a specific and nonlethal alteration in the pattern of hereditary materials, considered to comprise or be intimately surrounded by deoxyribonucleic acid. As a second requirement, it would be necessary that the *one* induced change would lead directly by means of complex metabolic pathways to the development of an adaptive physiological system now resistant to the chemical action of the drug. Thus, the drug would have a double specificity limited to reaction with (1) the determiners of heredity, and (2) the drug-sensitive biochemical pathway. The element of teleology thus introduced is in disagreement with contemporary genetic evidence that mutations are not primarily purposeful.

Even if the toxic drug is considered as a nonspecific mutagen, theoretical difficulties prevent the ready acceptance of Fig. 1c as a model for the origin of drug resistance. It will be noted that for survival the mutation must achieve phenotypic expression within one generation, an unusual situation in the light of our experimental information. The difficulty may be circumvented by employing agents that permit several terminal cell divisions before the drug becomes effective, or by using subinhibitory concentrations of the toxic agent. Drug-induced mutations originating under these special circumstances might find opportunity for delayed expression. Such interpretations could account for the occasional necessity of subculturing bacteria for prolonged periods at subinhibitory concentrations of drug before a resistant strain can be isolated. During the period of slow growth an increased opportunity would exist for the appearance and selection of new mutants with higher grades of resistance.

The problem of drug-induced mutation to resistance has been considered by Bellamy and Klimek (1948), Linz (1950), Voureka (1952), and Newcombe (1955). Linz (1950) suggests that the development of bacterial resistance to streptomycin may be in part the consequence of streptomycin-induced mutation. The production of mutations in *E. coli* to radiation resistance ($B \rightarrow B/r$) by ultraviolet light (Witkin, 1947) could contribute to the high apparent mutation rate when this agent is used for isolating the resistant organisms. A lower rate is noted if the B/r mutants are selected from a parental radiation-sensitive population by means of furadroxyl (Szybalski and Nelson, 1954). Since many drugs and chemicals, including the known mutagen, nitrogen mustard, can be used to isolate radiation-resistant mutants (Bryson, 1948; Bryson *et al.*, 1951), the occurrence of drug-induced mutation appears highly probable in appropriate examples. We may find that a great number of substances act as weak mutagens when used at inhibitory concentrations (Demerec, Bertani, and Flint, 1951; Voureka, 1952). The pronounced influence of many agents on the dividing nuclei of higher plants (Levan, 1951) or on bacteria (DeLamater *et al.*, 1955) can also be observed cytologically. Several bacteriostatic antibiotics selectively inhibit the separation of complementary bacterial structures resembling chromosomes, with lesser effect on their multiplication. Similar results, with the production of "transient polyploidy," can be obtained by chilling actively growing *Bacillus megaterium* to a suboptimal temperature (Szybalski and Hunter-Szybalska, 1955).

(ii) *Genetic exchange.* Variation resulting from the interchange of hereditary determinants between different individuals is a most important basis for the operation of natural or artificial selection in higher organisms, including as it does the manifestation of sexuality. In many microorganisms, the existence of sexual processes is still highly problematical. At the present time, it appears unlikely that sexual mechanisms contribute to any great extent in the development of drug-resistant bacterial strains. Genetic exchange could be illustrated by Figs. 1a, 1b, and 1c, with the qualification that *M* now designates the introduction of genetic material from outside the cell by recombination or transduction. New genetic information transferred by the exchange mechanisms may be carried by entire cells (gametes), by viruses, and by "unpackaged" deoxyribonucleic acid. Among the bacteria, persistence of a haploid phase during the vegetative state excludes the buffering effect of ploidy and accelerates the evolutionary testing of both mutations and genetic exchanges. Even though mutation has greater significance in the origin of drug resistance, a study of genetic exchange has provided new facts of extreme theoretical interest.

Sexual recombination between strains of *Escherichia coli* suitably differentiated by genetic markers has not only made possible the establishment of new genotypes but has also provided evidence that streptomycin resistance behaves as a recessive character in an exceptional heterozygous strain (Lederberg, 1951a). Crossing of strains resistant to sodium azide by others resistant to streptomycin provides further evidence that these properties are determined by factors analogous to the genes of higher organisms, although complications in the inheritance patterns of bacteria suggest that further research is required before a complete analogy is drawn (Lederberg, 1950). Also, chloromycetin resistance in *E. coli* is now known to be dependent on several genetic factors (Cavalli and Maccacaro, 1952), as described more fully in section V.

Transduction results from the infection of a host cell by genetic material obtained as a filtrable derivative of donor cells. The means of conveyance is a bacteriophage. Among the new genetic properties said to be transduced to lysogenic host cells of the genus Salmonella is resistance to streptomycin (Zinder and Lederberg, 1952). Obviously, the donor cells must have the necessary streptomycin-resistant constitution. It would appear that some lysogenic bacteriophages, when moving from one cell to another of different genetic constitution, carry over units of bacterial heredity. It is not certain whether these units are transported passively as foreign material, or are incorporated into the genotype of the phage as heredity shared in common with bacterial host cells. Later unpublished experiments by P. E. Hartman (azide resistance), V. Bryson (polymyxin resistance) and Z. Demerec (streptomycin resistance) show that the transfer of resistance properties by transduction may be more difficult than was originally assumed, if indeed it is possible.

Transformation represents a special example of transduction, and is well known through the classical studies of Avery, MacLeod, and McCarty (1944) on the production of genetic changes in the pneumococcus by treatment with purified DNA (deoxyribonucleic acid). More recently, Hotchkiss (1951) has shown by similar methods a stepwise transfer of penicillin resistance in pneumococci. In contrast, the transfer of high streptomycin resistance may be accomplished in *Hemophilus influenzae* as a one-step process if the nucleic acid is obtained originally from a fully resistant strain (Alexander and Leidy, 1953).

Genetic exchanges provide a strict proof that drug resistance can be transferred *after* primary origin, by genetic mechanisms; and that a sensitive cell may become resistant in the absence of a drug. No conclusions may be drawn on the role of drugs in the origin of resistance without a complete history of the genetic materials. A more extensive survey of these problems has been made by Cavalli-Sforza and Lederberg (1953).

b. *Resistance Dependent upon Nongenetic Change of Phenotype.* If resistance is to arise without genetic change, it must occur in cells endowed with a genotype capable of responding to the adaptive stimuli responsible for alterations in sensitivity level. Microorganisms capable of phenotypic change in response to substrate alterations may be termed inducible, *I*, and can arise from noninducible organisms by mutation. The first illustration of nongenetic adaptation to drug resistance is given in Fig. 2a. All cells are genetically inducible, but actual induction occurs only in occasional individuals, following a normal or Poissonian distribution. The change is confined to a few physiologically competent cells, and the majority are sterilized before induction can take place. With some variation in the degree of inducibility there may also be another form of heterogeneous adaptation, resulting in the selection of progressively fitter individuals with increased time as illustrated in one of the two adapted clones. During homogeneous nongenetic adaptation the role of selection is minimized, and all cells respond equally to the toxic inducer to produce a resistant phenotype without change in genotype (Fig. 2b).

By definition, phenotypic adaptation results from induced changes, characteristically of an extranuclear nature. Some alterations in the cytoplasm of the cell may be directly observable, as in the destruction of formed cytoplasmic particles by chemical agents. Thus, euflavine (2,8-diamino-10-methyl acridine) removes the mitochondria of yeasts with attendant biochemical changes (Ephrussi and Hottinguer, 1951), and streptomycin may damage or eliminate the chloroplasts of Euglena (Provasoli, Hutner, and Pintner, 1951). It has been said that a cell may be "cured" of the presence of replicating but dispensable cytoplasmic constituents, e.g., kappa particles in *Paramecium* (Brown, 1950), or lysogenic phage in bacteria (Lwoff, 1953).

Permanent elimination of a formed cytoplasmic constituent, with consequent inherited alteration in phenotype, is in conformity with a broad definition of mutation as proposed by Luria (1947). In a stricter sense, mutation has been confined by most workers to a change of nuclear origin, presumably chromosomal. Induced alterations of the cytoplasm of a permanent nature, therefore, occupy an intermediate position between mutations as conventionally defined and induced physiological changes.

14   VERNON BRYSON AND WACLAW SZYBALSKI

The elimination of cytoplasmic elements will have an effect on drug resistance only if there is a corresponding change of function with adaptive consequences.

It would be difficult to exhaust all possible examples of phenotypic adaptation. The subsequent section will be confined to a relatively well studied area, the consideration of drug resistance as related to changes in enzyme systems. "Induced enzyme synthesis" (Cohn and Monod, 1953) will substitute for the less accurate term "enzymatic adaptation," with obvious advantages, if the enzyme is synthesized in response to a nonutilizable substrate of no apparent adaptive significance.

(i) *Induction of a new physiological function.* Two notable examples are provided by the induced synthesis of β-galactosidase in *E. coli* (Cohn and Monod, 1953) and penicillinase in *B. cereus* (Pollock, 1953). In both cases, a substrate or related chemical compound induces the synthesis of an enzyme. Some of the most active inducers are not able to serve as substrates. β-galactosidase maintains significant levels only in the continued presence of an inducer, whereas penicillinase may continue to be formed for some time after removal of the inducing agent (see section III, 2). The production of an *inducer-inactivating enzyme* might act as a general mechanism of phenotypic adaptation in the development of drug resistance, particularly if the inducer is the toxic agent as in the penicillin-penicillinase system. Several illustrations of phenotypic adaptation to drug resistance in *Paramecium*, suggesting the inductive synthesis of drug-inactivating enzymes, are reviewed by Beale (1953). If induction resulted in the synthesis of an entire chain of enzymes along a metabolic pathway, as proposed by Stanier (1947), the adaptive latitude of the induced change would tend to be increased.

(ii) *Elimination of a cytoplasmic particle.* Several representative examples of the loss of cytoplasmic inclusions have already been considered. Emphasis is now placed on cytoplasmic particles as sites of enzyme formation. Yeast mutants without mitochondria are unable to produce cytochrome oxidase, succinic dehydrogenase, and numerous other enzymes most recently listed by Slonimski (1953). As another example, the pivotal role of chloroplasts in photosynthesis suggests an intimate relationship between these structures and the enzyme systems required by phototrophic microorganisms. Since the development of drug resistance is frequently accompanied by a loss of synthetic functions (cf. Sevag, 1946), it is at least possible that mitochondria or smaller cytoplasmic units of biochemical importance may disappear simultaneously with a loss of drug sensitivity.

There are several observations indicating a possible role of streptomycin in cytoplasmic inheritance. One is the finding by Provasoli,

Hutner, and Pintner (1951) that streptomycin irreversibly damages chloroplasts of green plants. Another is the evidence for non-Mendelian inheritance of low-grade streptomycin resistance in *Chlamydomonas* (Sager, 1954), as revealed by irregular ratios in tetrad analysis.

(iii) *Accumulation of a drug-inactivating factor.* That resistance to antibacterial agents may depend on the accumulation of drug-inactivating substances has been proposed by Hinshelwood (1949). In barest essential, Hinshelwood assumes two linked enzyme systems, *A* and *B*, which are vital for the multiplication of the cells. System *A* furnishes intermediates necessary for the reproduction of *B*. The drug, without impeding the reproduction of *A*, cuts down the output of intermediates so that synthesis of *B* is retarded. Multiplication must be delayed until, despite the inactivating action of the drug, enough intermediate is produced to allow synthesis of a critical amount of system *B*. With time, the amount of *A* has become progressively greater than normal, providing for an increased cellular output of the critical intermediate.

Later development of this theory of "automatic adjustment" shows that the situation would essentially remain unchanged, even if the simple reaction represented only part of a complex net of interlocking reaction cycles (Hinshelwood, 1953). Moreover, in the steady state, reactions of this pattern are autocatalytic, simulating superficially the behavior of replicable genetic units, or genes.

Hinshelwood's model, stimulating though it may be, fails to consider the experimentally established complexity of cellular structure.

If a single criticism may be raised, it is that elaborate mathematical analyses and elegant rational arguments will never suffice to establish the theory without the support of more complete biochemical and genetic investigation.

(iv) *Selection of an alternative physiological function.* Selection on a subcellular level may be presumed in special cases to result in phenotypic adaptation. Thus, instead of inducing a new physiological function, the drug may cause a selective change in the relative emphasis upon two or more preexistent enzymatic pathways, leading to the formation of an essential metabolite. An early example that may represent this type of adaptation was provided by Sevag and Green (1944). Their experiments demonstrated that a strain of *Staphylococcus aureus*, resistant to sulphonamides in the presence of glucose, could not grow if pyruvate was substituted. It may be inferred, although not proven, that a blocked enzymatic pathway leading from glucose to an essential metabolite by way of pyruvate has been by-passed in the drug-resistant strain.

Enzymatic changes leading to phenotypic adaptation may be interrelated by recourse to an idealized and undoubtedly oversimplified model.

It will be assumed that enzyme synthesis occurs by the organization of single amino acids into complex molecules that are impressed with specificity on the template surface of an *enzyme-forming site*, EFS. Our foregoing examples of phenotypic adaptation may therefore be considered in the following terms: (i) *modification* of EFS, the direct consequence of surface attachment of the inducer, and resulting in structural alteration of the template, (ii) *loss* of EFS, (iii) *accumulation* of identical EFS and (iv) *selection* of alternate EFS.

In the interpretation of drug resistance, consideration of EFS has certain advantages over a more restricted attention to the enzymes themselves. If the specificity of EFS is governed by genotype, but this entity is also self-reproducible, then phenotypic adaptation might easily persist as stable changes after removal of the inducing agent. In specific instances, we have seen that the inducing agent may be the toxic substance. Ribonucleic acid (RNA) could well serve as a hypothetical constituent of an EFS. RNA does not correspond to the predominant nucleic acid of the nucleus (DNA), considered to carry the main body of nuclear hereditary determinants. On the other hand, RNA, as a main component of some plant viruses, gives evidence of intracellular replication. It would be possible to construct a similar model for induced changes in antigenicity or serotype, since these changes are also thought to depend on molecular rearrangement. Reference could be made, for example, to an antigen-forming site.

There are undeniably many factors in the development of resistance that cannot be related, at least directly, to enzyme function. Changes in cell permeability are believed to result in the resistance of trypanosomes to arsenicals (Yorke, Murgatroyd, and Hawking, 1931). Altered permeability remains as an alternative to many interpretations of drug resistance. The dependence of resistance in defined media upon the presence of a specific substrate suggests, however, that altered permeability may not be of great significance as a causative factor in most instances (Harris and Kohn, 1943). The origin of permeability differences could, of course, be either genic or non-genic.

Many other considerations might be entertained in describing phenotypic adaptations leading to resistance. We will join with Beale (1953) in describing these adaptations as resulting from "reorganization of the protoplasm," a definition with a remarkable margin of safety.

c. *Resistance Involving No Adaptive Change.* It is well known that the sensitivity of microorganisms to antibiotics is profoundly influenced by the conditions of the test (Shwartzman, 1946; Rosanoff and Sevag, 1951; Sevag and Rosanoff, 1952). For example, sterilization of *E. coli* by streptomycin is greatly retarded in synthetic media requiring induced enzyme synthesis, or lacking substrates for metabolism (Rosenblum and Bryson, 1953). Figure 4 illustrates one of several possible effects of substrate upon the survival of a microbial population under exposure to a drug of uniform concentration. In contrast with all previous examples, there is no *necessary* indication that a resistant phenotype has been selected, or has developed in the surviving individuals grown in medium B. The process is therefore not properly defined as the development of resistance (section I, 3). This does not deny that growth on a widely different substrate may, in time, produce enzymatic changes of adaptive value in the presence of toxic chemicals, added simultaneously or later.

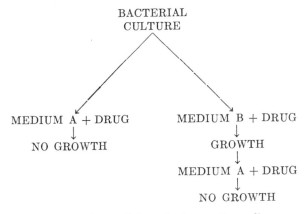

BACTERIAL
CULTURE

MEDIUM A + DRUG   MEDIUM B + DRUG
↓   ↓
NO GROWTH   GROWTH
↓
MEDIUM A + DRUG
↓
NO GROWTH

FIG. 4. "Resistance" dependent upon the medium.

Also, substitution of a new substrate in minimal media may by-pass a blocked reaction. However, the measurement of these changes must be made under one set of environmental conditions. This criterion is not met by the model in Fig. 4. If, after several transfers in new medium, a bacterial strain is found to tolerate higher drug concentrations than at the first transfer, the problem is no different than in previous considerations of genetic and nongenetic adaptation. The investigator must determine the mode of development of resistance.

Another instance that may lead to spurious illusions of differences in resistance level arises through failure to recognize the distinction between bactericidal and bacteriostatic effects. Determination of resistance to bactericidal drug action involves two experimental steps: the microorganisms are exposed to the drug for a limited time, and the proportion of surviving cells is then measured in the *absence* of the toxic agent. Again, the surviving cells may be relatively resistant, but this is not a necessary assumption, since the complete killing of even a homogeneous population requires a period of time. In comparison, bacteriostasis must be measured in the *presence* of the toxic agent. The degree of resistance is determined through the use of turbidometry, or by counting bacteria selected on the basis of their ability to form clones (colonies) capable of growth in drug-containing media.

d. *Borderline Examples.* A special problem of resistance is presented by the occurrence of colonies formed at bacteriostatic drug levels that do not grow upon subculture to a similar environment. Their appearance in a semi-solid medium might depend on uneven distribution of the drug, resulting in a favorable microenvironment. Alternate interpretations involve temporary changes at the cell level in the nature of polyploidy, clumping, capsule formation, or the unusual accumulation of chemical substances favoring survival. Creation of a favorable microenvironment may also become a race between the sterilizing capacity of the drug and the rate of bacterial multiplication. Occasional cells with a temporary adaptive advantage at the outset might form a self-created propitious microenvironment and continue to multiply. The statement that bacteria, persisting in drug-containing agar media, represent the chance survivors of a normal probability distribution is not sufficiently comprehensive, since colonies obviously represent clones and not single individuals. The adaptive advantage of persistors is nongenetic by definition, and so transitory as to defy demonstration after subculture. In interpreting the temporary resistance of a restricted group of cells to toxic agents, recourse is often taken to the normal variations in cytological or physiological state found within any population as shown, for example, by the presence of a distinct component exhibiting noninheritable resistance to radiation within populations of *E. coli* strain B, exposed to ultraviolet (Cavalli and Visconti di Modrone, 1949). An interpretation of the nature of "persistors" surviving temporary exposure to penicillin is provided by Bigger (1944). Another interesting example arises from the observation that *Streptomyces fradiae* changes its level of resistance to neomycin during the cultivation of this organism in the commercial production of the drug (Waksman, 1953). Sensitivity assays by the agar-streak dilution method show that the resistance of *S. fradiae* increases during fermentation almost fivefold, decreasing again at the end of the process. Decrease in reproductive activity during the progress of fermentation may be partially responsible for the apparent decrease in susceptibility to neomycin, but the possibility of population changes should not be overlooked. The problem of borderline examples has been described more fully by Wyss (1950).

e. *Resistance Dependent upon Composite Changes.* In the normal course of events, it is probable that drug resistance arises through a combination of the illustrated examples, either superimposed or in sequence. Thus, the multistep development of resistance to be described in a later section (Fig. 6) may be depicted by a simple tandem duplication of Fig. 1a, with increased resistance at each new mutation. A combination of genetic and nongenetic events may lead to the production of a resistant strain as shown in Fig. 3.

This example involves spontaneous mutation from sensitivity to inducibility ($S \to I$) with the resultant formation of potentially resistant, but phenotypically sensitive, clones. When the population is subsequently exposed to the drug, phenotypic adaptation to resistance occurs only in type I individuals. Possible illustrations are mutations that provide the *ability* to form antibiotic-destroying adaptive enzymes such as penicillinase (Pollock, 1953), and chloramphenicolase (Merkel and Steers, 1953). This experimental material awaits a rigorous genetic analysis. An analogous example involving both genetic and nongenetic changes has been analyzed by Ryan (1952) in his study of mutations in *E. coli* resulting in the origin of potentially lactose-positive strains from lactose-negative parents. In the presence of lactose, only I mutants can synthesize β-galactosidase. A further step in evolution is the mutation $I \to R$ under special selective conditions (alternating transfers in glucose or lactose media) favoring overgrowth of the parental population (Cohen-Bazire and Jolit, 1953). Lam and Sevag (1955) have proposed a composite origin of streptomycin resistance in micrococci. These investigators suggest that mutants isolated by replica plating are only potentially streptomycin resistant, their biochemical properties being different before and after exposure to the antibiotic. However, there is indication that pure cultures of potentially streptomycin resistant clones were not obtained from the drug-free master plates. Thus, the "resistant" R_0 cultures did not grow at streptomycin concentrations of ten micrograms per milliliter.

A full discussion of all possible composite examples would be superfluous. The illustrations provided by Figs. 1, 2, and 3 present at least a systematic basis for the comparison of different theories.

2. *Establishment of Drug-Resistant Microbial Populations*

a. *Uniform Change of All Individual Cells under the Influence of a Toxic Agent.* Consideration of the origin of drug-resistant cells does not dispose entirely of the problems inherent in the establishment of resistant strains. At least two general systems may be visualized leading to the production of large resistant populations, and related more or less directly to population genetics.

The first system is phenotypic adaptation of genetically identical, physiologically sensitive individuals under the influence of the toxic agent or other suitable inducers. As a *sole* mechanism, this method appears highly improbable, as it excludes genetic variability and denies the important role of selection in population dynamics. Experimental demonstration of physiological adaptation without selection can best be made under conditions that prohibit both cell multiplication and cell death. In practice, these conditions are rarely met. On the other hand, as a contributing mechanism to the establishment of resistant strains, phenotypic adaptation may have some significance, as suggested by the experiments of Eagle, Fleischman, and Levy (1952) on the development of chloramphenicol resistance in *E. coli*, and of Dean and Hinshelwood (1952) on the establishment of proflavine-resistant populations of *Aerobacter aerogenes*. Some of these experiments lack the rigorous proof that selection of spontaneous mutants is excluded. Attempts to rule out the possibility of selection in phenotypically adaptive processes have been made by recourse to nonmultiplying or ultraviolet-killed bacterial populations (Dean and Hinshelwood, 1951; Kaplan, Rosenblum, and Bryson, 1953). An example of uniform adaptation is shown in Fig. 2b. The implied position that reacting populations at any given time are both genetically homogeneous and identical in their degree of physiological adaptation is hardly tenable. The apostle of this view is soon faced with the microbiological equivalent of George Orwell's masterpiece of deliberate *non sequitur*, "All animals are equal, but some animals are more equal than others."

b. *Selection of Resistant Cells.* The second and more important aspect of the establishment of drug resistance is the selection of resistant clones, whose mode of origin has already received our attention. The fundamental assumptions are elementary: (1) Some microorganisms in a predominantly sensitive population are relatively drug resistant. (2) By suitable experimental methods or as a result of clinical treatment, the resistant microorganisms survive and multiply under toxic conditions unfavorable for the more prevalent sensitive type. (3) The resulting selective displacement of the drug-sensitive cells favors the isolation of resistant clones, leading to diminution or complete exclusion of the original sensitive component.

(i) *Methods of isolation of resistant strains.* A classic method for the isolation of resistant populations of bacteria has been cultivation in liquid nutrient containing a graded series of drug dilutions, followed by subculture of surviving organisms obtained at the level of partial inhibition. As required, the process is repeated using higher drug concentrations. To maintain the concentration of the drug at a *constant* level, Gezon and Carpenter (1953) used a porcelain filter to separate the culture from the main reservoir of media ("constant treatment" system). The somewhat ambiguous term "training" (Work and Work, 1948; Gale, 1948; Hinshel-wood, 1949) was once frequently used in describing such methods, but has significantly been omitted in a later edition of Gale's book (1951).

Considerably more information can be obtained if the resistant population is isolated on semisolid media. Here, the resistant clones remain *in situ* as colonies instead of being dispersed at random.

Either method may have limitations in the isolation of resistant strains capable of drug inactivation. As an example, individual penicillinase producing micrococci, arising as mutants in a culture of nonproducers, are characteristically inactivated when widely dispersed as single cells at inhibitory concentrations of the drug. However, clumps or aggregates of penicillinase-producers may grow very well under the same conditions. *In vitro* growth of a clone from the single, drug-inactivating mutants requires the establishment of a favorable nontoxic microenvironment, which is probable only in an area where the drug is present at a relatively low concentration (Szybalski, 1953a).

TABLE 2

Methods of Isolating Resistant Strains*

Direct methods (in the presence of toxic drug)

| Increase of drug concentration | Medium | |
	Liquid	Solid
Stepwise	Serial dilutions (test tubes)	Serial dilutions (agar plates)
Continuous Nonproportional	Turbidostat + direct feeding system	Reservoir agar plate
Proportional	Turbidostat + proportional feeding system	Gradient agar plate

Indirect methods (in the absence of the toxic drug)

Examples:
    Selection by associated characters
    Random selection and replica plating

* From Bryson, V., and Szybalski, W., 1952. *Science* **116,** 45–51.

Classification of methods used in the isolation of resistant strains has been compiled in outline form (Table 2), as developed during a previous study of microbial selection (Bryson and Szybalski, 1952).

(ii) *Patterns of resistance development.* Studies of survival curves, obtained by exposing bacterial populations to different drug concentrations in agar media, have provided further insight into both the origin and establishment of drug resistance. Two principal varieties of survival curve are obtained, the penicillin type and the streptomycin type (Demerec, 1948). In a more inclusive nomenclature, we may recognize the origin of resistant populations by way of a multistep pattern, a facultative single-step (or one step) pattern, and an obligatory single-step (or one step) pattern. These terms allow the definition of streptomycin resistance as single step, and therefore conform more closely to the usual terminology than the original designations of Hsie and Bryson (1950). In performing the experiments, petri plates are prepared with graded concentrations of drug and seeded with an inoculum adjusted when possible to give between

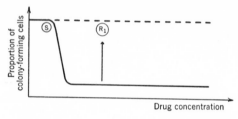

Fig. 5. One step, or single-step pattern.

50 and 500 survivors at the specific drug level employed. One or more of the resulting colonies is picked from the parental population (P) at a drug concentration indicated on the survival curves in Figs. 5–8 by arrows. The isolate is then subcultured to form a large R_1 population and, if necessary, the process is repeated until a highly resistant strain is obtained.

Single-step pattern. A simple alternative exists in the obligatory single-step pattern (Fig. 5). The microorganisms can be either sensitive or fully resistant. When the sensitive strain is exposed to the drug, a characteristic plateau of resistant survivors is obtained over a wide range of higher concentrations. These survivors prove to be nearly identical in sensitivity. Any clone obtained at high drug levels will serve at once to provide a fully resistant population (R_1). Examples of this pattern are found in the resistance of *E. coli* to bacteriophage (Luria and Delbrück, 1943), azide (Lederberg, 1950), and valine (Manten and Rowley, 1953); and in the resistance of *B. megaterium* to sodium p-aminosalicylate, isoniazid, erythromycin, cinnamycin (Szybalski and Bryson, 1953a; Szybalski, 1954). The step to azide resistance is comparatively small (Lederberg, 1950). Clinical information suggests that the resistance of virulent Mycobacteria to thiosemicarbazone and sodium p-aminosalicylate may be of the same kind.

Multistep pattern. This is the pattern of penicillin, and is typical for the development of bacterial resistance to most other antibiotics including the tetracyclines, viomycin, neomycin, and chloromycetin. The multistep pattern may be recognized by the necessary intervention of a series of intermediate steps between sensitivity and a high degree of resistance. The average resistance of each new isolate in a series of consecutive experiments then tends to increase in comparison with all previous populations until, finally, a highly resistant strain is derived.

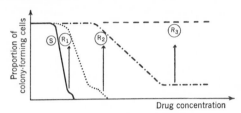

FIG. 6. Multi-step pattern.

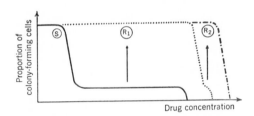

FIG. 7. Multi-step pattern (with wide first step).

Figures 6 and 7 illustrate this type of resistance pattern. The first (Fig. 6) appears very commonly and is exemplified by the survival curves obtained for *Micrococcus pyogenes* exposed to penicillin (Demerec, 1945), or *Mycobacterium ranae* in the presence of neomycin (Hsie and Bryson, 1950).

The pattern in Fig. 7 is more rare and is seen in the development of furadroxyl resistance by *E. coli* strain B (Szybalski and Nelson, 1954). Here, the first step represents a 30 to 40-fold decrease of sensitivity (B → B/r). This pattern might easily be confused with an obligatory single-step pattern, if determined within a range of concentrations limited by clinical considerations.

The foregoing classification remains relatively free of ambiguities only when applied to a particular strain. We see that in Fig. 6, strains S, R_1, and R_2 show a typical multistep pattern. Strain R_3, however, if isolated directly from a naturally occurring strain resembling R_2, would be considered as arising from the operation of an obligatory single-step pattern. The last step of a multistep pattern is often phenotypically large, suggesting that accumulating mutations have effects that are more than additive. Antibiotics eliciting this pattern are the least likely as a class to cause the clinical development of resistance. In the case of penicillin, however, the existence of a separate category of presumably single-step, penicillinase-producing mutants may be held partly responsible for the alarming clinical increase of penicillin-resistant staphylococci. This type of mutant escapes determination in survival curves (Szybalski, 1953a).

Facultative single-step pattern. The best known example of the facultative single-step pattern, the streptomycin pattern (Demerec, 1948), is found in the isolation of bacterial strains resistant to streptomycin.

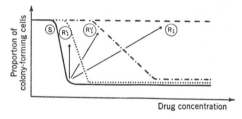

FIG. 8. Facultative one-step pattern.

If a bacterial culture consisting of ten billion or more streptomycin-sensitive *E. coli* is plated in the presence of 12 µg of antibiotic per milliliter, many cells will survive to form colonies. If these colonies are now subcultured, each will be characterized by an average level of resistance that may be slight, intermediate, or high. It has hence been possible for cells of all grades or resistance to arise in one step as represented in Fig. 8. Fastness to streptomycin may also be attained by a series of steps as in Fig. 6. The mode of development of high-level streptomycin resistance is therefore facultative. Other examples of the facultative single-step pattern are found by analysis of *Mycobacterium ranae* populations exposed to isoniazid (Szybalski and Bryson, 1952b). In all cases, surviving clones with a low grade of resistance greatly outnumber the more resistant types, but are screened out at high drug concentrations.

Significance of resistance patterns. It has been observed as a general rule that the resistance pattern is characteristic for a particular antibiotic (Bryson and Demerec, 1950). Thus, microorganisms sensitive to penicillin, but of differing genera, may be expected to follow the multistep pattern and not the facultative or obligatory single-step patterns. Similarly, saprophytic and virulent Mycobacteria show similar patterns in the development of streptomycin and isoniazid resistance, notwithstanding great differences in growth rate. Exceptions are occasionally found. For example, *E. coli* develops resistance to chloramphenicol by a typical multistep pattern, whereas *B. megaterium* does not readily change its sensitivity, and *M. ranae* becomes completely resistant in a single step (Szybalski and Bryson, 1954). For the isolation of a highly resistant cell by the patterns shown in Fig. 6, at least three steps of selection are necessary, since it is highly improbable that three mutations would occur in a single cell within the experimentally practical size of a bacterial population. The curves represented in Figs. 5–8 are statistical abstractions, derivable in actual experiment by averaging several sets of data.

Our consideration of resistance patterns has been presented from a descriptive viewpoint, without any attempt to define the origin of resistant strains obtained from colonies appearing on the downward slope of survival curves. The use of this analytical method, however, has been stressed by proponents of the genetic interpretation of resistance (Demerec, 1945; Szybalski and Bryson, 1953a). It has been implied by these investigators that the number of experimental steps required to develop any level of resistance corresponds approximately to the number of mutations necessary to produce the equivalent phenotype. The experimental evidence on this point is inadequate. Indirect indication of discrete steps leading to progressively higher grades of resistance is provided by bacterial transformation studies.

Exact correlation between number of experimental steps and number of mutations is difficult to establish, since the range of phenotypic variability within a single genotype always tends to obscure the discontinuous nature of polygenic differences (Cavalli, 1952), thus simulating in form a continuous spectrum (Eagle, Fleischman, and Levy, 1952). Phenotypic variation changes the vertical parts of survival curves to more inclined ones. For many drugs, however, the survival curve breaks off very sharply. This facilitates exact sensitivity determinations of a given strain. A comparison of sensitivities is much simplified, and accuracy is increased when several strains are plated on a single gradient plate (Szybalski, 1952). For example, by employing a 10 × 30-cm rectangular dish, it was possible by transverse streaking to assay the sensitivities of over 50 independently isolated furadroxyl-resistant *E. coli*. The isolates belonged to a few distinct classes of specific sensitivity. Mutants with interclass resistance levels were absent (W. Szybalski, unpublished). If no evidence of discontinuous variation remains after analysis of the quantitative information, several interpretations may be advanced: (1) genetic differences do not form the basis for resistance development, (2) resistance depends on a very large number of genetic factors (cf. Waddington, 1953), (3) phenotypic variation within any genotype may be very marked, or (4) replication of experiments, microenvironmental variation, and other unevaluated factors obscure any genetic differences that may exist. An apparently continuous distribution of sensitivities resulted in an attempt by Yudkin (1953) to provide an interpretation of resistance on the basis of clonal variation followed by selection, without any direct recourse to conventional genetic systems.

The prolonged evolutionary change resulting in the production of stable, resistant strains depends not only upon the selection of mutants of increased resistance level, but also may involve periodic selection of mutants with similar resistance which have better growth characteristics. Phenotypic adaptation also plays an important role, allowing survival and multiplication in otherwise drug-inhibited populations, and thus incidentally increasing the probability that better fitted mutants will appear.

This evidence leads to a general conclusion that the development of resistance is a highly complex evolutionary process, consisting potentially of many different mechanisms occurring simultaneously or in sequence. These mechanisms include many alternating phases of selection and physiological adaptation, with the possibility that toxic drugs will contribute additional variability as inducing or mutagenic agents. Prolonged exposure to highly selective conditions will almost invariably result in the isolation of new and varied mutants, at rates relatively slow in microorganisms with a well-buffered genotype as in *Paramecium* (Beale, 1953). The diversity of mechanisms observed in operation during evolutionary change is in itself the strongest argument against any extreme or dogmatic position in attempts to explain the origin of resistance.

III. Stability of Resistance

A prevalent, but erroneous, belief has been established that resistant strains derived by the selection of mutants are of necessity more permanent under conditions of subculture than are strains arising as a result of nongenetic changes. If a resistant culture reverts rapidly to sensitivity when subcultured in drug-free medium, it is illogically concluded that the basis for resistance *must* be phenotypic adaptation. The stability of resistance is based on a constellation of factors and does not yield to such a simple classification. Some of the factors tending to introduce instability into bacterial cultures or favor the loss of specific phenotypes (including resistance) are now considered.

1. *Overgrowth by Drug-Sensitive Clones of Better Adaptive Value in the Absence of the Drug*

In this example (Fig. 9a), mutation restores the original drug-sensitive phenotype, or a reasonable facsimile, through reverse mutation or some other genetic change with a corresponding effect. Many populations of resistant mutants are at a selective disadvantage in the absence of the drug, and tend to be replaceable by cells phenotypically closer to the original (wild type) strains (Mitchison, 1953; Hsie and Bryson, 1953). Competitive superiority of a bacterial clone in mixed populations need not depend entirely on a comparatively greater growth rate (Fig. 9a), or lower lag period and death rate of the adaptively favored type, as revealed by studies of population components in pure culture (Witkin, 1947). Complex interaction between competing strains, resulting from the production or accumulation of selectively toxic metabolites may condition

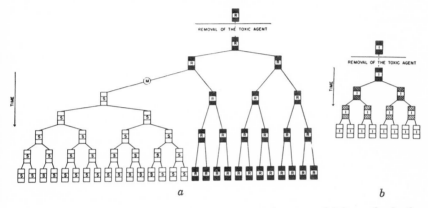

a   *b*

Fig. 9a. Loss of resistance dependent upon mutation to sensitivity and selective overgrowth of sensitive mutants.

Fig. 9b. Loss of resistance dependent upon dilution of a cytoplasmic constituent in the absence of the drug.

shifts in the proportions of genetically dissimilar clones (Goodlow, Mika, and Braun 1950). This may explain the observation of Dean and Hinshelwood (1954) that progressive deadaptation is sometimes paradoxically connected with temporary decreases in the growth rate of the deadapting bacteria.

2. *Dilution of a Cytoplasmic Constituent in the Absence of the Drug*

If the drug-resistant property has resulted in physiological adaptation, removal of the drug or inducer could easily permit a rapid reversion to sensitivity by a dilution of the induced system during growth and cell division (Fig. 9b). The rapidity of this diluting process and consequent loss of resistance might depend on several factors. Self-reproducibility, high activity, and a considerable accumulation of the biochemical system responsible for resistance would result in slow deadaptation. Induced synthesis of penicillinase is considered to be a rather permanent property and is caused by prolonged, inductive action of penicillin bound irreversibly with some components of the cell as shown by studies with radio-active sulfur (cf. Pollock, 1953). *Bacillus cereus* mutants producing constitutive penicillinase have also been found (P. H. A. Sneath, 1954, personal communication). Synthesis of penicillinase by staphylococci seems to be a constitutive property (Bondi *et al.*, 1954) but is destroyed by extreme conditions of exposure to unrelated antibiotics (Chandler *et al.*, 1951).

Phenotypic deadaptation as a cause of progressive diminution of resistance has been stressed by Dean and Hinshelwood (1954). These investigators found that strains of *Aerobacter aerogenes* adapted to grow in the presence of several drugs (proflavine, propamidine isethionate, chloramphenicol) might eventually revert to normal sensitivity, depending on the length of previous "training" and the conditions of deadaptation. The exhaustive, painstaking, but sometimes inconclusive data suggest a complex origin of the loss of resistance with back selection and phenotypic deadaptation as simultaneous or consecutive mechanisms.

Systems 9a and 9b may usually be distinguished by an analysis of clones arising from several individual cells obtained at the same time from the deadapting cultures. A separation of the two systems becomes difficult if resistance depends on a highly polygenic system, producing in combination with normal nongenetic variation an almost continuous range of phenotypes.

3. *Other Factors Contributing to Instability of Resistance*

Forward and reverse mutation rates may differ by a factor of at least 20 (Atwood, Schneider, and Ryan, 1951). In the absence of selection, rates of mutation to and from resistance should result in a population equilibrium at a point determined by their ratio. The resulting mixture of sensitive and resistant cells would be analogous to the example described by Stocker (1949) in his study of antigenic phase in *Salmonella typhimurium*. Genetic stability of bacteria may also be influenced by the residual genotype (Treffers, Spinelli, and Belser, 1954) and by the presence of mutagens. In the absence of a toxic drug, reverse mutation to sensitivity, with some correlated adaptive advantage, is thought to provide a basis for the selective loss of resistance on subculture. If the mutation rate or selective pressure were high, loss could be very rapid. It is commonly found that the culture with restored sensitivity is not exactly the same as the original culture. In the better-studied genetic systems involving the synthesizing capacities of microorganisms, so-called reversions are often the consequence of a "suppressor" mutation, and may provide only a mimic of the parent strain. Restoration of the original sensitive type is also less probable if a long chain of mutations separates the fully sensitive and fully resistant strain. The intermediate, slow-growing, partially resistant mutants might not have any selective advantage over the thoroughly drug-adapted strains, even in the absence of the drug.

Certain other factors may be significant in the loss or maintenance of selected strains with specific genetic properties. These include the existence of persistent cytoplasmic changes or "Dauermodifikationen" (Jollos, 1921), the stabilizing effects of periodic selection (Atwood, Schneider, and Ryan, 1951), and the profound influence of laboratory media on selective pressure. The eventual reappearance of a wild type clone is not unexpected, since this is the type best fitted by definition for survival in the absence of the drug.

IV. EXPERIMENTAL EVIDENCE FOR THE ORIGIN OF DRUG RESISTANCE

It is now necessary to re-examine the origin of drug resistance more critically with the aid of our illustrative models. Do resistant strains arise as a result of: microbial mutation followed by selection, by direct interaction of the toxic agent and microorganism, or by some more general type of adaptation? Admittedly, the answer may depend on the system studied and may involve combinations of methods.

As postulated by numerous investigators, the origin of heritable drug resistance before drug contact should lead to both the development of resistant clones and the isolation of resistant strains in the absence of the drug. On the other hand, by the theory of drug-induced mutations or of phenotypic adaptation, contact with the drug or a substitute inducer would be required for development of resistance. Hence no resistant cells, or clones of cells, should exist in untreated populations. The choice of suitable techniques to demonstrate the presence of families of resistant cells (clones) originating before drug contact has required considerable ingenuity, as has the isolation of resistant cultures in the absence of the drug. Considering only the more important methods, the detection of drug-resistant clones has been based on the following considerations as reviewed more extensively by Cavalli (1952), Braun (1953), and Cavalli-Sforza and Lederberg (1953).

1. The Fluctuation Test

Luria and Delbrück (1943) have provided a demonstration that the distribution of resistant cells in replicate cultures grown from a small mutant-free inoculum of sensitive cells does not conform to a Poisson distribution. Although originally performed as an analysis of phage resistance, the method may be applied with equal facility to the problem of resistance to drugs (Demerec, 1945). Cultures are grown to saturation in the absence of the drug and then plated in their entirety into drug-containing media. The high variance in the number of resistant cells, encountered when different cultures are compared, is postulated to depend on the presence of clones, increasing in size with each generation, and therefore related exponentially to the number of generations following the change of one or a few single cells from sensitivity to resistance. Because of their heritable nature, the changes are often considered to arise by a gene mutation, an assumption verifiable only by genetic test in microorganisms possessing a sexual phase.

If a very large clone of resistant cells is found in one of the replicate experiments, mutation is considered to have occurred early in the growth of that particular culture, at a time when the total number of cells per culture was small and the chance for mutation correspondingly reduced. Late mutation produces small clones or single resistant cells, and occurs more frequently, since the opportunity for mutation is greater in large populations. The fluctuation test has been performed with sulfathiazole (Oakberg and Luria, 1947), streptomycin (Demerec, 1948; Newcombe and Hawirko, 1949) and several other drugs (Szybalski, 1953b). Certain potential sources of unreliability exist if exact quantitative study is attempted. These sources include (1) selective elimination or overgrowth of resistant clones before application of the drug, (2) existence of several different types of resistant mutants within the same population, (3) delayed response of sensitive cells to the inhibitory action of the drug upon plating, (4) delayed expression of mutation, (5) uncontrollable environmental variability between independent cultures, (6) back mutations, and (7) use of a cell population so large as to swamp the initial variance. With due attention to these difficulties, validity of the variance test can be demonstrated by the fact that it is not simply a qualitative model. The Luria-Delbrück test allows quantitative predictions of the magnitude of any variance dependent upon mutation. By means of statistical models it has been possible to predict the exact distribution and size of clones if the mutational theory is applicable (Lea and Coulson, 1951; Armitage, 1952). Results obtained by experiment (Newcombe and Hawirko, 1949) showed the clonal origin of streptomycin resistance, as implied by the mutation theory.

Dean and Hinshelwood (1952) claimed to find a typical Luria-Delbrück non-Poisson distribution in variance tests performed with *Aerobacter aerogenes* plated in the presence of chloramphenicol and phenol. These investigators state that no adaptation to phenol resistance occurs, whereas adaptation to chloramphenicol appears readily. Even though no mutations to resistance were found, it was observed that the variance test failed to show a Poisson distribution. However, Berger and Wyss (1953) have described a considerable range of adaptation to phenol in *Micrococcus pyogenes* suggesting "mutation with superimposed adaptation." It appears possible that Dean and Hinshelwood may not have been justified in assuming genetic homogeneity for phenol resistance. Where adaptation is exclusively phenotypic, a Poisson distribution may indeed be observed (Spiegelman, Sussman, and Pinska, 1950), strengthening the argument that the variance or "fluctuation" test has a special genetic significance.

2. The Statistical Clone Test

Two groups of petri plates containing solidified nutrient are spread with a number of sensitive bacteria, sufficient to permit the isolation of resistant individuals after a few hours incubation, but small enough to exclude the presence of resistant individuals in the original inoculum as determined by direct test, regardless of the mode of origin. After a period of incubation permitting several cell divisions, one group of plates is respread by mechanical means, destroying individual microcolonies and redistributing the bacteria. The other group of plates is left undisturbed and a selective agent (phage) is immediately applied as an aerosol, thus producing no further disturbance in the position of the cells (Newcombe, 1949). According to the view that resistance must arise *after* contact with the toxic or selective agent, no clones of resistant bacteria could consist *a priori* in some microcolonies, and therefore redistribution would not increase the number of resistant colonies finally observed, as compared with the control plates. Neglecting the unlikely possibility that redistribution itself favors the origin of resistance, the usual presence of higher numbers of resistant colonies, developed on plates treated by mechanical redistribution of microcolonies, is taken as evidence that some of the microcolonies consisted of resistant clones before administration of the selective agent. Thus, a redistributed microcolony or clone of eight cells would later form eight resistant colonies, whereas its undistributed counterpart would form only one resistant microcolony. In its original form the test was applicable only to study of resistance to agents easily applied as aerosols. The introduction of membrane filters, upon which bacterial colonies may be transferred from one medium to another without disturbance, permits application of the method to a study of drug resistance (Bornschein, Dittrich, and Höhne, 1951; Dittrich, 1951).

3. Correlation between Clonal Distribution of Resistance and Associated Characters

In performing the Luria-Delbrück variance test, it is sometimes noticed when inspecting the petri dishes that all resistant colonies on a single plate (derived from a single independent culture) belong to one or two unique morphological types. Cavalli-Sforza and Lederberg (1953) have emphasized the significance of correlated characters as evidence of clonal relationship. If independent resistant mutants usually differ in morphology, the distinctive but identical appearance of all resistant cells in a single independent culture strongly suggests that they are related by descent. The bacteria, therefore, most probably comprise a clone originating before exposure to the drug, and dispersed at random on one dish during the plating procedure. On the other hand, variation in morphology between plates may be quite high, also indicating the independent origin of mutants in independent cultures. Distinctive properties of mutants taken from separate cultures are clearly visible when studying the resistance of *M. ranae* to isoniazid (Szybalski and Bryson, 1952b). In addition to morphological differences, other closely linked secondary properties of resistant strains may be similarly analyzed (Mitchison, 1953; Cavalli, 1952).

4. Lack of Correlation between Incidence and Degree of Resistance

As previously mentioned, one criticism of the fluctuation test attributes the high variation between independent cultures to uncontrollable environmental differences, rather than to the consequences of random mutations. In considering this problem, Cavalli-Sforza and Lederberg (1953) have suggested that if the action of environment were significant, then the same environmental factor, which increases the number of resistant cells, should also increase their average level of resistance. This could be compared with the action of wind; an increase in force would not only blow more leaves off a tree, but would also carry them further. Our analogy may be more colorful than informative, and several investigators have expressed doubt concerning the basic premise itself.

The experimental data (Cavalli, 1952) show no correlation between the number of resistant mutants in independent cultures and their average level of resistance. If the argument of Cavalli-Sforza and Lederberg is accepted, this weakens the view that variance between cultures depends on uncontrollable environmental factors, producing quantitative and qualitative changes in the same direction. It correspondingly strengthens the genetic interpretation wherein quantity and quality may be independent.

5. Increase in Proportion of Resistant Cells during Prolonged Cultivation

By means of manual transfer or mechanical devices, microorganisms may be cultured continuously at variable or fixed population densities. The proportion of drug-resistant mutants arising in these populations in the absence of the drug, increases in linear fashion if no selective pressures exist (Atwood, Schneider, and Ryan, 1951; Novick and Szilard,

1951). The mere maintenance of a constant proportion of resistant cells is evidence of clonal reproduction since, unless resistant cells reproduced themselves by cell division, their percentage would immediately decrease upon addition of fresh nutrient. The increasing proportion of mutants, with time, in the chemostat (Novick and Szilard, 1951) or turbidostat (Bryson and Szybalski, 1952) is dependent on the action of mutation or selection, superimposed on a horizontal curve provided by clonal reproduction of preexistent mutants.

6. Indirect Selection

The basis of indirect selection is the isolation of resistant or easily inducible cells without exposure to drug action. Several methods for indirect selection are available.

a. *Selection by Associated Characters.* The microorganism *Micrococcus pyogenes*, selected for faster growth rate on a semisynthetic medium, may become simultaneously less sensitive to streptomycin (English and McCoy, 1951) or may prove to be penicillin resistant when similarly selected for prototrophy (Gale, 1949).

b. *Random Selection and Replica Plating.* Logically, a simple method would be to prepare millions of independent clones derived from single cells and test a small part of each one for resistance. In this way, a clone might eventually be found that, without exposure to the drug, will yield only resistant cells. This method, however, in its primitive form is unduly tedious. The technical difficulty is overcome by the replica plating technique (Lederberg and Lederberg, 1952). Samples from almost innumerable, immobile clones on an agar surface can be transferred to the antibiotic-containing assay plate without seriously disturbing their spatial arrangement. This transfer is accomplished by stamping consecutive plates with a carefully oriented piece of sterile velveteen. The vertical fibers of cloth act as thousands of parallel bacteriological transfer needles.

By replica plating, it has been possible to show the drug-independent origin of mutants resistant to phage, streptomycin (Lederberg and Lederberg, 1952), and isoniazid (Bryson and Szybalski, 1952).

7. Genetic Origin of Mutants

In the foregoing paragraphs we have spoken rather freely of the existence of mutants. If a mutation is considered as a sudden hereditary discontinuous change, the term may be appropriate. However, all the tests described serve only to indicate the existence or nonexistence of drug resistant clones in the absence of the drug. They tell little about the *origin* of resistance. It is true that clones may arise by mutation, but this does not automatically exclude all other causes. In a strict sense,

34   VERNON BRYSON AND WACLAW SZYBALSKI

proof that clones of drug-resistant cells depend in origin upon mutation can be supported only by genetic tests, for example, study of bacterial recombination, transduction, transformation, or analysis of the segregation of nuclear hereditary determinants (Witkin, 1951).

8. *Drug-Induced Resistance*

Inability to demonstrate a spontaneously occurring clonal appearance of resistant mutants (Section IV, 1–6) may indicate that resistance arises by phenotypic adaptation or drug-induced mutation. In simple cases, analysis by sexual crossings may distinguish between these possibilities. An independent, but technically difficult indication of phenotypic adaptation, is its demonstration in the absence of multiplication; the existence of phenomic lag would characteristically prevent the expression of mutation without cell division. Induced enzyme synthesis is suggested by the demonstration of an inducer devoid of influence on selection within a population. The evidence for one complex case of phenotypic and genotypic adaptation, as illustrated in Fig. 3, was supplied by Ryan (1952) in experiments on the utilization of adaptive carbon sources. More complicated cases may not be amenable to exact experimental analysis.

A single, drug-induced, total and seemingly purposeful change in relatively stationary bacterial populations was recently described by Akiba (1955). The induced streptomycin resistance has subsequently been shown to be genic (nuclear) as determined by recombination analysis (Szybalski, 1955). Doubts, however, still exist as to the non-selectional origin of the high-level resistance encountered, especially because of the lower limit in the number of treated bacteria (10^5–10^6) necessary for successful and complete "conversions," and because not all samples of streptomycin are active. (Szybalski, unpublished.)

The role of phenotypic adaptation as a contributing factor in the development of resistance may seem to have been neglected. This has been necessary in order to condense discussion of a problem that could fill endless volumes with facts and speculation. At the present time, phenotypic adaptation appears to be less important than genetic variation in the development of drug resistance in microorganisms.

V. GENETIC PROPERTIES AND SPECIFICITY OF RESISTANT STRAINS

If resistance is frequently the consequence of enzymatic alteration, and if enzyme systems may be changed by genetic modification, then it may be predicted that sensitive and resistant organisms will frequently exhibit genetic dissimilarity. The first chromosome mapping of drug resistance in bacteria was performed by Lederberg (1947) who was able to establish phage and azide resistance as chromosomal markers. More recently, an extensive genetic analysis of resistance to chloramphenicol and oxytetracycline has been made by Cavalli (1952) by crossing resistant and sensitive strains of *E. coli* K12. As would be expected for a resistance pattern of the obligatory multistep type, there are several independent genetic loci, capable of segregation following genetic recombination. Strains showing the greatest resistance to chloramphenicol are produced by specific combinations of resistance markers, and not merely by the highest accumulation of resistant genes. These may be identified by their linkage relationship to genetic factors controlling properties of fermentation and other phenotypic traits. Thus a considerable loss of resistance might be caused by a single reverse mutation, destroying a specific configuration of genes.

Demerec (1950) and Newcombe and Nyholm (1950) have succeeded, by the use of bacterial recombination studies, in locating the factor or factors for streptomycin resistance in *E. coli*. As distinct from terramycin and chloramphenicol resistance, the genetic control of resistance to streptomycin is restricted to genes at a single locus (alleles) or to very closely linked factors ("pseudoalleles").

Severe limitations are imposed, by the present fragmentary knowledge of sex in bacteria, on any general application of bacterial recombination studies to the problem of resistance. Wide generalities have been drawn from a paucity of evidence. This has distressed a few bacteriologists of the older school who had been so busy guarding the door of bacteriology against onslaught by the biochemists that the geneticists were able to enter unnoticed through the bedroom window, taking notes as they came. In defense of the tendency of bacterial geneticists to extrapolate from a few favorable examples, it must be admitted that the evident existence of sexuality in only a limited number of bacterial strains is not a valid basis for assuming them to be otherwise unusual. It is more economical to conclude, at least tentatively, that one property of drug-resistant strains may be a distinct genotype, irrespective of crossability.

Let us represent the main property of resistance in bacterial mutants as R. Careful analysis often shows that R is a collective property, shared by many different kinds of mutants. The exact degree of resistance may vary. Even among mutants with identical degrees of resistance to a specific drug, distinction can typically be made by a comparison of collateral properties (Mitchison, 1953), or by other drugs of analogous structure (Treffers, Belser, and Alexander, 1953). As a collective property, resistance (R) tends to be associated with concomitant properties (x) representing unique qualities of individual allelic mutations, or possibly the modifying effects of a variable residual genotype. Different resistant mutants may be designated $Rx_1x_2x_3$, $Rx_1x_4x_6$, $Rx_2x_3x_5$, etc. It would not be too difficult to defend the position that very few bacterial mutants are exactly alike, suggesting for single-locus mutations an extensive system of multiple alleles. Where numerous independent loci can give rise to first-step, drug-resistant mutants, the determination of mutation rate also becomes a collective statistic, unless recombination analysis is employed to establish separability of the mutants within a single, general, phenotypic category.

The concomitant properties of drug-resistant mutants are highly important. They impart a specificity to almost every genetically independent clone. Independent mutants resistant to the same environmental agents may differ in colonial morphology (Braun and Lewis, 1950), type of metabolic deficiency (Gale, 1949), degree of cross resistance (Szybalski and Bryson, 1952a, 1954; Szybalski, 1953c, 1954), virulence (Middlebrook and Cohn, 1953), antigenicity (Gezon, 1948), collateral sensitivity (Szybalski and Bryson, 1952a), cytology (Hunter, Mudd, and Woodburn, 1950), and dependence (Miller and Bohnhoff, 1947; Bertani, 1951). The wide variability in secondary characteristics of mutants, primarily resistant to the same agent, provides an opportunity for clones corresponding in resistance, but differing in concomitant properties, to be further subdivided by appropriate selective procedures.

VI. Methods for Preventing the Development of Resistance

On a theoretical basis, the abolition of drug resistance may be accomplished by preventing either the origin or the establishment of resistant clones. Selective elimination of strains already established is a third alternative in attempts to minimize drug resistance as a clinical problem. Practically, great difficulties attend any attempt to interfere with the *origin* of resistance dependent upon genetic changes. Mutations arise from unknown causes with a measurable frequency that may, with few exceptions, easily be accelerated. In contrast, the depression of mutation rates by the use of antimutagens is difficult to accomplish, and until very recently was considered unfeasible. Although this work needs more confirmation, the discovery by Novick and Szilard (1952) that spontaneous mutation rates in bacteria may be depressed by certain nucleosides gives some hope that a new field may be opened in the control of mutation, even as the concept of metabolic analogues (Woods, 1940) gave impetus to a new and valuable trend in chemotherapy.

In certain instances, the origin of phenotypic adaptation might be controlled *in vitro* by the use of drugs that inhibit the induction or alteration of enzyme systems. As in chemotherapy generally, sufficient specificity would be required to permit use of the inhibitor *in vivo* without prohibitive toxic effects. To many geneticists, an attempt to prevent the origin of drug-resistant microorganisms by chemical means appears analogous to similar efforts aimed at the prevention of neoplasia. In both cases the present, and possibly temporary, limitations in our knowledge suggest a more fruitful approach, which is the selective control or elimination of biologically undesirable cell populations *after* they have originated. However, both the origin and establishment of resistant strains may be affected by several factors of more or less practical value:

(1) Multiple chemotherapy is based on the assumption that cells resistant to one drug may be eliminated by another. The spontaneous occurrence of multiply-resistant mutants is very rare. Theoretically, the probability of double mutation is equal to the product of individual mutation rates. For example, if the first mutant resistant to drugs A or B appears in a population composed of one million cells (10^6), populations one million times larger (10^{12}) would be necessary to find one doubly resistant mutant. Recent *in vitro* evidence indicates that experimental values may deviate slightly from the theoretical prediction (Szybalski and Bryson, 1953a).

Not all combinations of drugs are well suited for multiple chemotherapy. Those related by cross resistance or exhibiting antagonism should be avoided (Szybalski, 1953b).

It is often disputed whether two drugs should be used simultaneously or in sequence. Whenever possible, simultaneous treatment is preferred in efforts to prevent the establishment of multiply-resistant clones, which might otherwise form in a stepwise manner. Exceptionally, the existence of collateral sensitivity, or a possibility of induced phenotypic deadaptation, may favor the use of drugs in sequence, the second drug tending to eliminate resistance to the antibiotic previously used (Chandler et al., 1951). A more extensive theoretical discussion of multiple chemotherapy and the resistance problem has been made by Bryson and Demerec (1955).

(2) Choice of a drug of the multistep pattern, in preference to the single-step type, would tend to reduce the rate of resistance development. Likewise more effective would be agents which rarely select resistant cells because the rate of mutation to resistance is exceedingly low.

(3) Choice of a drug with rapid bacteriostatic or bacteriocidal action is desirable in efforts to prevent the continued growth of the bacteria, with attendant possibilities for phenotypic or genetic adaptation.

(4) Utilization of synergistic interactions between several drugs affords an additional method to reduce the significance of resistance and increase the efficiency of the therapeutic program (Jawetz and Gunnison, 1953). Physiological synergism may accelerate the disinfecting action of the drugs or decrease the concentration required to inhibit mutants with intermediate steps of resistance.

(5) Drug antagonisms must be avoided. An example of antagonism is found in the effects of subinhibitory concentrations of streptomycin on the action of isoniazid acting on *M. ranae* (Szybalski and Bryson, 1953b). In this case the streptomycin-induced decrease of bacterial growth rate and presumed reduction of metabolic turnover appears to protect cells from the action of isoniazid. Thus the residual growth is prolonged with consequent increase in probability of genotypic or phenotypic adaptation.

(6) Selection of drugs should favor those without mutagenic properties, and without the capacity to induce physiological changes to resistance.

(7) Use of antimutagens or anti-inducers in direct efforts to counteract both evolutionary (genetic) adaptation and physiological adaptation is an unexplored and perhaps useful approach to the problem of drug resistance.

(8) Sensitization of resistant cells is theoretically possible through recombination, transduction, transformation, or other exchange mechanisms. An avirulent strain might be used as the donor, providing the additional possibility of induced avirulence. The rarity of genetic exchanges among bacteria makes this suggestion highly impractical at present, but further research may increase both the number and efficiency of procedures designed to disturb the genetic equilibrium. A therapeutic program might require intermittent use of a drug with intervening drug-free periods directed toward deliberate restoration of drug sensitivity in the pathogen.

VII. Practical Application of Resistant Strains

Emphasis on the development of drug-resistant infections has obscured the fact that resistant strains may have value as analytical tools and be very useful in genetics, medicine, and industry. Analytical applications include the genetic mapping of bacterial chromosomes, wherein drug resistance is employed as one type of marker for establishing a locus. As a further example, to screen for bacterial recombination, a streptomycin-resistant strain of *E. coli*, having numerous metabolic deficiencies at separate loci, has been tested by crossing with numerous wild type strains (Lederberg, 1951b). Only by genetic exchange can a cell survive in a streptomycin medium, since recombination is required to produce a streptomycin-resistant prototroph able to grow in the synthetic medium used in the test. An additional genetic use has been the analysis of mutation rates, as in mutation from streptomycin dependence to nondependence (Bertani, 1951).

Resistant strains also provide a basis for the classification of both old and new antibiotics through analysis of cross resistance pattern

(Szybalski and Bryson, 1952a, 1954; Szybalski, 1953c, 1954). In this manner, families of antibiotics can be established having related effects and not suitable for simultaneous or consecutive clinical use.

The sensitivity of bioassay for certain antimicrobials might be increased by the use of resistant strains that have simultaneously become more sensitive to the assayed substance as in the example of collateral sensitivity (Szybalski and Bryson, 1952a).

Another whole class of utilitarian aspects pertains to the field of medicine. Present investigations indicate the feasibility of immunizing against diseases by means of drug-dependent or drug-resistant avirulent mutants The Valle strain of *M. tuberculosis* resistant to isoniazid may be used for the same purpose as BCG (Hobby, Lenert, and Auerbach, 1954). Burchenal, Waring, and Hutchison (1951) and Law (1952) have been using bacteria sensitive to antileukemic agents as convenient experimental material to investigate the development of resistance and dependence in the clinical treatment of leukemia.

Industrial uses of resistant strains include employment of actinophage- or bacteriophage-resistant strains for fermentation processes. These were formerly prone to constant interruption as a consequence of phage infection. As further examples, the bacterial strains used as lactic acid starters for butter production should be resistant to any antibiotics that might be contaminants of milk as a result of the treatment of cows for mastitis.

Many industrial oxidations or conversions performed by microorganisms may be retarded through inhibition of the organisms by accumulated metabolic products. Thus, the selective oxidation of sterols is inhibited by this substrate. Strains resistant to the inhibition effect, but not modified in the performance of industrially useful functions, will become of increasing value. Similarly, it has been noted that strains selected for higher resistance to streptomycin (Wilson *et al.*, 1951) and actinomycins (F. J. Gregory, private communication) are often better producers of the corresponding antibiotics. Random screening for microorganisms producing a given antibiotic is sometimes made easier by the fact that the producing organism may be more resistant to its own products (Villemin, Lechevalier, and Waksman, 1953).

VIII. Conclusions

It is both unfeasible and unnecessary to coerce the complex biological events contributing to the origin of resistance into a single theory. However, experimental evidence suggests that a few models will define most examples of resistance development, particularly if the models are so combined as to provide for either genotypic or phenotypic alterations of resistance level. If the body of present knowledge is to be kept sufficiently resilient to absorb new information without the impairment of established principles, it must be granted that resistance can arise in a variety of ways to be considered as complementary rather than mutually exclusive. This does not deny that a relatively important place must be assigned to certain methods of resistance development. Geneticists have been concerned with the spontaneous origin of resistance by mutation and the subsequent establishment of mutant clones by selective action of the drug. One alternative model, i.e. drug-induced resistance, appears to occupy a position of lesser importance. Evidently, induced resistance may be either genetic or nongenetic, inducibility *per se* providing no basis for distinction. In addition, selection operates not only upon mutants, but also upon transient phenotypic differences in resistance level that do not arise from heritable modifications. To define the problem in terms of mutation selection versus adaptation is therefore misleading.

In the final assessment, a mutational origin of resistance is most convincingly proven by a recombination analysis, allowing the specific localization of genes for resistance in the bacterial linkage groups (chromosomes?). Increased attention to recombination, transduction, and transformation as tools for the analysis of drug fastness will provide the geneticist with material for fruitful research, and establish with more precision the role of heredity in the origin of microbial resistance. It is obvious and proper that skeptics will not be satisfied with anything less than the best of evidence.

IX. REFERENCES

Abraham, E. P., 1953. The development of drug resistance in microorganisms. *Symposia Soc. Gen. Microbiol. (London)* **3**, 201–230.

Akiba, T., 1955. Discussion of session I, *in* "Origins of Resistance to Toxic Agents" (M. G. Sevag, R. D. Reid, and D. E. Reynolds, eds.), pp. 82–85. Academic Press, New York.

Alexander, H. E., and Leidy, G., 1953. Induction of streptomycin resistance in sensitive *Hemophilus influenzae* by extracts containing desoxyribonucleic acid from resistant *Hemophilus influenzae*. *J. Exptl. Med.* **97**, 17–31.

Armitage, P., 1952. The statistical concept of bacterial populations subject to mutation. *J. Roy. Statistical Soc.* **B14**, 1–33.

Atwood, K. C., Schneider, L. K., and Ryan, F. J., 1951. Selective mechanisms in bacteria. *Cold Spring Harbor Symposia Quant. Biol.* **16**, 345–354.

Avery, O. T., MacLeod, C. M., and McCarty, M., 1944. Studies on the chemical nature of the substance inducing transformation of pneumococcal types. Induction of transformation by a desoxyribonucleic acid fraction isolated from *Pneumococcus* Type III. *J. Exptl. Med.* **79**, 137–158.

Beale, G. H., 1953. Adaptation in *Paramecium. Symposia Soc. Gen. Microbiol. (London)* **3**, 294–305.

Bellamy, W. D., and Klimek, J. W., 1948. Some properties of penicillin-resistant staphylococci. *J. Bacteriol.* **55**, 153–160.

Berger, H., and Wyss, O., 1953. Studies on bacterial resistance to inhibition and killing by phenol. *J. Bacteriol.* **65**, 103–110.

Bertani, G., 1951. A method for detection of mutations, using streptomycin dependence in *Escherichia coli*. *Genetics* **36**, 598–611.

Bigger, J. W., 1944. Treatment of staphylococcal infections with penicillin by intermittent sterilization. *Lancet* ii, 497–500.

Bondi, A., de Saint Phalle, M., Kornblum, J., and Moat, A. G., 1954. Factors influencing the synthesis of penicillinase by *Micrococcus pyogenes*. *Arch. Biochem. and Biophys.* **53**, 348–353.

Bornschein, H., Dittrich, W., and Höhne, G., 1951. Zur Entstehung der Chemoresistenz bei Bakterien. *Naturwissenschaften* **38**, 383–384.

Braun, W., 1953. "Bacterial Genetics," 238 pp. Saunders, Philadelphia.

Braun, W., and Lewis, K. H., 1950. Colony morphology of *E. coli* mutants as a tool for genetic studies. *Genetics* **35**, 97–98.

Brown, C. H., 1950. Elimination of Kappa particles from "killer" strains of *Paramecium aurelia* by treatment with chloromycetin. *Nature* **166**, 527.

Bryson, V., 1948. The effects of nitrogen mustard on *Escherichia coli*. *J. Bacteriol.* **56**, 423–433.

Bryson, V., and Demerec, M., 1950. Patterns of resistance to antimicrobial agents. *Ann. N. Y. Acad. Sci.* **53**, 283–289.

Bryson, V., and Demerec, M., 1955. Bacterial resistance. *Am. J. Med.* **18**, 723–737.

Bryson, V., and Szybalski, W., 1952. Microbial selection. *Science* **116**, 45–51.

Bryson, V., Rosenblum, E., Kaplan, S., Hershey, H., Cuneo, H., and Dittman, I., 1951. Genetic and biochemical studies of bacteria. *Ann. Rept. Biol. Lab. Cold Spring Harbor* **62**, 24–34.

Burchenal, J. H., Waring, G. B., and Hutchison, D. J., 1951. Development of resistance to 4-amino-N[10]-methyl pteroylglutamic acid (Amethopterin) by *Streptococcus fecalis*. *Proc. Soc. Exptl. Biol. Med.* **78**, 311–313.

Cavalli, L. L., 1952. Genetic analysis of drug resistance. *Bull. World Health Org.* **6**, 185–206.

Cavalli, L. L., and Maccacaro, G. A., 1952. Polygenic inheritance of drug resistance in the bacterium *Escherichia coli*. *Heredity* **6**, 311–331.

Cavalli, L. L., and Visconti di Modrone, N., 1949. Variazione di resistenza agli agenti mutageni in *Bacterium coli*. IV. Resistenza fenotipica. *Ricerca Sci.* **19**, 1002–1006.

Cavalli, L. L., and Visconti, N., 1948. Variations de resistance aux agents mutagenes chez Bacterium coli II gaz moutarde a l'azote. *Ricerca Sci.* **18**, 1569–1574.

Cavalli-Sforza, L. L., and Lederberg, J., 1953. Genetics of resistance to bacterial inhibitors. *6th Intern. Congr. Microbiol., Rome*, pp. 108–142.

Chandler, C. A., Davidson, V. Z., Long, P. H., and Monnier, J. J., 1951. Studies on resistance of staphylococci to penicillin: The production of penicillinase and its inhibition by the action of aureomycin. *Bull. Johns Hopkins Hosp.* **89**, 81–89.

Cohen-Bazire, G., and Jolit, M., 1953. Isolement par selection de mutants d'*Escherichia coli* synthetisant spontanement l'amylomaltose et le β-galactosidase. *Ann. inst. Pasteur* **84**, 937–945.

Cohn, M., and Monod, J., 1953. Specific inhibition and induction of enzyme biosynthesis. *Symposia Soc. Gen. Microbiol. (London)* **3**, 132–149.

Davenport, C. B., and Neal, H. V., 1895. Studies on morphogenesis. V. On the acclimitization of organisms to poisonous chemical substances. *Arch. Entwicklungsmech. Organ.* **2**, 564–583.

Dean, A. C. R., and Hinshelwood, Sir Cyril, 1951. Induced and other variations in bacterial cultures. *J. Chem. Soc.*, pp. 1157–1177.

Dean, A. C. R., and Hinshelwood, Sir Cyril, 1952. Colony formation by *Bact. lactis aerogenes* on solid media containing antibacterial agents. *Proc. Roy. Soc. (London)* **B140**, 339–352.

Dean, A. C. R., and Hinshelwood, C., 1953. Observations on bacterial adaptation. *Symposia Soc. Gen. Microbiol. (London)* **3**, 21–39.

Dean, A. C. R., and Hinshelwood, Sir Cyril, 1954. The stability of various adaptations of *Bact. lactis aerogenes* (*Aerobacter aerogenes*). *Proc. Roy. Soc. (London)* **B142**, 45–60.

DeLamater, E. D., Hunter, M. E., Szybalski, W., and Bryson, V., 1955. Chemically induced aberations of mitosis in bacteria. *J. Gen. Microbiol.* **12**, 203–212.

Demerec, M., 1945. Production of staphylococcus strains resistant to various concentrations of penicillin. *Proc. Natl. Acad. Sci. U.S.* **31**, 16–24.

Demerec, M., 1948. Origin of bacterial resistance to antibiotics. *J. Bacteriol.* **56**, 63–74.

Demerec, M., 1950. Reaction of populations of unicellular organisms to extreme changes in environment. *Am. Naturalist* **84**, 5–16.

Demerec, M., 1953. Reaction of genes of *Escherichia coli* to certain mutagens. *Symposia Soc. Exptl. Biol.* **7**, 43–54.

Demerec, M., and Fano, U., 1945. Bacteriophage-resistant mutants in *Escherichia coli. Genetics* **30**, 119–136.

Demerec, M., Bertani, G., and Flint, J., 1951. A survey of chemicals for mutagenic action on *E. coli. Am. Naturalist* **85**, 119–136.

Dittrich, W., 1951. Chemoresistänz von Bakterien und Newcombe-Test. *Experientia* **7**, 431–432.

Eagle, H., Fleischman, R., and Levy, M., 1952. Development of increased bacterial resistance to antibiotics. I. Continuous spectrum of resistance to penicillin, chloramphenicol, and streptomycin. *J. Bacteriol.* **63**, 623–638.

English, A. R., and McCoy, E., 1951. A study of streptomycin resistance in *M. pyogenes* var. *aureus. J. Bacteriol.* **61**, 51–56.

Ephrussi, B., and Hottinguer, H., 1951. On an unstable cell state in yeast. *Cold Spring Harbor Symposia Quant. Biol.* **16**, 75–84.

Florey, H. W., Chain, E., Heatley, N. G., Jennings, M. A., Sanders, A. G., Abraham, E. P., and Florey, M. E., 1949. "Antibiotics," 2 vols., 1774 pp. Oxford Univ. Press, London.

Frédéricq, P., and Betz-Bareau, M., 1952. Recombinants génétiques de souches marquées par résistance aux colicines et aux bactériophages. *Ann. inst. Pasteur* **83**, 283–294.

Gale, E. F., 1948. "The Chemical Activities of Bacteria," 199 pp. Univ. Tutorial Press, London.

Gale, E. F., 1949. The action of penicillin on the assimilation and utilization of amino acids by Gram-positive bacteria. *Symposia Soc. Exptl. Biol.* **3**, 233–242.

Gale, E. F., 1951. "The Chemical Activities of Bacteria," 213 pp. Univ. Tutorial Press, London.

Gezon, H. M., 1948. Antibiotic studies on beta hemolytic streptococci. *Proc. Soc. Exptl. Biol. Med.* **67**, 208–219.

Gezon, H. M., and Carpenter, R. R., Jr., 1953. Streptomycin resistance acquired by Shigella through continuous exposure to the antibiotic. "Antibiotics Annual 1953-1954," pp. 576–584. Medical Encyclopedia, New York.

Goodlow, R. J., Mika, L. A., and Braun, W., 1950. The effect of metabolites upon variation of *Brucella abortus. J. Bacteriol.* **60**, 291–300.

Harris, J. S., and Kohn, H. I., 1943. Factors influencing the development of resistance in *Escherichia coli* to the sulfonamides. *J. Immunol.* **46**, 189–194.

Hinshelwood, C. N., 1949. Adaptation of bacteria to resist drug action (with special reference to *Bact. lactis aerogenes*). *Symposia Soc. Exptl. Biol.* **3**, 243–252.

Hinshelwood, C. N., 1953. Autosynthesis. *J. Chem. Soc.*, pp. 1947–1956.

Hobby, G., Lenert, T. F., and Auerbach, C., 1954. The immunizing properties of an isoniazid-resistant mutant of the Valee strain of *M. tuberculosis* as compared to BCG. Observations in the mouse and guinea pig. *Trans. 13th Conf. Chemotherap. Tuberc.*, Vet. Admin. Army-Navy, St. Louis, pp. 251–254.

Hotchkiss, R. D., 1951. Transfer of penicillin resistance in pneumococci by the desoxyribonucleate derived from resistant cultures. *Cold Spring Harbor Symposia Quant. Biol.* **16**, 457–470.

Hsie, J., and Bryson, V., 1950. Genetic studies on the development of resistance to neomycin and dihydrostreptomycin in *Mycobacterium ranae*. *Am. Rev. Tuberc.* **62**, 286–299.

Hsie, J., and Bryson, V., 1953. Variability and relative growth rate of mycobacteria resistant to dihydrostreptomycin, neomycin and isoniazid. "Antibiotics Annual 1953–1954," pp. 585–594. Medical Encyclopedia, New York.

Hunter, M. E., Mudd, S., and Woodburn, M. A., 1950. The morphological characteristics of paired sulfonamide-susceptible and sulfonamide-resistant strains of *Staphylococcus aureus*. *J. Bacteriol.* **60**, 315–320.

Jawetz, E., and Gunnison, J. B., 1953. Antibiotic synergism and antagonism, an assessment of the problem. *Pharmacol. Revs.* **5**, 175–192.

Jollos, V., 1921. Experimentelle Protistenstudien. I. Untersuchungen uber Variabilitat und Verebung bei Infusorien. *Arch. Protistenk.* **43**, 1–222.

Kaplan, S., Rosenblum, E. D., and Bryson, V., 1953. Adaptive enzyme formation in radiation-sensitive and radiation-resistant *Escherichia coli* following exposure to ultraviolet. *J. Cellular Comp. Physiol.* **41**, 153–162.

Kossiakoff, M. G., 1887. De la propriété que possèdent les microbes de s'accommoder aux milieux antiseptiques. *Ann. inst. Pasteur* **1**, 465–476.

Lam, G. T., and Sevag, M. G., 1955. Mechanism of the development of resistance to streptomycin. II. Biochemical differences of replica colonies. *J. Bacteriol.* **69**, 184–187.

Law, L. W., 1952. Mechanism of resistance and dependence in growth of leukemic cells. *Texas Repts. Biol. Med.* **10**, 571–597.

Lea, D. E., and Coulson, C. A., 1949. The distribution of the numbers of mutants in bacterial populations. *J. Genet.* **49**, 264–285.

Lederberg, J., 1947. Gene recombination and linked segregations in *Escherichia coli*. *Genetics* **32**, 505–525.

Lederberg, J., 1950. The selection of genetic recombinations with bacterial growth inhibitors. *J. Bacteriol.* **59**, 211–215.

Lederberg, J., 1951a. Streptomycin resistance: a genetically recessive mutation. *J. Bacteriol.* **61**, 549–550.

Lederberg, J., 1951b. Prevalence of *Escherichia coli* strains exhibiting genetic recombination. *Science* **114**, 68–69.

Lederberg, J., and Lederberg, E. M., 1952. Replica plating and indirect selection of bacterial mutants. *J. Bacteriol.* **63**, 399–406.

Levan, A., 1951. Chemically induced chromosome reactions in *Allium cepa* and *Vicia faba*. *Cold Spring Harbor Symposia Quant. Biol.* **16**, 233–243.

Linz, R., 1950. Sur le mecanisme de l'action de la streptomycine. II. La résistance à la streptomycine. *Ann. inst. Pasteur* **78**, 105–114.

Luria, S. E., 1947. Recent advances in bacterial genetics. *Bacteriol. Revs.* **11**, 1–40.

Luria, S. E., and Delbrück, M., 1943. Mutations of bacteria from virus sensitivity to virus resistance. *Genetics* **28**, 491–511.

Lwoff, A., 1953. Lysogeny. *Bacteriol. Revs.* **17**, 269–337.

Manten, A., and Rowley, D., 1953. Genetic analysis of valine inhibition in the K-12 strain of *Bacterium coli. J. Gen. Microbiol.* **9**, 226–233.

Merkel, J. R., and Steers, E., 1953. Relationship between "chloramphenicol reductase activity" and chloramphenicol resistance in *Escherichia coli. J. Bacteriol.* **66**, 389–396.

Middlebrook, G., and Cohn, M. L., 1953. Some observations on the pathogenicity of isoniazid-resistant variants of tubercle bacilli. *Science* **118**, 297–299.

Miller, C. P., and Bohnhoff, M., 1947. Two streptomycin-resistant variants of meningococcus. *J. Bacteriol.* **54**, 467–481.

Miller, C. P., and Bohnhoff, M., 1950. The development of bacterial resistance to chemotherapeutic agents. *Ann. Rev. Microbiol.* **4**, 201–222.

Mitchison, D. A., 1953. The ecology of tubercle bacilli resistant to streptomycin and isoniazid. *Symposia Soc. Gen. Microbiol. (London)* **3**, 253–274.

Newcombe, H. B., 1949. Origin of bacterial variants. *Nature* **164**, 150–151.

Newcombe, H. B., and Hawirko, R., 1949. Spontaneous mutation to streptomycin resistance and dependence in *E. coli. J. Bacteriol.* **57**, 565–572.

Newcombe, H. B., 1955. Spontaneous and induced mutations to drug resistance in *Escherichia coli. in* "Origins of Resistance to Toxic Agents" (M. G. Sevag, R. D. Reid, and D. E. Reynolds, eds.), pp. 4–19. Academic Press, New York.

Newcombe, H. B., and Nyholm, M. H., 1950. The inheritance of streptomycin resistance and dependence in crosses of *E. coli. Genetics* **35**, 603–611.

Novick, A., and Szilard, L., 1951. Experiments on spontaneous and chemically induced mutations of bacteria growing in the chemostat. *Cold Spring Harbor Symposia Quant. Biol.* **16**, 337–343.

Novick, A., and Szilard, L., 1952. Anti-mutagens. *Nature* **170**, 926–927.

Oakberg, E. F., and Luria, S. E., 1947. Mutations to sulfonamide resistance in *Staphylococcus aureus. Genetics* **32**, 249–261.

Pollock, M. R., 1953. Stages in enzyme adaptation. *Symposia Soc. Gen. Microbiol. (London)* **3**, 150–177.

Provasoli, L., Hutner, S. H., and Pintner, I. J., 1951. Destruction of chloroplasts by streptomycin. *Cold Spring Harbor Symposia Quant. Biol.* **16**, 113–120.

Rosanoff, E. J., and Sevag, M. G., 1951. The role of amino acids in the development of resistance to streptomycin. *Bacteriol. Proc.* p. 56.

Rosenblum, E. D., and Bryson, V., 1953. Rate of bacterial metabolism and the action of streptomycin. *Antibiotics & Chemotherapy* **3**, 957–965.

Ryan, F. J., 1952. Adaptation to use lactose in *Escherichia coli. J. Gen. Microbiol.* **7**, 69–88.

Sager, R., 1954. Mendelian and non-mendelian inheritance of streptomycin resistance in *Chlamydomonas reinhardi. Proc. Natl. Acad. Sci. U.S.* **40**, 356–363.

Sevag, M. G., 1946. Enzyme problems in relation to chemotherapy, "adaptation," mutations, resistance and immunity. *Advances in Enzymol.* **6**, 33–127.

Sevag, M. G., and Green, M. N., 1944. The mechanism of resistance to sulfonamides. *J. Bacteriol.* **48**, 623–630.

Sevag, M. G., and Rosanoff, E. I., 1952. Mechanism of the development of resistance to streptomycin. I. Origin of resistant strains. *J. Bacteriol.* **63**, 243–251.

Shwartzman, G., 1946. Studies on the nature of resistance of Gram-negative bacilli to penicillin. Antagonistic and enhancing effects of amino acids. *J. Exptl. Med.* **83**, 65–88.

Slonimski, P. P., 1953. A specific relation between enzymic adaptation and cytoplasmic mutation. *Symposia Soc. Gen. Microbiol. (London)* **3**, 76–94.

Spiegelman, S., Sussman, R. R., and Pinska, E., 1950. On the cytoplasmic nature of "long-term adaptation" in yeast. *Proc. Natl. Acad. Sci. U.S.* **36**, 591–606.

Stanier, R. Y., 1947. Simultaneous adaptation: a new technique for the study of metabolic pathways. *J. Bacteriol.* **54**, 339–348.

Stanier, R. Y., 1953. Adaptation, evolutionary and physiological: or Darwinism among the micro-organisms. *Symposia Soc. Gen. Microbiol.* **3**, 1–14.

Stocker, B. A. D., 1949. Measurements of rate of mutation of flagellar antigenic phase in *Salmonella typhi-murium*. *J. Hyg.* **47**, 398–413.

Szybalski, W., 1952. Microbial selection. Part I. Gradient plate technique for study of bacterial resistance. *Science* **116**, 46–48.

Szybalski, W., 1953a. "Natural" and "artificial" penicillin resistance in Staphylococcus (*Micrococcus pyogenes* var. *aureus*). *Antibiotics & Chemotherapy* **3**, 915–918.

Szybalski, W., 1953b. Multiple chemotherapy and antagonism between antimicrobial agents. *6th Intern. Congr. Microbiol., Rome, Abstr. Communs.* **1**, 318–319.

Szybalski, W., 1953c. Genetic studies on microbial cross resistance to toxic agents. II. Cross resistance of *Micrococcus pyogenes* var. *aureus* to thirty-four antimicrobial drugs. *Antibiotics & Chemotherapy* **3**, 1095–1103.

Szybalski, W., 1954. Genetic studies on microbial cross resistance to toxic agents. IV. Cross resistance of *Bacillus megaterium* to forty-four antimicrobial drugs. *Appl. Microbiol.* **2**, 57–63.

Szybalski, W., 1955. "Lamarckian" inheritance of streptomycin resistance "Antibiotics Annual 1954–1955."

Szybalski, W., and Bryson, V., 1952a. Genetic studies on microbial cross resistance to toxic agents. I. Cross resistance of *Escherichia coli* to fifteen antibiotics. *J. Bacteriol.* **64**, 489–499.

Szybalski, W., and Bryson, V., 1952b. Bacterial resistance studies with derivatives of isonicotinic acid. *Am. Rev. Tuberc.* **65**, 768–770.

Szybalski, W., and Bryson, V., 1953a. One step resistance development to isoniazid and sodium p-aminosalicylate. *J. Bacteriol.* **66**, 468–469.

Szybalski, W., and Bryson, V., 1953b. Conditional antagonism between isoniazid and other antibacterial agents. *Am. Rev. Tuberc.* **68**, 280–283.

Szybalski, W., and Bryson, V., 1954. Genetic studies on microbial cross resistance to toxic agents. III. Cross resistance of *Mycobacterium ranae* to twenty-eight antimycobacterial agents. *Am. Rev. Tuberc.* **69**, 267–279.

Szybalski, W., and Bryson, V., 1955. Origin of drug resistance in microorganisms. *in* "Origins of Resistance to Toxic Agents" (M. G. Sevag, ed.), pp. 20–41. Academic Press, New York.

Szybalski, W., and Hunter-Szybalska, M. E., 1955. Synchronization of nuclear and cellular division in *Bacillus megaterium*. *Bacteriol. Proc.* **1955**, in press.

Szybalski, W., and Nelson, T. C., 1954. Genetics of bacterial resistance to nitrofurans and radiation. *Bacteriol. Proc.* 51–52.

Treffers, H. P., Belser, N. O., and Alexander, D. C., 1953. Genetic studies on resistance to streptomycin and to substituted streptomycin (N'-γ-hydroxypropylstreptomycylamine). "Antibiotics Annual" 1953–1954, pp. 595–603. Medical Encyclopedia, New York.

Treffers, H. P., Spinelli, V., and Belser, N. O., 1954. A factor (or mutator gene) influencing mutation rates in *Escherichia coli*. *Proc. Natl. Acad. Sci. (U.S.)* **40**, 1064–1071.

Villemin, P. F., Lechevalier, H. A., and Waksman, S. A., 1953. Antibiotics of actinomyces with special reference to their role in the physiology of the organisms producing them. *6th Intern. Congr. Microbiol., Symp. Actinomycetales, Rome,* pp. 147–173.

Voureka, A., 1952. Induced variations in a penicillin-resistant staphylococcus. *J. Gen. Microbiol.* **6,** 352–360.

Waddington, C. H., 1953. Genetic assimilation of an acquired character. *Evolution* **7,** 118–126.

Waksman, S. A., 1949. "Streptomycin," 619 pp. Williams and Wilkins, Baltimore.

Waksman, S. A., 1953. "Neomycin," 219 pp. Rutgers University Press, New Brunswick, New Jersey.

Wilson, E., Koffler, H., Coty, V. F., and Tetrault, P. A., 1951. The effect of streptomycin on the respiration and growth of various strains of *Streptomyces griseus. Bacteriol. Proc.* p. 15.

Witkin, E. M., 1947. Genetics of resistance to radiation in *E. coli. Genetics* **32,** 221–248.

Witkin, E. M., 1951. Nuclear segregation and the delayed appearance of induced mutants in *Escherichia coli. Cold Spring Harbor Symposia Quant. Biol.* **16,** 357–371.

Woods, D. D., 1940. The relation of p-aminobenzoic acid to the mechanism of action of sulfonilamide. *Brit. J. Exptl. Pathol.* **21,** 74–90.

Work, T. S., and Work, E., 1948. "The Basis of Chemotherapy," 435 pp. Interscience, New York.

Wyss, O., 1950. Bacterial resistance. *Ann. N. Y. Acad. Sci.* **53,** 183–190.

Wyss, O., and Haas, F. L., 1953. Genetics of microorganisms. *Ann. Rev. Microbiol.* **7,** 47–82.

Yorke, W., Murgatroyd, F., and Hawking, F., 1931. Studies on chemotherapy. V. Preliminary contribution on the nature of drug resistance. *Ann. Trop. Med. Parasitol.* **25,** 351–358.

Yudkin, J., 1953. Origin of acquired drug resistance in bacteria. *Nature* **171,** 541–546.

Zinder, N. D., and Lederberg, J., 1952. Genetic exchange in salmonella. *J. Bacteriol.* **64,** 679–699.

The "Obscura Group" of the Genus Drosophila

Adriano A. Buzzati-Traverso

*Istituto di Genetica, Pavia, Italy and Scripps Institution of Oceanography,
La Jolla, California*

AND

Renzo E. Scossiroli

Istituto di Genetica, Pavia, Italy

|---|---|
I. Introduction	47
II. Taxonomic History	48
III. The Nearctic Members	52
1. Geographic Distribution	53
2. Chromosomes	54
3. Genetics	55
IV. The Palaearctic Members	55
1. Geographic Distribution	55
2. Chromosomes	59
3. Genetics	61
4. Biology	63
V. Mating Behavior	64
VI. Interspecific Hybrids	65
VII. Relationships	79
VIII. Acknowledgments	86
IX. References	86

I. Introduction

The wealth of data collected in the last sixteen years and the importance of the results obtained by Dobzhansky and his coworkers have made *D. pseudoobscura* and related species living on the American continent a classical material for experimental studies of evolution.

In the last decade, studies on the European species belonging to the same natural group have also been developed by several workers from the viewpoints of taxonomy, genetics, cytology, and experimental evolution.

The present paper brings together both published and unpublished data with the purpose of offering a unified picture of the phylogenetic and distributional relationships between Eurasiatic and American members of the group.

II. Taxonomic History

During its first century, the history of *D. obscura* was uneventful from the taxonomic point of view, but during the last thirty years remarkable changes have taken place.

In 1823 Fallèn described a species of Drosophila from southern Sweden which he named *Drosophila obscura*. Its most easily recognizable characters, when compared with other European species, were its very dark body color and the presence of two sex combs on the front tarsi of the male. For about a century, specimens regarded as this species were collected by several systematists in Europe. It was not until 1916, however, that a related species was found in North America, when Sturtevant described *D. affinis*, found in the eastern part of the continent. Later (1921) he mentioned a species from the Pacific coast which seemed to fit Fallèn's description of *D. obscura*. Thus began the subsequent splitting of this taxonomic entity into nineteen described species to which at least three more forms should probably be added. All of them would fit the original description given in 1823.

In 1926 Frolowa pointed out that a strain of *D. obscura* collected in Russia had a chromosome set different from that described by Metz and Moses (1923) for the supposed American form of this species. She came to the conclusion, therefore, that it had been uncorrectly classified under this name. In a later study (Frolowa and Astaurov, 1929), it was shown that even though both forms could fit into the original description they could easily be distinguished on morphological as well as on biological grounds. As a consequence, the American form was considered as distinct from the European one, and was given the name of *D. pseudoobscura* Frolowa. These authors described at the same time another strain morphologically very close to what they considered as the true *D. obscura* but having a different chromosome configuration. This form, which had been studied for its sex ratio peculiarity by Gershenson (1928), was later considered as a different taxonomic entity under the name "*D. obscura* Gershenson" (Sturtevant, 1940).

In 1935 Dobzhansky described *D. miranda*, which occurs more or less continuously along the Pacific coast from Vancouver Island to the Monterey Peninsula and in isolated localities of the Sierra Nevadas. This species was morphologically indistinguishable from *D. pseudoobscura* but can be crossed to it, giving F_1 hybrids which are mostly sterile. In the following year, five more species (*algonquin, athabasca, azteca, narragansett,* and *seminole*) were found on the North American Continent and described by Sturtevant and Dobzhansky (1936).

In England, at the same time, Collin (1936) found an *obscura*-like form which can be easily distinguished from the type of *D. obscura* Fallèn. This species was accordingly named *D. subobscura*.

In 1937 Dubinin, Sokolov, and Tiniakov published a paper on the chromosome structure of Drosophila species occurring in Russia. They spoke of a "*D. obscura*," a "*D. obscura-2*" and a "*D. obscura-3*." On the basis of the few morphological and cytological details published by them, one can surmise that *D. obscura-3* of the Russian authors corresponds to *D. subobscura* Collin. This interpretation was confirmed by a later note (Sokolov and Dubinin, 1941).

In 1938 Buzzati-Traverso collected a large series of flies in northern Italy and Germany which also corresponded to Fallèn's description. All possible crosses between the different strains were made and it was found that the collected material fell into five distinct groups which could not be crossed with one another. One of these forms was identified as *D. subobscura* Collin, and another was first regarded as the variety *tristis* of *D. obscura* Fallèn, but was later raised to specific rank as *D. tristis*. The whole material was handed over to Pomini (1940) who described and named the three remaining forms as *D. ambigua, D. bifasciata** and *D. obscuroides*. Reference to the name *D. obscura* was avoided, for it was uncertain whether any of them was identical with Fallèn's type, the war preventing comparison with type specimens. The following year a description of the mitotic chromosomes of these five species was published by Buzzati-Traverso (1941b) together with a discussion of the possible taxonomic relationships between them.

Two more species from the North American continent, also related to *obscura*, were later named *D. dobzhanskii* (Patterson, 1943) and *D. tolteca* (Patterson and Mainland, 1944).

In 1929 Lancefield distinguished two races (A and B) of *D. pseudoobscura* on the grounds of chromosome morphology. This distinction was later confirmed by cytological and genetic investigations of Dobzhansky and Boche (1933) who found that the two races were intersterile. The latter distinction later (1944) led to the segregation of race B as *D. persimilis* Dobzhansky and Epling, even though it was morphologically indistinguishable at the time (Mather and Dobzhansky, 1939). Ritzki has only recently (1951) found a consistent difference in the male genitalia of the two species.

* In Pomini's description (1940), a systematic account of the new species *D. bilineata* is given. This name is used by Pomini throughout the paper, but in the determination key (page 163) the same fly is referred to as *D. bifasciata*. Buzzati-Traverso pointed out (1948b) that, since the name bilineata had been previously used by Williston for a quite different species (see Sturtevant, 1921), the species described by Pomini and belonging to the European "obscura group" should be named *D. bifasciata* Pomini.

In 1945 Smart pointed out that a species found in Kenya and named *D. subobscura* by Seguy (1938) had to be given another name, inasmuch as *D. subobscura* was previously chosen by Collin to describe a form certainly distinct from the African one. Smart accordingly named the latter *D. seguyi* Smart.

Two more European species of the group, *D. helvetica* and *D. alpina*, were described in 1948 by Burla. Finally in 1949 Wheeler found another species in North America and named it *D. frolovae*.

Thus a complex of 19 species has been described, all closely related to the first named, *D. obscura*.

The question has been recently raised by Buzzati-Traverso (1949b) as to which of the species referred to in this discussion should be regarded as synonymous with *D. obscura* Fallèn. Living material collected through the kind offices of Prof. K. Anders, University of Lund, at Esperöd (Sweden), the *terra typica* of *D. obscura*, was a mixture of *D. obscuroides* and *subobscura*. Comparison of the male external genitalia of several species with those of Fallèn's type, labeled *D. obscura* in his own handwriting, was later made by Cain, Collin, and Demerec (1952) and proved that *D. obscuroides* Pomini is synonymous with *D. obscura* Fallèn. Thus, two lines of evidence indicate beyond doubt that the name *D. obscura* Fallèn should be correctly applied only to the species described as follows (according to Pomini, 1940; Buzzati-Traverso, 1941b; and Burla, 1951):

Drosophila obscura Fallèn, described in 1823, has the synonyms *D. obscura*-1 Frolowa (1929) and *D. obscuroides* Pomini (1940).

Male: Arista with 7 branches. Second joint of the antenna yellow-brown, with brown spot on the posterior side; third joint dark brown. Front opaque dark brown, with anterior part lighter. Orbits and ocellar triangle shining brown. Second orbital ⅓ of the third. Second oral bristle ⅓ of the first. Face and proboscis yellow. Brownish palpi; brown, broad, and high carina. Cheeks brownish yellow, their greatest width about ⅓ greatest diameter of eyes. Eyes dark red.

Mesonotum and scutellum brown, pollinose, with grayish and bronze colored reflexes. Two dark brown shining longitudinal stripes, from scutellum to neck, between dorsocentral bristles. The conspicuousness of the stripes varies with age. Sometimes, instead of the two stripes, one single broad, dark stripe extends forward from the scutellum.

Scutellum dark brown with lighter margins. Pleurae dark brown, 8 rows of acrostichal hairs. Sterno-index about 0.55. Apical bristles on first and second tibiae, preapicals on all. Small comb of short, stout, curved, black bristles, obliquely placed with respect to the main axis of the joint, on the inner side of each of the two basal joints of each front tarsus. Wings clear, veins brownish-yellow. There are 2 bristles in front of the costal break. Stout costal bristles over $\frac{2}{5}$ of the third costal section. Costal index about 2.9, fourth-vein index about 1.9, 4c index about 0.9, 5x index about 1.5.

Abdominal tergites dark brown. A series of about 9 black, tooth-shaped bristles on each of the forcipes.

Length of body: 2.4–3.7 mm, 2.2–3.1 mm; length of wings: 2.4–3.3 mm, 2.2–2.8 mm.

Females agree, except no tarsal combs. Yellow spots on the sides of the 4–6 tergites, in anterior marginal position.

Internal characters of imagines: Testes dull orange; proximal portion sac-like, short, and thin; distal portion elliptic, large. Spermathecae spherical, chitinized. Ventral receptacle, N-shaped tube, lying against the ventral surface of the uterus. Anterior and posterior arms of Malpighian tubules free.

Eggs: 2 filaments, with distal ends expanded.

Puparia: Yellow brown, each anterior spiracle with 8–10 branches.

The above is a chronological history from a purely nomenclatorial viewpoint. In 1942, however, Sturtevant brought the classification of Drosophila up to date and proposed a subdivision of the genus Drosophila into several subgenera, some of which were further subdivided into "species groups." According to Sturtevant's data, the species referred to above belong to the "*obscura* group" of the subgenus Sophophora.

The *obscura* group includes dark species with the following characters (Patterson and Stone, 1952):

"No opaque areas on tergites, sex combs present, preapical on first tibiae usually long, sterno-index 0.6, anterior scutellars convergent, second oral bristle small, middle orbital bristle large, and larvae do not skip."

The group is subdivided into two subgroups (Table 1): *obscura* subgroup, forms with several teeth in the distal sex comb, acrostical hairs in eight rows, ventral receptacle short, testes elliptical and carina broad and flat; *affinis*-subgroup, forms with one or two teeth in the distal sex comb, acrostical hairs in six rows, ventral receptacle nearly as long as in the *melanogaster* group, testes rather short and spirally coiled, carina narrow and not flat.

Besides the described species, there certainly are others of this group which await description. Such are, for example, *obscura-X* mentioned by Burla (1951), another form found in Scotland which will be called *D. silvestris* (Basden, personal communication) and probably one undescribed species close to *D. athabasca* found in Japan (Makino *et al.*, 1952). In the following discussion of the taxonomic, cytologic, and genetic relationships of the species belonging to the *obscura* group, only those species will be considered which are known from living material, and have thus made careful biological studies possible. The genus Drosophila has provided an exceptional material for evolutionary studies (see Patterson and Stone, 1952) because of the unparalleled qualities of many of its species: short life cycle, remarkable fecundity and hardiness, ease and cheapness of rearing, unusual cytological material. It is our opinion that the most reliable conclusions about relationships between species can be

TABLE 1

Species of Drosophila Belonging to the *Obscura* Group

obscura subgroup	*affinis* subgroup
Nearctic forms	Nearctic forms
frolovae Wheeler, 1949*	*affinis* Sturtevant, 1916
miranda Dobzhansky, 1935c	*algonquin* Sturtevant et Dobzhansky, 1939
persimilis Dobzhansky et Epling, 1944	*athabasca* Sturtevant et Dobzhansky, 1936
pseudoobscura Frolowa et Astaurov, 1929	*azteca* Sturtevant et Dobzhansky, 1936
Palaearctic forms	*dobzhanskii* Patterson, 1943*
alpina Burla, 1948*	*narragansett* Sturtevant et Dobzhansky, 1936
ambigua Pomini, 1940	*seminole* Sturtevant et Dobzhansky, 1936*
bifasciata Pomini, 1940	*tolteca* Patterson et Mainland, 1944*
obscura Fallèn, 1823	Palaearctic forms†
silvestris Basden, 1954	*helvetica* Burla, 1948
subobscura Collin, 1936	
tristis Fallèn, 1823	
obscura-X Burla, 1950	
Ethiopian form	
seguyi Smart, 1945*	

* Not reared in the laboratory.
† A species close to *athabasca* has also been found (Makino *et al.*, 1952a, undescribed).

drawn not from morphological similarities alone, but only when they are supported by experiments which disclose their reproductive and cytological compatibilities.

III. The Nearctic Members

Numerous papers of a detailed sort as well as reviews of the American representatives of the *obscura* group are available. We will not, therefore, enter into a discussion of these species except for data pertinent to topics to be discussed presently and we will refer the reader especially to the following publications, Dobzhansky and Epling's "Taxonomy, Geographic Distribution, and Ecology of *Drosophila pseudoobscura* and Its Relatives" and Patterson and Stone's "Evolution in the Genus Drosophila."

1. Geographic Distribution

The four American species belonging to the *obscura* subgroup occur chiefly west of the continental divide (Fig. 1). *D. pseudoobscura* has the widest range, the northernmost localities are in British Columbia and

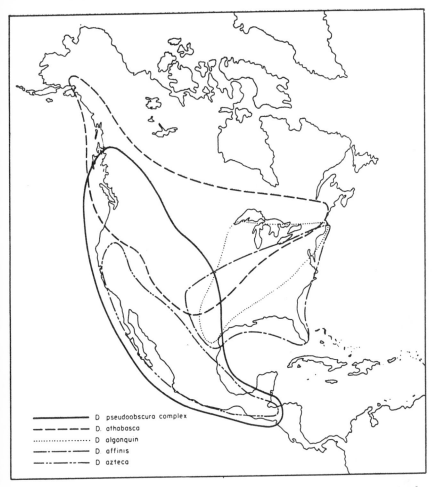

Fig. 1. Distribution of the most representative species of the *obscura* group in the Nearctic region (based on data by Patterson and Wagner, 1943).

the southernmost in Guatemala, it ranges west of the main mountain chains to the Pacific coast and on islands off it. *D. persimilis* occurs from Vancouver Island and central British Columbia to south central California, and from the Pacific to the eastern slope of the Sierra Nevada and Cascade ranges; it is also found in the Coso and Panamint ranges. *D. miranda* is distributed more or less continuously along the Pacific coast from Vancouver Island to the Monterey Peninsula. It has also been found in an isolated locality in the Sierra Nevadas, and quite recently in the San Jacinto Mountains (Epling, personal communication). *D. frolovae* has been found only once in a forest in the mountains about 19 miles east of Morelia, Michoacan, Mexico.

The distribution of *affinis* subgroup is wider and more varied. *D. athabasca* has been recorded as far north as Alaska, as far south as New Mexico, and extends from the North Pacific coast to the eastern slope of the Rocky Mountains and to Tennessee. *D. azteca* has been recorded in Guatemala, in several Mexican states, and in Texas, New Mexico, Arizona, and California. *D. affinis* and *D. algonquin* seem to have an overlapping distribution covering the South, the Middle West, and the Eastern United States. *D. narragansett* has been found in Massachusetts, Connecticut, Ohio, and Texas. *D. dobzhanskii* and *D. tolteca* seem to be limited to some areas in Mexico. *D. seminole* has been recorded only from Alabama.

2. *Chromosomes*

The metaphase configurations of American members of the *obscura* group are presented in Fig. 2. A detailed summary of the cytological evidence on the subject is given by Patterson and Stone (1952, pp. 130–133 and 191–207). Here mention will be made only of the following points: (1) The members of the *obscura* subgroup have basically the same metaphase configuration, with one dot and the five long elements, basic to the genus Drosophila, arranged in three rods and one V-shaped chromosome, derived by the fusion of elements A and D of Muller's classification (1940). *D. miranda* has a peculiar sex-determining mechanism with two X chromosomes. (2) The members of the *affinis* subgroup show three different configurations, in which the X chromosome is derived from the fusion of elements A and D, and the autosomes have various shapes as a result of pericentric inversions and addition of heterochromatin in the basic remaining elements. (3) In the salivary gland nuclei, heterochromatin is mostly concentrated in the chromocenter, always well evident. (4) More than one gene arrangement has been found in every chromosome of the studied species, except chromosome C (element B) in *D. azteca*. (5) Element C shows a higher variability than the other chromosomes in *D. pseudoobscura* and *D. persimilis* (Chromosome 3), *D. athabasca* (Chromosome C) and *D. azteca* (Chromosome A), whereas in *D. algonquin* all the chromosomes have a uniformly low variability. (6) This variability in element C has allowed the reconstruction of a

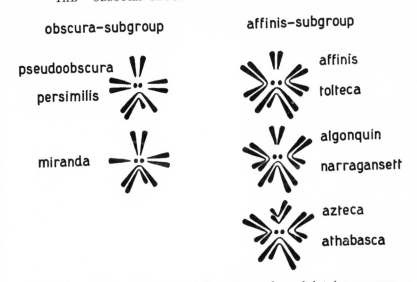

FIG. 2. Metaphase configurations of Nearctic members of the *obscura* group.

very convincing chromosome phylogeny for the complex *pseudoobscura-persimilis-miranda* and for *D. athabasca*.

3. *Genetics*

The genetics of the complex *D. pseudoobscura-persimilis-miranda* has been worked out by Lancefield (1922), Tan (1935b, 1936), and Dobzhansky and Tan (1936); genetic data on *D. affinis* have been discussed by Sturtevant (1940). These works made it possible to establish homologies between the chromosome elements of these species and those of *D. melanogaster* and other species, thereby showing the genetic relationships between members of the *obscura* group and of other groups and subgenera (Muller, 1940; Sturtevant and Novitski, 1941). Homologies between *D. affinis* and other species of that subgroup have been based on cytological studies (Miller, 1939; Dobzhansky and Sokolov, 1939).

IV. THE PALAEARCTIC MEMBERS

Taxonomic descriptions of the European members of the *obscura* group has been given by Collin (1936), Pomini (1940), and Burla (1948, 1951).

1. *Geographic Distribution*

The range is fairly well known for western Europe, but scarcely at all for eastern Europe and Asia. More extensive information about this vast area is badly needed, for we know that at least two members of the group occur as far east as Japan and at least one as far south as Lebanon

(Basden, 1952, 1954; Burla, 1948, 1951; Burla *et al.*, 1950; Buzzati-Traverso, 1941b; Hadorn *et al.*, 1952; Makino *et al.*, 1952a,b; Moriwaki *et al.*, 1951, 1952a,b, 1953; Pipkin, 1951; Pomini, 1940; Prevosti, 1952).

   D. obscura (Fig. 3) has been found practically everywhere in Europe, at all elevations, from the Atlantic coast to central Germany (Berlin) and eastern Austria, as far north as Scotland and southern Sweden and as

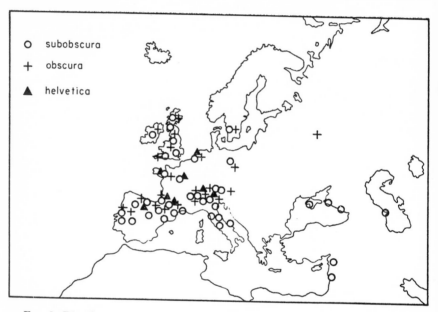

○   subobscura

+   obscura

▲   helvetica

FIG. 3. Distribution of the known records for Europe of *D. subobscura* and *D. obscura*, belonging to the *obscura* subgroup, and of *D. helvetica*, belonging to the *affinis* subgroup.

far south as the Ebro river in Portugal and the Po Valley in Italy. It apparently does not occur further east, except perhaps in European Russia. This conclusion is based on Gershenson's report (1928) of finding two females of *D. obscura* near Moscow (Zvenigorod). A few generations consisting almost exclusively of females were reared and were studied cytologically by Frolowa. She found that the chromosome set was comparable to that of *D. obscura*. The entities ascribed to *D. obscura* by Frolowa and Astaurov (1929) from the neighborhood of Moscow, and by Dubinin, Sokolov, and Tiniakov (1937) from Moscow, Alma Ata (Semirechije) Gori (Transcaucasia) and Samarkand (central Asia) are *D. bifasciata* (see below). The species is very frequent in woods and bushes, and prefers a rather humid environment, being very rare in dry areas, and in clearings.

D. subobscura (Fig. 3) is by far the most commonly collected species in western Europe. It has been recorded all over Europe from the Atlantic coast to the Black and Caspian seas and from Scotland and Sweden to southern Italy, Syria, and Lebanon. It occurs from the sea level to timber line and can be found wherever trees or bushes are present.

D. ambigua (Fig. 4), too, has been found in very different ecological conditions such as the dry climate of southern Europe (Iberic and Italian

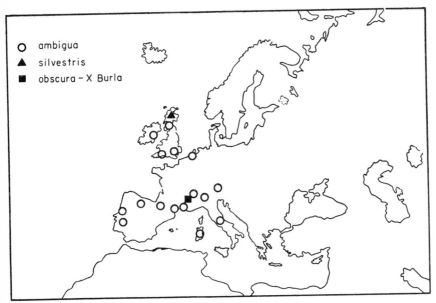

Fig. 4. Distribution of the known records of *D. ambigua*, *D. silvestris*, and *D. obscura-X*, Burla, belonging to the *obscura* subgroup.

peninsulas, Sardina) and the more humid conditions of northern France, Holland, and Great Britain. It has been found as far east as Austria.

D. bifasciata (Figs. 5 and 6) has been found in France, Germany, the Iberic peninsula, Italy, Switzerland, Holland, and has recently been captured in northern Japan where it is the most abundant species all over the mountain districts throughout the year (Moriwaki *et al.*, 1951, 1952a,b, 1953). The species from Russia referred to *D. obscura* by Frolowa and Astaurov (1929) and by Dubinin, Sokolov, and Tiniakov (1937) is considered to be *D. bifasciata* for the following reasons: (1) identity of the metaphase chromosome configurations; not only does the general description of Frolowa correspond well to that of Buzzati-Traverso, but the peculiarity of the dot chromosome being somewhat larger than in most Drosophila species is emphasized independently by both authors;

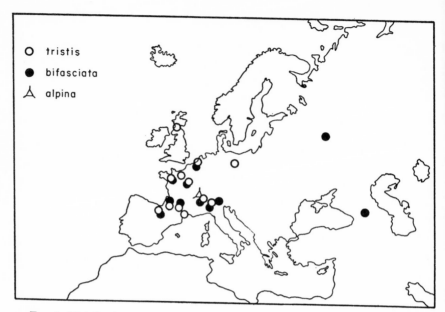

FIG. 5. Distribution of the known records for Europe of *D. tristis, D. bifasciata,* and *D. alpina,* belonging to the *obscura* subgroup.

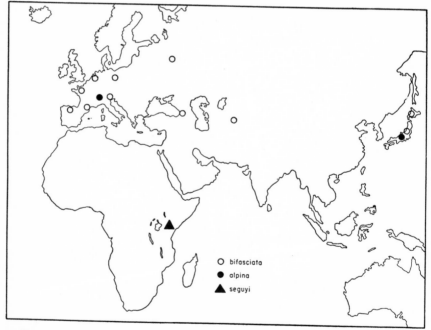

FIG. 6. Distribution of the known records for the Palaearctic region of *D. bifasciata* and *D. alpina,* and of *D. seguyi* for the Ethiopian region.

(2) the correspondence in the number of teeth on the clasper's combs (10) in Frolowa and Astaurov's as well as in Pomini's and Burla's description; (3) the correspondence in the teeth number of sex combs on male tarsi. It seems, therefore, that *D. bifasciata* occurs more or less continuously in Eurasia from the Atlantic to the Pacific. It is accordingly the member

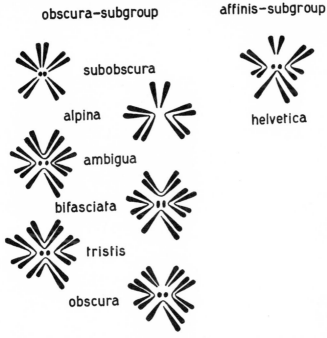

obscura-subgroup   **affinis-subgroup**

subobscura

alpina

ambigua

bifasciata

tristis

obscura

helvetica

FIG. 7. Metaphase configuration of Palaearctic members of the *obscura* group.

of the *obscura* group with the widest range for it comprises the whole Palaearctic.

D. tristis (Fig. 5) has been found in Scotland, Cornwall, France, Spain, Pyrenees, Holland, Switzerland, and northern Italy. Its area is discontinuous, however, because it is confined to very humid areas in the neighborhood of rivers and springs, irrespective of altitude.

D. alpina (Fig. 5) has been certainly recorded only for Switzerland and more recently for Japan.

D. helvetica (Fig. 3) has been found only in France, Holland, Germany, Switzerland, and in Italy on the southern slopes of the Alps.

2. Chromosomes

The metaphase configurations of Palaearctic members of the *obscura*-group are given in Fig. 7. They have been described by Frolowa and

Astaurov (1929), Emmens (1937), Buzzati-Traverso (1941b), Philip (1941), Burla (1950), and Moriwaki *et al.* (1952b, 1953). Salivary gland chromosome maps are available for *subobscura* (Frizzi, 1950; Mainx, Koske, and Smital, 1953), *ambigua* (Mainx *et al.*, 1953; Frumento, 1954), and *obscura* (Mainx, Koske, and Smital, 1953). A comparison of the salivary gland chromosomes of the last two species and of *bifasciata* and *tristis* has been given by Prevosti (1950).

The only species belonging to the *affinis* subgroup has a metaphase configuration similar to that of some of the Nearctic species of the group. Salivary gland chromosomes have not been studied.

The members of the *obscura* subgroup show a variety of patterns. *D. subobscura* has the cytological configuration that has been considered as the basic for the genus (Muller, 1940; Sturtevant and Novitsky, 1941), i.e., five rods and a dot, the Y chromosome has the same length as the X. *D. alpina* has only three chromosomes, i.e., one rod and two V-shaped chromosomes, probably derived from two fusions of four of the long elements. This is the only species of the *obscura* group that does not have the dot chromosome, and has been recently confirmed by Kurokawa through examination of larval ganglion and salivary gland cells (Moriwaki, personal communication). *D. ambigua* and *tristis* have a similar set, with a V-shaped X chromosome, probably derived from the fusion of two basic elements (see discussion in Section VII), three V-shaped autosomes and one dot. The former species has a rod-shaped Y, while the latter has a J-shaped Y chromosome. *D. bifasciata* has a similar arrangement, but differs from the last two species in that the limbs of the X chromosome are shorter and the small chromosome looks more like a short rod than like a dot. This unusual shape is probably due to the presence of heterochromatin, since this element does not seem particularly elongated in the salivary gland chromosomes. The Y chromosome is rod shaped. As pointed out in Section IV, 1 of this paper, the morphological and cytological description of Russian "obscura" corresponds to that of *D. bifasciata;* this Russian form should be considered as belonging to the said species and with the just described chromosome set. *D. obscura* has three V-shaped chromosomes, one of which is the X, two rods and one dot; the Y chromosome is rod shaped. This configuration corresponds to that given for the so-called "*obscura* Gershenson," as pointed out by Buzzati-Traverso (1941b, also see Section IV, 1 of this chapter); this Russian form should accordingly be considered as *D. obscura.*

While the remaining species have a very easily distinguishable chromocenter, *D. subobscura* salivary nuclei have practically no such structure. The salivary chromosomes of this species have, on the other hand, a striking amount of heterochromatin distributed in intercalary position

(Frizzi, 1950); this originates the formation of "puffs" which make the observation of chromosomes difficult, particularly in aged larvae. Natural populations of *subobscura* show a very remarkable amount of chromosome variability. At least 40 different inversions have been recorded and practically every individual is heterozygous for more than one inversion; the five long chromosomes are affected (Stumm-Zollinger, 1953; Mainx, Koske, and Smital, 1953, and unpublished data). Observations in nature, as well as experimental tests, indicate that this extreme polymorphism in the gene arrangements is sustained not merely by a selective advantage of the inversion heterozygotes, as demonstrated for one inversion in chromosome 5 by J. and S. Maynard Smith (1954), but by the presence of balanced lethals. This conclusion is proved by the following facts: (1) Practically every studied larva descending from free-living females has proved to be heterozygous for more than one inversion involving the five chromosomes. Sokolov and Dubinin (1941) as well as Philip *et al.* (1944) have accordingly regarded this species as a permanent hybrid. (2) In the inbred progeny of flies captured in the wild a great amount of embryonic mortality is observed, which has made the breeding of some strains especially hard (Buzzati-Traverso, 1941a; Frizzi, 1950, and unpublished data); accordingly, attempts to secure strains homozygous for certain inversions have failed. (3) The only free-living individuals found that were structurally homozygous in all the five chromosomes, even though captured at such widely separated localities as Küsnacht, Switzerland (Zollinger, 1950), Esperöd, Sweden, Mergozzo, Italy (unpublished data), and Alpach, Austria (Mainx, Koske, and Smital, 1953), all proved to have the same gene arrangement. This is probably the only one viable in homozygous condition. The chromosomal polymorphism found in *D. subobscura* populations does not seem to be correlated with the ecological characteristics of the habitat occupied by the species (Stumm-Zollinger, 1953).

No comparable amount of work has been concentrated on the study of chromosome variability in the remaining five species. Disregarding *D. alpina* for which no data at all are available, it can be said, however, that inversions have been found in every case. According to reports of the Austrian geneticists, it appears probable that the amount of chromosomal polymorphism of *D. tristis* is comparable to that of *subobscura*, while that of *ambigua*, *bifasciata*, and *obscura* is much more limited.

3. *Genetics*

The present knowledge of the genetics of Palaearctic species of the group under discussion is satisfactory for only one species, *D. subobscura*. An imposing amount of data has been collected on this species during the last eighteen years at the Department of Biometry of the University of London. Thanks to the efforts of these workers (Biometry Department, 1946, 1948, 1949; Bird, 1946a,b; Boyd et al., 1939; Christie, 1939; Clarke, 1951, 1952; Fahmy, 1952; Goldberg, 1950; Gordon, 1936; Gordon et al., 1939; Haldane, 1945; Hipsch, 1952; Hornibrook, 1952; Jermyn et al., 1943; Milani, 1949; J. and S. Maynard Smith, 1952, 1954; Philip, 1941, 1946; Philip et al., 1944; Rendel, 1943, 1945; Rendel and Spurway, 1940; Rendel and Suley, 1946; Spurway, 1939a,b, 1945, 1946a,b, 1948, 1951; Spurway and Haldane, 1954; Spurway and Philip, 1952; and Suley, 1953) it is now possible to establish genetic homologies between American and European species. Unfortunately the data have never been summarized, so that it is necessary to bring together bits of information which are scattered through several papers and in notes published in the Drosophila Information Service, 1946, 1948, 1949; Mainx, 1949, 1950; Prevosti, 1952.

A total of 233 mutants have been reported. Of these, 79 have not been localized. The remaining belong to the various chromosomes as follows (the terminology of Dr. H. Spurway-Haldane will be used): chromosome X, 94 visible mutants, 2 lethals, 29 loci; chromosome 2, 20 visible mutants, 13 loci; chromosome 3, 7 visible mutants, 5 loci; chromosome 4, 15 mutants, 11 loci; chromosome 5, 15 mutants, 8 loci; chromosome 6, 3 mutants, 3 loci. On the basis of the parallelism shown by the phenotype of some of these localized mutants with respect to that of mutants known in other species, it has been possible to establish the following homologies:

Chromosome X (e.g., bobbed, cut, crossveinless, dusky, lozenge, miniature, scute, singed, white, yellow) corresponds to element A.

Chromosome 2 (e.g., scarlet, sepia, hirsute, interrupted) corresponds to element D.

Chromosome 3 (e.g., net) probably corresponds to element B.

Chromosome 4 (e.g., plexus, poppy, pointed) corresponds to element C.

Chromosome 5 (e.g., aristapedia, Bare, Delta, vermilion) corresponds to element E.

Chromosome 6 corresponds to element F.

It appears worth while to point out a peculiarity of the genetic map of Chromosome X, namely that of having just one limb and over 200 Morgan units.

For the remaining species very little is known. For D. ambigua, 9 visible mutants have been reported (Mainx, 1950a, 1951), for D. bifasciata, 8 visible mutants (Buzzati-Traverso, 1951a; Mainx, 1952a), for D.

obscura, 4 visible mutants (Mainx, 1950b), and for *D. tristis*, one mutant (Mainx, 1952b).

4. Biology

We will report here on some biological peculiarities of European members of the *obscura* group which seem of significance for the discussion to follow.

D. subobscura. As shown by Rendel (1945), this species is unable to mate in total darkness. Only one other Drosophila species, *D. auraria*, is known to have a similar behavior. Even though occurring in very hot climates such as in Lebanon, Syria, and southern Italy, *D. subobscura* seems to be very sensitive to high temperatures for it becomes easily sterile in the laboratory at about 25°C, and females prefer relatively low temperature (about 19°C) for egg laying.

Remarkable differences in sensitivity to temperature can be found within the distribution range of the species. Buzzati-Traverso (1941a) found two extreme "temperature races" in this species. An English race became sterile at more than 21°C, and a northern Italian one has its developmental optimum at 23°C.

Natural breeding habitats for *D. subobscura* are on record, these being the only ones for the European members of the *obscura* group. Specimens of these species were reared from diseased iris roots by Collin in England, as reported by Smart (1945). Buzzati-Traverso (1948c) found larvae of *D. subobscura* in several localities in northern Italy crawling in the fermenting pulp of cornel berries (*Cornus* sp.) decaying on the soil in mixed woods. A similar habitat has been reported on galls of *Biorrhiza pallida* (Oliv.) formed on oaks in southern England (Basden, 1952). Wild yeasts have been isolated from free living individuals and were shown to be preferred to baker's yeast by *D. subobscura* (Buzzati-Traverso, 1948d, 1949a).

As previously pointed out, *D. subobscura* is the prevailing species of this group in western Europe, followed by *D. obscura* in order of dominance. Both species can be considered as eurytopic forms. As shown by Burla (1951), however, *D. obscura* and *D. subobscura* show minor differences in their ecologic valence with respect to their distribution in various biotopes at different altitudes (see Fig. 8).

D. bifasciata is peculiar in that a large fraction of its wild females produce almost exclusively female progeny (Buzzati-Traverso, 1941c). This sex-ratio condition is transmitted through the female line and is probably dependent on the presence of a cytoplasmic factor which does not allow for the embryonic development or metamorphosis of Y-bearing zygotes (Magni, 1952, 1953a,b). This condition has been found in several wild populations, its frequency among free-living females being as high as 30% in one locality. A similar condition was observed once in the progeny of *D. obscura* females collected in northern Italy (Magni, 1952). The accidental loss of the strain prevented a detailed analysis. A different type of sex-ratio condition was described by Gershenson (1928) for a strain of a species collected in Russia. On the basis of the cytological

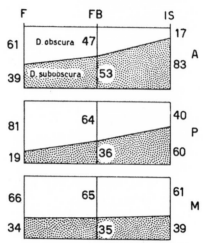

FIG. 8. Differences in the ecological valence of *D. obscura* and *D. subobscura* in various biotopes at different altitudes in Switzerland. The frequencies are given in relative percentage of the two species for: the Alps (A), the Pre-Alps (P) and for the region comprised between the Jura and the Pre-Alps (M); in the forest (F), at the edge of forests (FB), in meadows with scattered trees (IS) (from Burla, 1951).

description given by Frolowa, it is possible to say that this was *D. bifasciata*. In this case the sex-ratio condition was due to a gene producing abnormalities in the meiosis of males which could not produce Y-bearing sperms.

V. Mating Behavior

The mating behavior of the considered species follows a basically similar pattern. There are, however, two major variations on the same theme which enable us to separate the species of the *obscura* group into two subgroups, which fit very well into the morphologic distinction of *obscura* and *affinis* subgroups.

The basic mating behavior of the group consists (Spieth, 1952) of "the male's tapping, followed by posturing at the side, front, or rear of the female, but never involves licking at any time. The female accepts by spreading the vaginal plates but not the wings. The male achieves intromission by grasping the dorsolateral surface of the female's abdomen with his forelegs and bringing the tip of his abdomen forward and under;

he then immediately mounts and spreads the female's wings with his fore-legs, aided by the sex combs. The male assumes a 'forward' copulatory position, holding onto the bases of the female's wings with his fore tarsal claws".

The differences between the two subgroups, *obscura* and *affinis*, are related to the actions performed by the male just after "tapping". Those of the *obscura* subgroup posture at the side, front, or rear of the female, while the males of the *affinis* subgroup circle the female but never posture in front of her.

Minor differences in the mating behavior have been described for each of the species of the group (Milani, 1950, 1951a,b; Weidmann, 1951; Spieth, 1952). It should be pointed out that *subobscura* not only stands out with respect to the rest of the species of the group for its requirement of light in order to perform mating (Philip *et al.*, 1944; Rendel, 1945; Wallace and Dobzhansky, 1946; and Milani, 1951a) but that it shows a peculiar behavior in terms of posturing action when compared with the remaining European species of the *obscura* subgroup. As we shall see later, *subobscura* is divergent from these in some morphological traits, too.

According to Spieth, *subobscura* engages a posturing movement which is almost identical to that of *pseudoobscura*, *persimilis*, and *miranda*. This author therefore concludes: "this movement is so distinct and so similar in all four species that it seems logical to conclude that this element of the mating behavior was possessed by an ancestor common to all four species".

VI. INTERSPECIFIC HYBRIDS

Attempts to obtain hybrids among species of Drosophila have proved very useful for ascertaining the degree of genetic affinity and the possible phylogenetic relationships between the tested entities (*e.g.*, Patterson and Stone, 1952). Numerous tries of this sort have been made for species of the *obscura* group. While crosses between the three most studied Nearctic species of the *obscura* subgroup gave interspecific hybrids, which made it possible to establish genetic homologies between the chromosomes of *D. pseudoobscura*, *persimilis*, and *miranda*, no results were obtained in extensive experiments with European species (Table 2). Hybrids were obtained, however, from the cross between species living on different continents: *D. ambigua* from Europe crossed with *D. pseudoobscura*, *persimilis*, and *miranda* from North America (Buzzati-Traverso and Scossiroli, 1952; Koske, 1952, 1953). Koske (1953) states that hybrid larvae were obtained from the crosses of *D. pseudoobscura* and *persimilis* with *D. tristis* and *bifasciata* but presented no data. The present authors have not been able to confirm this statement (Table 2). In the *affinis*

TABLE 2
Crosses Between Members of the *obscura* Group

Crosses female × male	F_1 Hybrids ♀♀	♂♂	Gene exchange possible	References
		obscura subgroup		
Nearctic members				
1. *pseudoobscura* × *persimilis*	Fertile	Sterile	Yes	Lancefield, 1929
2. *persimilis* × *pseudoobscura*	Fertile	Sterile	Yes	Lancefield, 1929
3. *pseudoobscura* × *miranda*	Fertile	Sterile	Yes	Dobzhansky, 1935a, 1937
4. *miranda* × *pseudoobscura*	Fertile	Sterile	Yes	Dobzhansky, 1935a, 1937
5. *persimilis* × *miranda*	Fertile	Sterile	Yes	Dobzhansky, 1935a, 1937
6. *miranda* × *persimilis*	Fertile	Sterile	Yes	Dobzhansky, 1935a, 1937
Palaearctic members				
7. *subobscura* × *tristis*	No progeny		—	Buzzati-Traverso, 1941b
8. *tristis* × *subobscura*	No progeny		—	Buzzati-Traverso, 1941b
9. *subobscura* × *bifasciata*	No progeny		—	Buzzati-Traverso, 1941b
10. *bifasciata* × *subobscura*	No progeny		—	Buzzati-Traverso, 1941b
11. *subobscura* × *obscura*	No progeny		—	Buzzati-Traverso, 1941b
12. *obscura* × *subobscura*	No progeny		—	Buzzati-Traverso, 1941b
13. *subobscura* × *ambigua*	No progeny		—	Buzzati-Traverso, 1941b
14. *ambigua* × *subobscura*	No progeny		—	Buzzati-Traverso, 1941b
15. *tristis* × *bifasciata*	No progeny		—	Buzzati-Traverso, 1941b
16. *bifasciata* × *tristis*	No progeny		—	Buzzati-Traverso, 1941b
17. *tristis* × *obscura*	No progeny		—	Buzzati-Traverso, 1941b
18. *obscura* × *tristis*	No progeny		—	Buzzati-Traverso, 1941b
19. *tristis* × *ambigua*	No progeny		—	Buzzati-Traverso, 1941b
20. *ambigua* × *tristis*	No progeny		—	Buzzati-Traverso, 1941b
21. *bifasciata* × *obscura*	No progeny		—	Buzzati-Traverso, 1941b
22. *obscura* × *bifasciata*	No progeny		—	Buzzati-Traverso, 1941b
23. *bifasciata* × *ambigua*	No progeny		—	Buzzati-Traverso, 1941b
24. *ambigua* × *bifasciata*	No progeny		—	Buzzati-Traverso, 1941b
25. *ambigua* × *obscura*	No progeny		—	Buzzati-Traverso, 1941b
26. *obscura* × *ambigua*	No progeny		—	Buzzati-Traverso, 1941b
Palaearctic × Nearctic members				
1. *ambigua* × *miranda*	Only pupae		No	Buzzati-Traverso, 1951b, Buzzati-Traverso and Scossiroli, 1952

TABLE 2. (*Continued*)

Crosses female × male	F_1 Hybrids		Gene exchange possible	References
	♀ ♀	♂ ♂		
Palaearctic × Nearctic members				
2. *miranda* × *ambigua*	No progeny		—	Buzzati-Traverso, 1951b; Buzzati-Traverso and Scossiroli, 1952
3. *ambigua* × *pseudoobscura*	Only pupae		No	Buzzati-Traverso, 1951b; Buzzati-Traverso and Scossiroli, 1952; Koske, 1953
4. *pseudoobscura* × *ambigua*	No progeny		—	Buzzati-Traverso, 1951b; Buzzati-Traverso and Scossiroli, 1952
	Sterile	Sterile	No	Koske, 1953
5. *ambigua* × *persimilis*	Only pupae		No	Buzzati-Traverso, 1951b; Buzzati-Traverso and Scossiroli, 1952
	Sterile	Sterile	No	Koske, 1953
6. *persimilis* × *ambigua*	No progeny		No	Buzzati-Traverso, 1951b, Buzzati-Traverso, and Scossiroli, 1952
	Only pupae			Koske, 1953
7. *tristis* × *miranda*	No progeny		—	Buzzati-Traverso and Scossiroli, unpubl.
8. *miranda* × *tristis*	No progeny		—	Buzzati-Traverso and Scossiroli, unpubl.
9. *tristis* × *pseudoobscura*	No progeny		—	Buzzati-Traverso and Scossiroli, unpubl.
10. *pseudoobscura* × *tristis*	No progeny		—	Buzzati-Traverso and Scossiroli, unpubl.
	Only pupae		No	Koske, 1953
11. *tristis* × *persimilis*	No progeny		—	Buzzati-Traverso and Scossiroli, unpubl.
	Only pupae		No	Koske, 1953
12. *persimilis* × *tristis*	No progeny		—	Buzzati-Traverso and Scossiroli, unpubl.
13. *subobscura* × *miranda*	No progeny		—	Buzzati-Traverso and Scossiroli, unpubl.
14. *miranda* × *subobscura*	No progeny		—	Buzzati-Traverso and Scossiroli, unpubl.

TABLE 2. (*Continued*)

Crosses female × male	F_1 Hybrids ♀♀ ♂♂	Gene exchange possible	References
Palaearctic × Nearctic members			
15. *subobscura* × *pseudoobscura*	No progeny	—	Buzzati-Traverso and Scossiroli, unpubl.
16. *pseudoobscura* × *subobscura*	No progeny	—	Buzzati-Traverso and Scossiroli, unpubl.; Rendel, 1943
17. *obscura* × *miranda*	No progeny	—	Buzzati-Traverso and Scossiroli, unpubl.
18. *miranda* × *obscura*	No progeny	—	Buzzati-Traverso and Scossiroli, unpubl.
19. *obscura* × *pseudoobscura*	No progeny	—	Buzzati-Traverso and Scossiroli, unpubl.
20. *pseudoobscura* × *obscura*	No progeny	—	Buzzati-Traverso and Scossiroli, unpubl.
21. *obscura* × *persimilis*	No progeny	—	Buzzati-Traverso and Scossiroli, unpubl.
22. *persimilis* × *obscura*	No progeny	—	Buzzati-Traverso and Scossiroli, unpubl.
23. *bifasciata* × *miranda*	No progeny	—	Buzzati-Traverso and Scossiroli, unpubl.
24. *miranda* × *bifasciata*	No progeny	—	Buzzati-Traverso and Scossiroli, unpubl.
25. *bifasciata* × *pseudoobscura*	No progeny	—	Buzzati-Traverso and Scossiroli, unpubl.
26. *pseudoobscura* × *bifasciata*	No progeny	—	Buzzati-Traverso and Scossiroli, unpubl.
27. *bifasciata* × *persimilis*	No progeny	—	Buzzati-Traverso and Scossiroli, unpubl.
28. *persimilis* × *bifasciata*	No progeny	—	Buzzati-Traverso and Scossiroli, unpubl.
	Only pupae	No	Koske, 1953
***affinis* subgroup**			
Nearctic members			
1. *athabasca* × *azteca*	Sterile Sterile	No	Sturtevant and Dobzhansky, 1936
2. *azteca* × *athabasca*	Sterile Sterile	No	Sturtevant and Dobzhansky, 1936
3. *affinis* × *athabasca*	Sterile Sterile	No	Miller, 1941
4. *algonquin* × *athabasca*	Fertile Sterile	Yes	Miller, 1941

TABLE 2. *(Continued)*

Crosses female × male	F_1 Hybrids ♀♀	F_1 Hybrids ♂♂	Gene exchange possible	References
Palaearctic × Nearctic Members				
1. *affinis* × *helvetica*	No progeny		—	Buzzati-Traverso, 1951c
2. *helvetica* × *affinis*	No progeny		—	Buzzati-Traverso and Scossiroli, unpubl.
3. *algonquin* × *helvetica*	No progeny		—	Buzzati-Traverso and Scossiroli, unpubl.
4. *helvetica* × *algonquin*	No progeny		—	Buzzati-Traverso and Scossiroli, unpubl.
5. *narragansett* × *helvetica*	No progeny		—	Buzzati-Traverso and Scossiroli, unpubl.
6. *helvetica* × *narragansett*	No progeny		—	Buzzati-Traverso and Scossiroli, unpubl.
7. *azteca* × *helvetica*	No progeny		—	Buzzati-Traverso and Scossiroli, unpubl.
8. *helvetica* × *azteca*	No progeny		—	Buzzati-Traverso and Scossiroli, unpubl.
9. *athabasca* × *helvetica*	No progeny		—	Buzzati-Traverso and Scossiroli, unpubl.
10. *helvetica* × *athabasca*	No progeny		—	Buzzati-Traverso and Scossiroli, unpubl.
Crosses between subgroups				
1. *pseudoobscura* × *helvetica*	No progeny		—	Buzzati-Traverso and Scossiroli, unpubl.
2. *helvetica* × *pseudoobscura*	No progeny		—	Buzzati-Traverso and Scossiroli, unpubl.
3. *persimilis* × *helvetica*	No progeny		—	Buzzati-Traverso and Scossiroli, unpubl.
4. *helvetica* × *persimilis*	No progeny		—	Buzzati-Traverso and Scossiroli, unpubl.
5. *miranda* × *helvetica*	No progeny		—	Buzzati-Traverso and Scossiroli, unpubl.
6. *helvetica* × *miranda*	No progeny		—	Buzzati-Traverso and Scossiroli, unpubl.
7. *obscura* × *affinis*	No progeny		—	Buzzati-Traverso and Scossiroli, unpubl.
8. *affinis* × *obscura*	No progeny		—	Buzzati-Traverso and Scossiroli, unpubl.

TABLE 2. (*Continued*)

Crosses female × male	F_1 Hybrids		Gene exchange possible	References
	♀♀	♂♂		
Crosses between subgroups				
9. *obscura* × *algonquin*	No progeny		—	Buzzati-Traverso and Scossiroli, unpubl.
10. *algonquin* × *obscura*	No progeny		—	Buzzati-Traverso and Scossiroli, unpubl.
11. *obscura* × *narragansett*	No progeny		—	Buzzati-Traverso and Scossiroli, unpubl.
12. *narragansett* × *obscura*	No progeny		—	Buzzati-Traverso and Scossiroli, unpubl.
13. *obscura* × *azteca*	No progeny		—	Buzzati-Traverso and Scossiroli, unpubl.
14. *azteca* × *obscura*	No progeny		—	Buzzati-Traverso and Scossiroli, unpubl.
15. *obscura* × *athabasca*	No progeny		—	Buzzati-Traverso and Scossiroli, unpubl.
16. *athabasca* × *obscura*	No progeny		—	Buzzati-Traverso and Scossiroli, unpubl.
17. *obscura* × *helvetica*	No progeny		—	Buzzati-Traverso and Scossiroli, unpubl.
18. *helvetica* × *obscura*	No progeny		—	Buzzati-Traverso and Scossiroli, unpubl.
19. *subobscura* × *affinis*	No progeny		—	Buzzati-Traverso and Scossiroli, unpubl.
20. *affinis* × *subobscura*	No progeny		—	Buzzati-Traverso and Scossiroli, unpubl.
21. *subobscura* × *algonquin*	No progeny		—	Buzzati-Traverso and Scossiroli, unpubl.
22. *algonquin* × *subobscura*	No progeny		—	Buzzati-Traverso and Scossiroli, unpubl.
23. *subobscura* × *narragansett*	No progeny		—	Buzzati-Traverso and Scossiroli, unpubl.
24. *narragansett* × *subobscura*	No progeny		—	Buzzati-Traverso and Scossiroli, unpubl.
25. *subobscura* × *azteca*	No progeny		—	Buzzati-Traverso and Scossiroli, unpubl.
26. *azteca* × *subobscura*	No progeny		—	Buzzati-Traverso and Scossiroli, unpubl.

TABLE 2. (*Continued*)

Crosses female × male	F_1 Hybrids ♀♀	F_1 Hybrids ♂♂	Gene exchange possible	References
Crosses between subgroups				
27. *subobscura* × *athabasca*	No progeny		—	Buzzati-Traverso and Scossiroli, unpubl.
28. *athabasca* × *subobscura*	No progeny		—	Buzzati-Traverso and Scossiroli, unpubl.
29. *subobscura* × *helvetica*	No progeny		—	Buzzati-Traverso and Scossiroli, unpubl.
30. *helvetica* × *subobscura*	No progeny		—	Buzzati-Traverso and Scossiroli, unpubl.
31. *bifasciata* × *affinis*	No progeny		—	Buzzati-Traverso and Scossiroli, unpubl.
32. *affinis* × *bifasciata*	No progeny		—	Buzzati-Traverso and Scossiroli, unpubl.
33. *bifasciata* × *algonquin*	No progeny		—	Buzzati-Traverso and Scossiroli, unpubl.
34. *algonquin* × *bifasciata*	No progeny		—	Buzzati-Traverso and Scossiroli, unpubl.
35. *bifasciata* × *narragansett*	No progeny		—	Buzzati-Traverso and Scossiroli, unpubl.
36. *narragansett* × *bifasciata*	No progeny		—	Buzzati-Traverso and Scossiroli, unpubl.
37. *bifasciata* × *azteca*	No progeny		—	Buzzati-Traverso and Scossiroli, unpubl.
38. *azteca* × *bifasciata*	No progeny		—	Buzzati-Traverso and Scossiroli, unpubl.
39. *bifasciata* × *athabasca*	No progeny		—	Buzzati-Traverso and Scossiroli, unpubl.
40. *athabasca* × *bifasciata*	No progeny		—	Buzzati-Traverso and Scossiroli, unpubl.
41. *bifasciata* × *helvetica*	No progeny		—	Buzzati-Traverso and Scossiroli, unpubl.
42. *helvetica* × *bifasciata*	No progeny		—	Buzzati-Traverso and Scossiroli, unpubl.
43. *tristis* × *helvetica*	No progeny		—	Buzzati-Traverso and Scossiroli, unpubl.
44. *helvetica* × *tristis*	No progeny		—	Buzzati-Traverso and Scossiroli, unpubl.

TABLE 2. (*Continued*)

Crosses female × male	F_1 Hybrids		Gene exchange possible	References
	♀ ♀	♂ ♂		
Crosses between subgroups				
45. *affinis* × *tristis*	No progeny		—	Buzzati-Traverso and Scossiroli, unpubl.
46. *algonquin* × *tristis*	No progeny		—	Buzzati-Traverso and Scossiroli, unpubl.
47. *narragansett* × *tristis*	No progeny		—	Buzzati-Traverso and Scossiroli, unpubl.
48. *azteca* × *tristis*	No progeny		—	Buzzati-Traverso and Scossiroli, unpubl.
49. *athabasca* × *tristis*	No progeny		—	Buzzati-Traverso and Scossiroli, unpubl.
50. *ambigua* × *affinis*	No progeny		—	Buzzati-Traverso and Scossiroli, unpubl.
51. *affinis* × *ambigua*	No progeny		—	Buzzati-Traverso and Scossiroli, unpubl.
52. *ambigua* × *algonquin*	No progeny		—	Buzzati-Traverso and Scossiroli, unpubl.
53. *algonquin* × *ambigua*	No progeny		—	Buzzati-Traverso and Scossiroli, unpubl.
54. *ambigua* × *narragansett*	No progeny		—	Buzzati-Traverso and Scossiroli, unpubl.
55. *narragansett* × *ambigua*	No progeny		—	Buzzati-Traverso and Scossiroli, unpubl.
56. *ambigua* × *azteca*	No progeny		—	Buzzati-Traverso and Scossiroli, unpubl.
57. *azteca* × *ambigua*	No progeny		—	Buzzati-Traverso and Scossiroli, unpubl.
58. *ambigua* × *athabasca*	No progeny		—	Buzzati-Traverso and Scossircli, unpubl.
59. *athabasca* × *ambigua*	No progeny		—	Buzzati-Traverso and Scossiroli, unpubl.
60. *ambigua* × *helvetica*	No progeny		—	Buzzati-Traverso and Scossiroli, unpubl.
61. *helvetica* × *ambigua*	No progeny		—	Buzzati-Traverso and Scossiroli, unpubl.

subgroup, interspecific crosses were successful only among some North American representatives.

The discovery that one Palaearctic species, which cannot be crossed with other representatives from the same region, gives hybrids when crossed with species from the Nearctic is of interest because it gives us a clue to the relationships between two geographically separated groups. The experimental evidence on this point, however, is partly

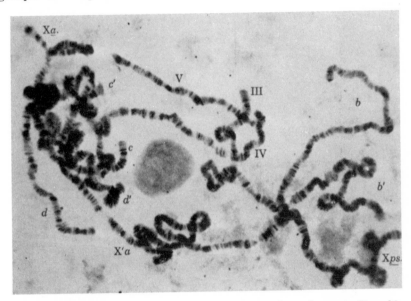

FIG. 9. Salivary gland chromosomes of hybrid larva from the cross: *D. ambigua* (Swiss strain) × *D. pseudoobscura* (Arrowhead gene arrangement, Aspen strain). *D. ambigua*'s chromosomes are indicated according to Frumento's terminology (Xa-X'a; b-b'; c-c'; d-d'); *D. pseudoobscura*'s chromosomes are indicated with Roman numbers, except for the X chromosome (Xps).

controversial. The present authors found in 1950 that when *ambigua* females are crossed to any of the three mentioned North American species, a small number of hybrids are formed, some of which complete development and pupate but do not undergo metamorphosis; the reciprocal crosses did not give any result. Cytological studies of the hybrid larvae showed that in the salivary gland nuclei the chromosome strands of the parental species do not undergo synapsis, and therefore one can observe 13 free arms (5 of *pseudoobscura* and 8 of *ambigua*) originating from a common chromocenter in which the two small dot chromosomes (Figs. 9 and 10) can be seen. Koske (1953), on the other hand, using the same strains, reported that she obtained a few hybrid adults from one cross of *ambigua* ♀ × *persimilis* ♂, and from one of *pseudoobscura* ♀ × *ambigua* ♂. Furthermore, she observed salivary glands pairing between both *pseudoobscura* and *persimilis* chromosomes and those of *ambigua*. Such results would make it possible to ascertain homologies between cytological elements of the American and European species. Miss Koske kindly communicated her results to us and we made extensive but futile attempts to repeat them. In view of the interest of such observations,

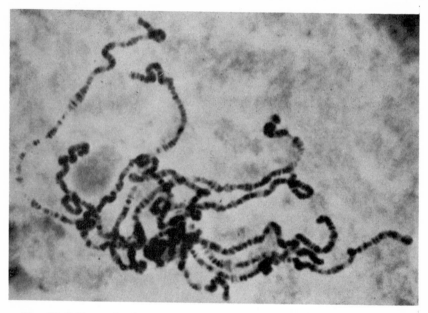

Fig. 10. Salivary gland chromosomes of hybrid larva from the cross: *D. ambigua* (Swiss strain) × *D. pseudoobscura* (Oaxaca strain). The 13 long arms of the parental species are well distinguishable.

extensive attempts were carried out to analyze further this phenomenon. Unfortunately, however, the results were completely negative.

In the course of these investigations, it turned out that the percentage of eggs which hatch to give larvae differs when different strains of both species are crossed (Table 3). This observation led to a further checking on this point.

Culture bottles with a minimum of 15 virgin *ambigua* females and 25 *pseudoobscura* (or *persimilis*, or *miranda*) males were set up and the number of pupae obtained during a period of 20 days was recorded. Four replications were made for each cross (Buzzati-Traverso and Scossiroli, 1952; Scossiroli, 1951, 1954). Table 4 gives the results of a first series of tests. It appears that the Chiricahua gene arrangement of *D. pseudo-*

obscura may be more successful in producing hybrid pupae than any of the other gene arrangements tested. If so, this might depend upon (1) a specific effect of the Chiricahua gene arrangement, or (2) a nonspecific effect due to the whole genotype. In order to test which of these assumptions was correct, a second series of tests was carried out, taking advantage of special strains constructed by Dr. Donald F. Mitchell for his experiments on the selective value of third chromosome types of *D. pseudoobscura*. Chiricahua and Standard third chromosome gene arrangements derived from Keen Camp and Pinon Flat, respectively, had been

TABLE 3

Percentage of Hatched Eggs and Pupae Recovered from Eggs Laid by *D. ambigua* (Swiss Strain) Females Kept with *D. pseudoobscura*, *D. persimilis*, and *D. miranda* Males

♂♂	No. of eggs tested	Percent of eggs hatched	Percent of pupae recovered
pseudoobscura Pinon, Standard g.a.	10,230	0.078	0.059
pseudoobscura Pinon, Arrowhead g.a.	10,084	0.323	0.188
pseudoobscura Aspen, Arrowhead g.a.	10,204	0.020	0.020
pseudoobscura Amecameca	10,077	0.050	0.030
pseudoobscura Tree Line, Morelia g.a.	10,106	0.059	0.020
pseudoobscura Pinon, Chiricahua g.a.	10,127	0.188	0.128
persimilis Sequoia, Standard g.a.	10,000	0.090	0.070
persimilis Porcupine, Arrowhead g.a.	10,009	0.070	0.030
persimilis Hope, Klamath g.a.	10,000	0.030	0.010
miranda Big Basin	10,100	0.0	0.0

combined with the other chromosomes from Mather (Epling, Mitchell, and Mattoni, 1953).

The results shown in Table 5 (Scossiroli, 1954) indicate further that the Chiricahua chromosome type has a specific effect in the production of interspecific hybrid pupae. At the same time, comparison of the percentage of successful crosses in which geographically different *ambigua* strains were used shows that the southern European strains used were more successful than the Scottish ones.

Several dozen larvae derived from crosses using several geographic strains of both parental species have been studied cytologically. Not a single case of pairing was found. The fact that the hybrid larvae are somewhat larger than those of either parental species, and the remarkable thickness of the salivary chromosomes, raised the suspicion that the

TABLE 4

Tests of Fertility of Crosses between Strains of *D. ambigua* (Females) and *D. pseudoobscura, persimilis,* and *miranda* (Males)

Strains and gene arrangements (g.a.) of the male parents	Strains of *D. ambigua* (♀♀)											
	Swiss		Terminillo		Admont		Dalkeith		Renfrew		Bonnyrigg	
	a*	b†	a*	b†	a*	b†	a*	b†	a*	b†	a*	b†
g.a. Klamath:												
persimilis, Hope	4/20	0.18	4/6	0.47	4/6	0.37	4/28	0.22	4/28	0.18	4/28	0.08
g.a. Standard:												
persimilis Sequoia	6/7	1.20	6/7	1.20	6/7	0.90	5/28	0.27	11/28	0.37	2/28	0.05
pseudoobscura Pinon	17/21	0.78	11/16	0.51	4/6	0.50	2/28	0.03	2/28	0.03	5/28	0.10
g.a. Arrowhead:												
pseudoobscura Aspen	18/26	0.82	4/6	2.27	5/6	1.07	6/28	0.13	13/28	0.28	8/28	0.20
pseudoobscura Pinon	11/19	1.21	8/8	0.52	4/5	0.57	9/28	0	3/28	0.05	2/28	0.05
g.a. Chiricahua:												
pseudoobscura Pinon	15/21	1.99	3/6	0.97	5/6	1.72	7/28	0.27	3/28	0	2/28	0.03
g.a. Tree Line:												
pseudoobscura Morelia	5/15	0.12	4/9	0.17	—		9/28	0	9/28	0	9/28	0
miranda Big Basin	0/15	0	9/15	0	3/6	0.52	2/28	0.02	3/28	0.08	9/28	0

* In columns *a,* the number of cultures with larva are given against the total number of culture started.
† In columns *b,* the number of pupa per parental females are given.

TABLE 5

Tests of Fertility of Crosses between Strains of *D. ambigua* (Females) and Strains of *D. pseudoobscura* (Males) Differing in the Gene Arrangements of Their Third Chromosomes*

	No. of ♀♀	No. of cultures	No. of fertile cultures	No. of pupae	No. of pupae per female
D. ambigua Dalkeith × *D. pseudoobscura*					
Keen Camp, g.a. Chiricahua, strain 304	60	28	7	12	0.20
Keen Camp, g.a. Chiricahua, strain 311	60	28	4	2	0.03
Keen Camp, g.a. Standard, strain 265	60	28	1	1	0.02
Keen Camp, g.a. Standard, strain 313	60	28	4	8	0.13
Pinon Flat, g.a. Chiricahua, strain 325	60	28	2	2	0.03
Pinon Flat, g.a. Chiricahua, strain 344	60	28	1	0	0.0
Pinon Flat, g.a. Standard, strain 284	60	28	1	0	0.0
Pinon Flat, g.a. Standard, strain 337	60	28	1	1	0.02
D. ambigua Swiss strain × *D. pseudoobscura*					
Keen Camp, g.a. Chiricahua, strain 304	60	28	10	52	0.87
Keen Camp, g.a. Chiricahua, strain 311	60	28	11	66	1.10
Keen Camp, g.a. Standard, strain 265	60	28	7	10	0.17
Keen Camp, g.a. Standard, strain 313	60	28	6	15	0.25
Pinon Flat, g.a. Chiricahua, strain 325	60	28	8	12	0.20
Pinon Flat, g.a. Chiricahua, strain 344	60	28	6	11	0.18
Pinon Flat, g.a. Standard, strain 284	60	28	7	26	0.43
Pinon Flat, g.a. Standard, strain 337	60	28	4	10	0.17
D. ambigua Admont × *D. pseudoobscura*					
Keen Camp, g.a. Chiricahua, strain 304	60	28	14	27	0.45
Keen Camp, g.a. Chiricahua, strain 311	60	28	7	15	0.25
Keen Camp, g.a. Standard, strain 265	60	28	6	21	0.35
Keen Camp, g.a. Standard, strain 313	60	28	6	15	0.25
Pinon Flat, g.a. Chiricahua, strain 325	60	28	8	4	0.07
Pinon Flat, g.a. Chiricahua, strain 344	60	28	7	7	0.12
Pinon Flat, g.a. Standard, strain 325	60	28	6	11	0.18
Pinon Flat, g.a. Standard, strain 337	60	28	8	14	0.23
D. ambigua Terminillo × *D. pseudoobscura*					
Keen Camp, g.a. Chiricahua, strain 304	60	28	12	41	0.68

TABLE 5. (*Continued*)

	No. of ♀ ♀	No. of cultures	No. of fertile cultures	No. of pupae	No. of pupae per female
D. ambigua Terminillo × *D. pseudoobscura*					
Keen Camp, g.a. Standard, strain 265	45	21	7	11	0.24
Keen Camp, g.a. Standard, strain 313	60	28	7	22	0.37
Pinon Flat, g.a. Chiricahua, strain 325	15	7	3	9	0.60
Pinon Flat, g.a. Chiricahua, strain 344	60	28	6	8	0.13
Pinon Flat, g.a. Standard, strain 284	30	14	2	2	0.06
Pinon Flat, g.a. Standard, strain 337	60	28	12	15	0.25

* Strain numbers as from C. Epling.

larvae were allopolyploids. This possibility was carefully checked by ascertaining whether any of the thirteen threads would show occasional unpaired regions and thus indicate diploid condition. No such case was found; furthermore, counts of mitotic metaphase plates in the hybrids do not seem to support this possibility.

In spite of the fact that it has not been possible to confirm Koske's results, they certainly are very interesting because they indicate that, on rare occasions, one may obtain hybrids between species which ordinarily cannot cross. Koske's proposed homologies between *pseudoobscura* and *ambigua* chromosomes, however, appear doubtful, especially with respect to the X chromosome. While there is a good correspondence in the relative length of the salivary gland chromosomes of *D. pseudoobscura* and *subobscura*, it turns out that the X chromosome of *ambigua* is about 20 units shorter than that of *pseudoobscura* (see Table 9). Similar, although less striking, discrepancies are to be found in the comparison of the remaining elements. Koske's diagram of cytologic homologies fails to account for these differences.

The results reviewed above indicate that, in the material examined, genetic divergence between species living in different zoogeographic regions has reached a point where (1) only a very small fraction of the produced hybrid zygotes undergoes development; (2) development of those hybrid zygotes that complete the embryonic stages is bound to come to a standstill during larval life, or at the latest during metamorphosis, probably as a consequence of the lack of pairing between somatic chromosomes; (3) only exceptional environmental circumstances allow chromosome pairing to take place and this is accompanied by complete ontogenesis.

TABLE 6

Homologies between Chromosomes of Species of the *obscura* Group and
D. melanogaster

| Species | Chromosome Elements | | | | | | Reference |
	A	B	C	D	E	F	
melanogaster	X	2L	2R	3L	3R	4	Muller, 1940
pseudoobscura	XL	4	3	XR	2	5	Lancefield, 1922
persimilis	XL	4	3	XR	2	5	Tan, 1935b
miranda	XL	4	X2	XR	2	5	Dobzhansky and Tan, 1936
affinis	XL	4	3	XR	2	5	Sturtevant, 1940
algonquin	XS	C	A	XL	B	D	Miller, 1939
azteca	XS	C	A	XL	B	D	Dobzhansky and Sokolov, 1939
athabasca	A	B	C	D	E	F	Novitski, 1946
subobscura	X	III	IV	II	V	VI	Dept. of Biometry, University College, London, 1936–54
subobscura	X	II	V	III	IV	VI	Frizzi, 1950
subobscura	A	E	U	J	O	D	Mainx, Koske, and Smital, 1953

VII. Relationships

With the possible exception of *D. seguyi*, whose inclusion in this group of species is doubtful, the *obscura* group has a typical Holarctic distribution. Both subgroups, *affinis* and *obscura*, are represented in the Old and the New Worlds, but the degree of differentiation they have undergone is remarkably different. Eight species belonging to the *affinis* subgroup are present in the Nearctic, while only one occurs in the Palaearctic; and, on the contrary, the four Nearctic forms of the *obscura* subgroup are matched by six described and probably more than two undescribed forms in the Palaearctic. The degree of ecologic valence of the two subgroups is very different in the two continents, too. While the distribution range of the *affinis* subgroup covers practically the whole North American continent, the *obscura* subgroup is represented by its various forms only west of the Rocky Mountains, and only one species, *D. pseudoobscura*, is widespread over a vast area and occupies ecologically different biotopes. On the Eurasian continent, on the other hand, the only species of the *affinis* subgroup, *D. helvetica*, has a very patchy distribution and seems to have rather restricted ecological requirements. The species of the *obscura* subgroup, on the contrary, occur all over the vast area comprised between the Atlantic and the Pacific Oceans, with four species, *D. bifasciata*, *alpina*, *subobscura*, and *obscura* distributed over very wide ranges, both in terms of geography and ecology. It appears that the *obscura* group has undergone a different type of evolution in the Palaearctic and in the

Nearctic. In the Palaearctic, the *obscura* subgroup has undergone a greater differentiation, producing a larger number of species capable of varied ecological adjustments, whereas the *affinis* subgroup has not produced many forms and remained ecologically restricted. In the Nearctic, an opposite tendency is evident; the *affinis* subgroup has evolved more species and thereby occupied a vaster area than the *obscura* subgroup. Such different evolutionary patterns of the two subgroups in the Holarctic regions, as revealed at the taxonomic level, are reflected in the morphology, the behavior, the cytology, and probably in the genetic systems of the species.

TABLE 7

Numbers of Characters in Common between Any Two Given Species of the *obscura* Subgroup. 48 Morphological Traits Have Been Considered

Species	obscura	tristis	bifasciata	ambigua	sub-obscura	per-similis	pseudo-obscura	miranda
obscura	—	25	27	24	17	13	16	14
tristis	25	—	19	26	21	14	17	13
bifasciata	27	19	—	17	21	12	12	13
ambigua	24	26	17	—	23	13	15	13
subobscura	17	21	21	23	—	13	12	11
persimilis	13	14	12	13	13	—	37	36
pseudo-obscura	16	17	12	15	12	37	—	40
miranda	14	13	13	13	11	36	40	—

Considering the morphology of the species belonging to the *obscura* subgroup first, we notice that the amount of differentiation in the three well-known North American species is very little (Reed and Reed, 1948), so little, in fact, that the two species *pseudoobscura* and *persimilis* were considered as physiological races of the same species for several years. The five Eurasian species can be distinguished more easily from one another, especially in the male sex. Only old males of *D. obscura* and *D. bifasciata* would usually be confused, but *D. tristis* and *D. obscura* females are practically indistinguishable. The degree of similarity between species can be directly evaluated in Table 7 where the number of morphological traits in common between any two species are given. Only those species are noted for which at least 48 morphological traits could be considered. It can be concluded that *D. subobscura* differs more from each of the members of the Eurasian subgroup than the latter differ from each other, but, at the same time, its differences with *D. obscura* and *D. bifasciata* are of a different sort than those with *D. ambigua* and *D. tristis*. These conclusions are in good agreement with the data presented by Weidman (1951) and Spieth (1952) concerning the mating behavior of these forms. A superficial comparison of the Eurasian with the American forms could lead one to believe that *D. obscura* and especially *D. bifasciata* are closer in their morphology to *D. pseudoobscura* than to other Palaearctic forms. As Table 7 shows, however, this is not the case; the morphological similarity is distinctly greater within forms of one continent than between forms of two continents. *D. ambigua*, as previously mentioned, can be crossed with *D. pseudoobscura, persimilis*, and *miranda;* its similarity to the American forms is, however, not greater than that of other European species. On the basis of Table 7 classification, in fact, *D. obscura* and *tristis* have a larger number of traits in common with the Nearctic forms.

TABLE 8

Numbers of Characters in Common between Any Two Given Species of the *affinis* Subgroup. 38 Morphological Traits Have Been Considered

Species	algonquin	affinis	athabasca	azteca	narragansett	tolteca	helvetica
algonquin	—	27	28	23	24	14	19
affinis	27	—	27	22	26	13	16
athabasca	28	27	—	25	27	15	22
azteca	23	22	25	—	24	17	24
narragansett	24	26	27	24	—	12	23
tolteca	14	13	15	17	12	—	12
helvetica	19	16	22	24	23	12	—

A similar table for the morphological comparison between the species of the *affinis* subgroup has been constructed (Table 8), taking into account 38 characters. Here it appears that *D. algonquin, affinis, athabasca, azteca,* and *narragansett* form a very homogeneous group, and this is well in agreement with the results of hybridization experiments. No data of this type are available for *narragansett*, but the morphology of this species with a limited geographic distribution does not depart appreciably from the others just mentioned. *D. tolteca*, the sixth Nearctic species, on the other hand, has a unique position with respect to the other five; in fact it deviates more than *D. helvetica*, the only representative of the subgroup in the Palaearctic. The latter, however, as shown in Table 2, does not produce any hybrid with the Nearctic relatives.

Summarizing the evidence derived from morphological comparisons it can be said that: (1) subgroups differ from one another more than species of the same subgroup belonging to different zoogeographical regions; (2) in the *obscura* subgroup species have diverged more between than within zoogeographical regions, and are represented by one complex (*pseudoobscura-persimilis-miranda*) in the Nearctic, two complexes (*obscura-bifasciata* and *ambigua-tristis*) and one widespread, abundant species (*subobscura*) in the Palaearctic; (3) in the *affinis* subgroup species have diverged to the same extent if not more, within rather than between zoogeographical regions, and are represented by one complex (*algonquin-affinis-athabasca-azteca-narragansett*) in the Nearctic, and two outstanding species, one in the Nearctic (*tolteca*) and one in the Palaearctic (*helvetica*).

Chromosome evolution within the *obscura* group has certainly been conspicuously greater than in other species groups. The cytological configuration with five rods and a dot, i.e., six separate chromosome elements, regarded as basic for the genus Drosophila (Muller, 1940; Sturtevant and Novitski, 1941; Patterson and Stone, 1952) is found in *D. subobscura*. The karyotypes of other species of the group have probably been derived either by fusions or by pericentric inversions. Homologies between the chromosome elements of *D. melanogaster* and of this group have been established for several American and for just one European species (Table 6). The integrity of the five long elements has been retained in spite of changes in the number and shape of the chromosomes. A comparison of the relative lengths of the long elements in the salivary gland chromosomes (Table 9) supports this conclusion. This also seems to hold true for *D. subobscura*, in spite of the appreciable amount of intercalary heterochromatin present. Similar data are presented in the lower part of Table 9 for some of the species for which chromosome homologies have not yet been established. (We consider *ambigua* in this group, since the homologies proposed by Koske do not seem convincing, as pointed out in Section IV.) The configuration of *D. alpina* is probably derived from three fusions, although it is not yet clear how the five basic elements have been repatterned to form the chromosome configurations of *D. ambigua*, *bifasciata*, *obscura*, and *tristis*. A more detailed study of the genetics and cytology of these species appears urgently needed for a complete understanding of the chromosome evolution within this species group.

A very interesting trait which appears typical of this group of species is the greater variability in the gene sequences presented by element C. As Novitski (1946) pointed out, the number of different gene arrangements found in element C of *D. pseudoobscura* and *persimilis* (Chromosome 3), as well as of *D. athabasca* (Chromosome C), *algonquin* (Chromosome A), and *azteca* (Chromosome A) is greater, or at least equal to that of any other chromosome. This trait is not limited to the Nearctic species, for Stumm-Zollinger (1953) found 11 different inversions in element C (Chromsome V) of *D. subobscura*, as contrasted with a maximum of 5 in the second most variable chromosome. The effect of the concentrating

TABLE 9

Relative Lengths of the Long Elements in the Salivary Glands Nuclei

Species	Element					References
	A	B	C	D	E	
algonquin	16.4	18.5	19.7	20.0	25.4	Miller, 1939
azteca	15.1	18.8	19.0	21.4	25.8	Dobzhansky and Sokolov, 1939
pseudoobscura	14.0	19.9	16.3	24.0	25.8	Tan, 1937; Dobzhansky and Tan, 1936
subobscura	17.3	20.9	17.0	20.5	24.3	Frizzi, 1950
subobscura	16.5	20.4	18.1	20.1	24.9	Mainx et al., 1953
	Terminology used and lengths					
obscura	A = X	E	I	O	U	
	9.6 + 10.0	9.7 + 14.0	15.8 + 17.4	10.5	13.0	Mainx et al., 1953
	3 + 3	4 + 5	1 + 2	1′	2′	Prevosti, 1950
	16.4 + 10.4	13.4 + 9.3	15.9 + 14.7	11.0	8.9	
ambigua	A	E	I	U		
	7.5 + 11.2	11.3 + 11.4	17.7 + 17.3	10.6 + 13.0	13.0	Mainx et al., 1953
	X	D	B	C		
	10.4 + 9.7	10.0 + 9.3	17.2 + 16.2	12.5 + 14.7		Frumento, 1954
	1	2	3	4		
tristis	16.7 + 15.2	16.1 + 12.6	13.2 + 11.5	7.3 + 7.4		Prevosti, 1950
	1	2	3	4		
bifasciata	16.5 + 17.6	17.6 + 12.7	9.0 + 13.5	7.7 + 5.4		Prevosti, 1950

of many gene sequences in one particular element and its significance for the evolution of the group is far from understood, especially since such inversions seem to perform different functions in different species. Thus, whereas in *D. pseudoobscura* seasonal variations in gene frequencies and the characteristic geographic distribution of certain inversions can be related to different adaptive values of the genetic material present in the various gene sequences (Dobzhansky, 1947, 1948, 1952; Heuts, 1948; Levine, 1952), in *D. subobscura* no seasonal cycles have been observed, no chromosomal geographic races have been identified, and no correlation has been found between the degree of chromosome polymorphism and the number of ecological niches available in any given locality. In *D. willistoni* and related species the greatest chromosome variability is found in element E (Dobzhansky, Burla, and Da Cunha, 1950), while in other widely distributed species, such as *D. melanogaster*, all the chromosome elements seem to be equally constant in their gene sequences. What factors are responsible for such marked differences in the genetic systems of various species, and what part they may have played in their evolution remains an open question, in spite of the great amount of work which has been aimed toward an understanding of the function of chromosome polymorphism in the Nearctic species. The fact that one particular chromosome element maintains a greater plasticity than any other throughout this species group and in different zoogeographical regions, points to the importance of the mechanism.

Finally, at the level of genetic variability, the *obscura* group provides us with a very fine example of how different ecological conditions can be met by different genetic systems. On one hand, we find species, such as *D. bifasciata* and *D. athabasca*, having an exceedingly wide longitudinal range of distribution, and also species showing the ability of withstanding a great variety of ecological conditions, such as *D. subobscura*, found in the Lebanon desert and in the highlands of Scotland, and *D. pseudoobscura* found in tropical Mexico and in the mountain forests of British Columbia. On the other hand, we have highly specialized entities such as *D. tristis*, found only in the neighborhood of rivers or springs, or *D. seminole*, which seems limited only to a small area in Alabama. Accordingly, we find temperature races, chromosomal polymorphism as well as an impressive amount of genetic heterogeneity in wild populations, and various genetic mechanisms, all developed to cope with a variety of environments.

The various lines of evidence which we have discussed indicate that the evolutionary history of this group of species has been very varied. Faced with the problem of conquering an increasingly wider range of habitats, the hypothetical ancestor of this group of species has given origin to a remarkable series of variations on the same theme. At some times, isolating mechanisms were established and accordingly new taxonomic entities were born, at other times a large genetic diversification took place within the previously existing specific limits. The presence of the two subgroups in both the Palaearctic and the Nearctic, together with the fact that differences within subgroups are smaller than between subgroups, even when comparing species living in different zoogeographical regions, point to an ancient origin of the two subgroups and of the whole complex of species. The evidence derived from cytological data is well in agreement with this view.

We could now attempt a reconstruction of the phylogenetic history of the *obscura* group, but we regard the data at our disposal as being too vague to justify any such attempt, except in particular cases such as that of the *D. pseudoobscura* complex of sibling species, mentioned above. We have been able to bring together enough information to show close taxonomic relationships and genetic affinities among the described species, and it has been possible to identify some common cytologic denominators in the evolution of the group. We are bound to assume that the genetic changes leading to the present conditions have taken place over a long period of time. Unfortunately, no known fossil records are available of the progenitors of the now living *Drosophila obscura* and, therefore, we should, in our attempt, rely exclusively on speculation. Sturtevant (1940) pointed out that probably *D. pinicola* is the most primitive living member of the genus and that the *obscura* group, being the closest to this species, could possibly be the most primitive species group. In view of the fact that we can base our conclusions only on those forms which are now living, and that we have no way of telling which may have disappeared in the past, we accept Sturtevant's conclusion but prefer not to construct a phylogeny of the species within the *obscura* group.

The history of the studies on the Drosophilae of the *obscura* group and the results obtained, which we have attempted to summarize and discuss, are the best proof of the fact that, even when they do not lead to a well constructed phylogenetic tree, investigations of this sort are very important for a better understanding of evolutionary mechanisms. As it always happens in science, a deeper knowledge opens wider horizons and brings out new, previously unsuspected problems. The study of evolutionary mechanisms within the *obscura* group is far from being exhausted; the data here collected indicate the directions along which further work will be likely to produce important information and make the origin of this group less obscure.

VIII. Acknowledgments

The authors are indebted to numerous persons to whom they wish to express their appreciation of help received. They are under obligation first of all to Mr. Giordano Peschiera for assistance over a period of many years with collections of specimens in nature, maintenance of stocks, and help in the course of experiments. They are grateful to the Department of Biometry, University College, London, and particularly to Dr. Helen Spurway-Haldane for communicating unpublished observations and for having made available many strains; they are likewise indebted to Prof. Felix Mainx, Vienna, Austria, and to Prof. Daigoro Moriwaki, Tokyo, Japan. We wish to express our appreciation to Prof. K. Anders, University of Lund, Sweden, for the collection of living specimens of *D. obscura* in its *terra typica*. Strains have been received from Mr. E. B. Basden, Edinburgh, Scotland; Prof. Th. Dobzhansky, New York, N.Y.; Prof. C. Epling, Los Angeles, California; Prof. E. Hadorn, Zürich, Switzerland; Professor D. D. Miller, Lincoln, Nebraska; Prof. J. T. Patterson, Austin, Texas; Dr. A. Prevosti, Barcelona, Spain; thanks are due to all these colleagues. The authors are indebted to Prof. Carl Epling for a critical reading of the manuscript and for numerous helpful comments.

IX. References

Basden, E. B., 1952. Some Drosophilidae (Diptera) of the British Isles. *Entomol. Monthly Mag.* **88**, 200–201.

Basden, E. B., 1954. The distribution and biology of Drosophilidae (Diptera) in Scotland, including a new species of Drosophila. *Trans. Roy. Soc. Edinburgh,* **62**, 603–654.

Biometry Department, University College, London, 1946. Report on *D. subobscura* mutants. *Drosophila Information Service* **20**, 82–83.

Biometry Department, University College, London, 1948. Report on *D. subobscura* mutants. *Drosophila Information Service* **22**, 66–68.

Biometry Department, University College, London, 1949. Report on *D. subobscura* mutants. *Drosophila Information Service* **23**, 77–78.

Bird, M. J., 1946a. X chromosome of *Drosophila subobscura*. *Drosophila Information Service* **20**, 84.

Bird, M. J., 1946b. A gene affecting the male genitalia in *Drosophila subobscura*. *Drosophila Information Service* **20**, 85.

Boyd, M. M. M., Rendel, J. M., and Spurway, H., 1939. (Linkage data of *D. subobscura.*) *Drosophila Information Service* **12**, 54.

Brunetto, A., 1954. I cromosomi politenici delle ghiandole salivari di *Drosophila ambigua*. II. Inversioni eterozigoti. *Scientia Genet. Turin* **4**, in press.

Burla, H., 1948. Die Gattung Drosophila in der Schweiz. *Rev. suisse zool.* **55**, 272–279.

Burla, H., 1950. Die Chromosomensätze der in der Schweiz vorkommenden Drosophila Arten *D. helvetica, D. kuntzei, D. limbata, D. testacea, D. littoralis* und *D. nigrospursa*. *Arch. Julius Klaus-Stift. Vererbungsforsch. Sozialanthropol. Rassenhyg.* **25**, 496–504.

Burla, H., 1951. Systematik, Verbreitung und Oekologie der *Drosophila* Arten der Schweiz. *Rev. suisse zool.* **58**, 23–175.

Burla, H., Ernst, F., Gloor, H., and Hadorn, E., 1950. Collecting wild *Drosophila* in southwestern Europe. *Drosophila Information Service* **24**, 79.

Buzzati-Traverso, A., 1941a. Genetica di popolazioni in *Drosophila:* I. Eterosi in *Drosophila subobscura* Collin. *Scientia Genet. Turin* **2**, 190–223.

Buzzati-Traverso, A., 1941b. Genetica di popolazioni in *Drosophila;* II. I cromosomi di 5 specie del "gruppo obscura" e la incrociabilità di varie razze geografiche. *Scientia Genet. Turin* **2**, 224–241.

Buzzati-Traverso, A., 1941c. An extreme case of sex-ratio in *D. bilineata*. *Drosophila Information Service* **14**, 49.

Buzzati-Traverso, A., 1948b. *D. bifasciata*, a systematic note. *Drosophila Information Service* **22**, 69.

Buzzati-Traverso, A., 1948c. Larvae of *D. subobscura* found in nature. *Drosophila Information Service* **22**, 69.

Buzzati-Traverso, A., 1948d. Wild yeasts from *D. subobscura* adults. *Drosophila Information Service* **22**, 69.

Buzzati-Traverso, A., 1949a. Preference of *D. subobscura* for wild yeasts. *Drosophila Information Service* **23**, 88.

Buzzati-Traverso, A., 1949b. What is *Drosophila obscura?* *Drosophila Information Service* **23**, 88–89.

Buzzati-Traverso, A., 1951a. Report on *D. bifasciata* mutants. *Drosophila Information Service* **25**, 94.

Buzzati-Traverso, A., 1951b. Interspecific crossings in the *obscura* subgroup. *Drosophila Information Service* **25**, 102.

Buzzati-Traverso, A., 1951c. Interspecific crossings in the *affinis* subgroup. *Drosophila Information Service* **25**, 102.

Buzzati-Traverso, A., and Scossiroli, R. E., 1952. Interspecific crosses between *Drosophila* species living on different Continents. *Trans. 9th Intern. Congr. Entomol., Amsterdam* **1**, 246–249.

Cain, A. J., Collin, J. E., and Demerec, V. R., 1952. Correct application of the name *Drosophila obscura* Fallèn and notes on the type of *D. tristis* Fallèn (Dipt., Drosophilidae). *Entomol. Monthly Mag.* **88**, 193–196.

Christie, A. L. M., 1939. The effect of X-rays on sex in *D. subobscura* and an account of some sex-linked characters. *J. Genet.* **39**, 1–46.

Clarke, J. M., 1951. Report on *D. subobscura* mutants. *Drosophila Information Service* **25**, 94.

Clarke, J. M., 1952. Report on *D. subobscura* mutants. *Drosophila Information Service* **26**, 87–88.

Collin, J. E., 1936. *Drosophila subobscura* n. sp. *J. Genet.* **39**, 60.

Dobzhansky, T., 1935a. Maternal effects as a cause of the difference between the reciprocal crosses in *Drosophila pseudoobscura*. *Proc. Natl. Acad. Sci. U.S.* **21**, 443–446.

Dobzhansky, T., 1935b. The Y chromosome of *Drosophila pseudoobscura*. *Genetics* **20**, 366–376.

Dobzhansky, T., 1935c. *Drosophila miranda*, a new species. *Genetics* **20**, 377–391.

Dobzhansky, T., 1937. Further data on *Drosophila miranda* and its hybrids with *Drosophila pseudoobscura*. *J. Genet.* **34**, 135–151.

Dobzhansky, T., 1947. Adaptive changes induced by natural selection in wild populations of Drosophila. *Evolution* **1**, 1–16.

Dobzhansky, T., 1948. Genetics of natural populations. XVI. Altitudinal and seasonal changes produced by natural selection in certain populations of *Drosophila pseudoobscura* and *Drosophila persimilis. Genetics* **33**, 158–176.

Dobzhansky, T., 1952. Genetics of natural populations. XX. Changes induced by drought in *Drosophila pseudoobscura* and *Drosophila persimilis. Evolution* **6**, 234–243.

Dobzhansky, T., and Boche, R. D., 1933. Intersterile races of *Drosophila pseudoobscura. Biol. Zentr.* **53**, 314–330.

Dobzhansky, T., Burla, H., and da Cunha, A. B., 1950. A comparative study of chromosomal polymorphism in sibling species of the *willistoni* group of *Drosophila. Am. Naturalist* **84**, 229–246.

Dobzhansky, T., and Epling, C., 1944. Taxonomy, geographic distribution, and ecology of *Drosophila pseudoobscura* and its relatives. *Carnegie Inst. Wash. Publ.* **554**, 1–46.

Dobzhansky, T., and Sokolov, D., 1939. Structure and variation of the chromosomes in *Drosophila azteca. J. Heredity* **30**, 3–19.

Dobzhansky, T., and Tan, C. C., 1936. Studies in hybrid sterility. III. A comparison of the gene arrangement in two species, *D. pseudoobscura* and *D. miranda. Z. indukt. Abstamm.-u. Vererbungsl.* **72**, 88–114.

Dubinin, N. P., Sokolov, N. N., and Tiniakov, G. G., 1937. Intraspecific chromosome variability. *Biol. Zhur.* **6**, 1007–1054.

Emmens, C. W., 1937. The morphology of the nucleus in the salivary glands of four species of *Drosophila* (*D. melanogaster, D. immigrans, D. funebris* and *D. subobscura*). *Z. Zellforsch. u. mikroskop. Anat.* **26**, 1–20.

Epling, C., Mitchell, D. F., and Mattoni, R. H. T., 1953. On the role of inversions in wild populations of *Drosophila pseudoobscura. Evolution* **7**, 342–365.

Fahmy, O. G., 1952. The cytology and genetics of *Drosophila subobscura*. VI. Maturation, fertilization, and cleavage in normal eggs and in the presence of the crossover suppressor gene. *J. Genet.* **50**, 486–506.

Fallèn, C. F., 1823. "Diptera Sueciae, Geomyzides" **2**, 1–8.

Frizzi, G., 1950. I cromosomi delle ghiandole salivari in *Drosophila subobscura* Collin. *Scientia Genet. Turin* **3**, 205–214.

Frolowa, S., 1926. Normale und polyploide Chromosomengarnituren bei einigen *Drosophila* Arten. *Z. Zellforsch. u. mikroskop. Anat.* **3**, 681–694.

Frolowa, S., and Astaurov, B. L., 1929. Die Chromosomengarnitur als systematischer Merkmal. *Z. Zellforsch. u. mikroskop. Anat.* **10**, 201–213.

Frumento, L., 1954. I cromosomi politenici delle ghiandole salivari di *Drosophila ambigua*, ordinamento tipo. *Scientia Genet. Turin* **4**, in press.

Gershenson, S., 1928. A new sex-ratio abnormality in *Drosophila obscura. Genetics* **13** 488–507.

Gershenson, S., 1939. *Drosophila* species near Kiev. *Drosophila Information Service* **11**, 44.

Goldberg, B., 1950. Report on *D. subobscura* mutants. *Drosophila Information Service* **24**, 77.

Gordon, C., 1936. The frequency of heterozygosis in free living populations of *Drosophila melanogaster* and *Drosophila subobscura. J. Genet.* **33**, 25–60.

Gordon, C., Spurway, H., and Street, P. A. R., 1939. An analysis of three wild populations of *D. subobscura. J. Genet.* **38**, 37–90.

Hadorn, E., Burla, H., Gloor, H., and Ernst, F., 1952. Beitrag zur Kenntnis der *Drosophila*-Fauna von Südwest-Europa. *Z. indukt. Abstamm.-u. Vererbungsl.* **84**, 133–163.

Haldane, J. B. S., 1945. Report on *D. subobscura* mutants. *Drosophila Information Service* **19**, 56.

Heuts, M. T., 1948. Adaptative properties of carriers of certain gene arrangements in *D. pseudoobscura*. *Heredity* **2**, 63–75.

Hipsch, R., 1952. Linkage groups and chromosomes of *Drosophila subobscura*. *Drosophila Information Service* **26**, 106.

Hornibrook, A., 1952. Report on *D. subobscura* mutants. *Drosophila Information Service* **26**, 88.

Jermyn, J. E., Philip, U., Rendel, J. M., and Spurway, H., 1943. Report on mutants and linkage data of *D. subobscura*. *Drosophila Information Service* **17**, 52–53.

Koske, T., 1952. A new species hybrid in the *obscura* group. Drosophila *Information Service* **25**, 108.

Koske, T., 1953. Artkreuzungsversuche in der *obscura*-Gruppe der Gattung *Drosophila*. *Z. indukt. Abstamm.-u. Vererbungsl.* **85**, 373–381.

Lancefield, D. E., 1922. Linkage relations of sex-linked characters in *D. obscura*. *Genetics* **7**, 335–384.

Lancefield, D. E., 1929. A genetic study of crosses of two races or physiological species of *Drosophila obscura*. *Z. indukt. Abstamm.-u. Vererbungsl.* **52**, 287–317.

Levine, R. P., 1952. Adaptative responses of some third chromosome types of *Drosophila pseudoobscura*. *Evolution* **6**, 216–233.

Magni, G. E., 1952. Sex ratio in *Drosophila bifasciata*. *Rend. ist. lombardo Sci.* **85**, 391–411.

Magni, G. E., 1953a. Sex-ratio un carattere "citoplasmatico" in *Drosophila bifasciata*. Convegno di Genetica, Napoli, 1–2 giugno 1952. *Ricerca sci.* Suppl. **23**, 59–64.

Magni, G. E., 1953b. "Sex-ratio": a non-Mendelian character in *Drosophila bifasciata*. *Nature* **172**, 81.

Mainx, F., 1949. Report on *D. subobscura* mutants. *Drosophila Information Service* **23**, 78–79.

Mainx, F., 1950a. Report on *D. ambigua* mutants. *Drosophila Information Service* **24**, 77.

Mainx, F., 1950b. Report on *D. obscuroides* mutants. *Drosophila Information Service* **24**, 77.

Mainx, F., 1950c. Report on *D. subobscura* mutants. *Drosophila Information Service* **24**, 77.

Mainx, F., 1951. Report on *D. ambigua* mutants. *Drosophila Information Service* **25**, 94.

Mainx, F., 1952a. Report on *D. bifasciata* mutants. *Drosophila Information Service* **26**, 87.

Mainx, F., 1952b. Report on *D. tristis* mutants. *Drosophila Information Service* **26**, 89.

Mainx, F., Koske, T., and Smital, E., 1953. Untersuchungen über die chromosomale Struktur europäischer Vertreter der *Drosophila obscura*-Gruppe. *Z. indukt. Abstamm.-u. Vererbungsl.* **85**, 354–372.

Makino, S., Momma, E., and Takada, H., 1952. Observed distribution of *Drosophila* species in relation to altitude on Mt. Asahidake, Hokkaido, Japan. *Drosophila Information Service* **26**, 109.

Makino, S., Momma, E., Takada, H., and Ishipara, T., 1952. Species of *Drosophila* collected so far in Hokkaido, Japan (1952), by localities. *Drosophila Information Service* **26**, 109–110.

Mather, K., and Dobzhansky, T., 1939. Morphological differences between the "Races" of *Drosophila pseudoobscura*. *Am. Naturalist* **73**, 5–25.

90 ADRIANO A. BUZZATI-TRAVERSO AND RENZO E. SCOSSIROLI

Maynard Smith, J., 1952. (Report on *D. subobscura* mutants.) *Drosophila Information Service* **26**, 88.

Maynard Smith, J., and Maynard Smith, S., 1954. Genetics and cytology of *Drosophila subobscura*. VIII. Heterozygosity, viability, and rate of development. *J. Genet.* **52**, 152–164.

Metz, C. W., and Moses, M. S., 1923. Chromosomes of *Drosophila*. *J. Heredity* **14**, 195–205.

Milani, R., 1949. Report on *D. subobscura* mutants. *Drosophila Information Service* **23**, 78.

Milani, R., 1950. Sexual behavior of *D. subobscura, ambigua, bifasciata, tristis, obscuroides*. *Drosophila Information Service* **24**, 88.

Milani, R., 1951a. Osservazioni sul corteggiamento di *Drosophila subobscura* Collin. *Rend. ist. lombardo Sci.* **84** (reprint), 1–12.

Milani, R., 1951b. Osservazioni comparative ed esperimenti sulle modalità del corteggiamento nelle cinque specie europee del gruppo "obscura." *Rend. ist. lombardo Sci.* **84** (reprint), 1–12.

Miller, D. D., 1939. Structure and variation of the chromosomes in *Drosophila algonquin*. *Genetics* **24**, 699–708.

Miller, D. D., 1941. Interspecific hybrids involving *Drosophila athabasca*. *Genetics* **26**, 161.

Moriwaki, D., Okada, T., Ohba, S., and Kurokawa, H., 1951. *Drosophila* species belonging to the *obscura* group found in Japan. *Drosophila Information Service* **25**, 116.

Moriwaki, D., Okada, T., Ohba, S., and Kurokawa, H., 1952a. *Bifasciata-* and *alpina*-like species of *Drosophila* found in Japan. *Drosophila Information Service* **26**, 112–113.

Moriwaki, D., Okada, T., Ohba, S., and Kurokawa, H., 1952b. *Drosophila* species belonging to the "obscura" group found in Japan. *Zool. Mag. Tokyo* **61**, 283–287.

Moriwaki, D., Okada, T., Ohba, S., and Kurokawa, H., 1953. Further information on *Drosophila* species belonging to the "*obscura*" group found in Japan. *Drosophila Information Service* **27**, 104.

Muller, H. J., 1940. Bearing of the *Drosophila* work on systematics. "*in* The New Systematics," pp. 185–268 (Huxley, ed.), Oxford Univ. Press, New York.

Novitski, E., 1946. Chromosome variation in *Drosophila athabasca*. *Genetics* **31**, 508–524.

Patterson, J. T., 1943. The Drosophilidae of the Southwest. *Univ. Texas Publ.* **4313**, 7–216.

Patterson, J. T., and Mainland, G. B., 1944. The Drosophilidae of Mexico. *Univ. Texas Publ.* **4445**, 9–101.

Patterson, J. T., and Stone, W. S., 1952. "Evolution in the Genus *Drosophila*." MacMillan, New York.

Patterson, J. T., and Wagner, R. P., 1943. Geographical distribution of species of the genus *Drosophila* in the United States and Mexico. *Univ. Texas Publ.* **4313**, 217–281.

Philip, U., 1941. The chromosomes of *Drosophila subobscura*. *Drosophila Information Service* **14**, 53–54.

Philip, U., 1946. Cytology of males in cultures with recessive crossover suppressor. *Drosophila Information Service* **20**, 90.

Philip, U., Rendel, J. M., Spurway, H., and Haldane, J. B. S., 1944. Genetics and kariology of *Drosophila subobscura*. *Nature* **154**, 260.

Pipkin, S. B., 1951. Seasonal fluctuations in *Drosophila* populations at different altitudes in the Lebanon Mountains. *Genetics* **36**, 571.

Pomini, F. P., 1940. Contributi alla conoscenza delle *Drosophila* (Diptera, Acalyptera) europee. I. Descrizione di alcune specie riferibili al gruppo *obscura*. *Boll. ist. entomol. univ. Bologna* **12**, 145–164.

Prevosti, A., 1950. Cromosomas gigantes de las glandulas salivales de cuatro especies europeas de *Drosophila*, pertenecientes al grupo de la *"obscura."* *Genet. iber.* **2**, 185–192.

Prevosti, A., 1952. Variabilidad genica en una poblacion natural de *Drosophila subobscura*. *Genet. iber.* **4**, 95–128.

Reed, S. C., and Reed, E. W., 1948. Morphological differences and problems of speciation in *Drosophila*. *Evolution* **2**, 40–48.

Rendel, J. M., 1943. *D. pseudoobscura A × D. subobscura*. *Drosophila Information Service* **17**, 64.

Rendel, J. M., 1945. Genetics and cytology of *D. subobscura*. II. Normal and selective matings in *Drosophila subobscura*. *J. Genet.* **46**, 287–302.

Rendel, J. M., and Spurway, H., 1940. Report on *D. subobscura* mutants. *Drosophila Information Service* **13**, 61.

Rendel, J. M., and Suley, A. C. E., 1946. Interspecific eye disc transplantation. *Drosophila Information Service* **20**, 91.

Ritzki, M. T. M., 1951. Morphological differences between two sibling species, *D. pseudoobscura* and *D. persimilis*. *Proc. Natl. Acad. Sci. U.S.* **37**, 156–159.

Scossiroli, R., 1951. Relation between successful interspecific crossings and gene arrangements. *Drosophila Information Service* **25**, 127.

Scossiroli, R., 1954. Rapporti tra razze geografiche, razze cromosomiche ed affinità genetica in incroci interspecifici. *Rend ist. lombardo Sci.* **87**, 167–181.

Séguy, E., 1938. Mission scientifique de l'Omo, Diptera. I. Nematocera et Brachycera. *Mem. museum hist. nat. Paris* [n. s.] **8**, 319–380.

Smart, J., 1945. *Drosophila subobscura* Collin: descriptive notes on its nomenclatorial status (Diptera). *Proc. Roy. Ent. Soc. (London)* **B14**, 53–56.

Sokolov, N. N., and Dubinin, N. P., 1941. Permanent heterozygosity in *Drosophila*. *Drosophila Information Service* **15**, 39–40.

Spieth, T. H., 1952. Mating behavior within the Genus *Drosophila* (Diptera). *Bull. Am. Museum Nat. Hist.* **99**, 401–473.

Spurway, H., 1939a. (Report on *D. subobscura* mutants). *Drosophila Information Service* **11**, 29.

Spurway, H., 1939b. (Report on *D. subobscura* mutants). *Drosophila Information Service* **12**, 53.

Spurway, H., 1945. The genetics and cytology of *D. subobscura*. I. Element A., Sex-linked mutants and their standard order. *J. Genet.* **46**, 268–286.

Spurway, H., 1946a. An extreme example of delay in gene action in *D. subobscura*. *Drosophila Information Service* **20**, 91.

Spurway, H., 1946b. A sex-linked recessive crossover suppressor in *D. subobscura*. *Drosphila Information Service* **20**, 91.

Spurway, H., 1948. Genetics and cytology of *D. suboscura*. IV. An extreme example of delay in gene action, causing sterility. *J. Genet.* **49**, 126–140.

Spurway, H., 1951. (Report on *D. subobscura* mutants). *Drosophila Information Service* **25**, 95–96.

Spurway, H., and Haldane, J. B. S., 1954. Genetics and cytology of *Drosophila subobscura*. IX. An autosomal recessive mutant transforming homogametic zygotes into intersexes. *J. Genet.* **52**, 208–225.

Spurway, H., and Philip, U., 1952. Genetics and cytology of *Drosophila subobscura*. VII. Abnormal gene arrangements in element A. *J. Genet.* **51**, 198–215.

Stumm-Zollinger, E., 1953. Vergleichende Untersuchungen über die Inversions-häufigkeit bei *Drosophila subobscura* in Populationen der Schweiz und Südwesteuropas. *Z. indukt. Abstamm.-u. Vererbungsl.* **85**, 382–407.

Sturtevant, A. H., 1916. Notes on the North American Drosophilidae with descriptions of twenty-three new species. *Ann. Entomol. Soc. Amer.* **9**, 323–343.

Sturtevant, A. H., 1921. The North American species of *Drosophila. Carnegie Inst. Wash. Publ.* **301**, 1–150.

Sturtevant, A. H., 1940. Genetic data on *Drosophila affinis* with a discussion of the relationships in the subgenus Sophophora. *Genetics* **25**, 337–353.

Sturtevant, A. H., 1942. The classification of the Genus *Drosophila* with description of nine new species. *Univ. Texas Publ.* **4213**, 5–51.

Sturtevant, A. H., and Dobzhansky, T., 1936. Observations on the species related to *Drosophila affinis* with descriptions of seven new forms. *Am. Naturalist* **70**, 574–584.

Sturtevant, A. H., and Novitzki, E., 1941. The homologies of the chromosome elements in the genus Drosophila. *Genetics* **26**, 517–541.

Suley, A. C. E., 1953. Genetics of *Drosophila subobscura*. VIII. Studies on the mutant *grandchildless. J. Genet.* **51**, 375–405.

Tan, C. C., 1935a. Salivary gland chromosomes in the two races of *Drosophila pseudoobscura. Genetics* **20**, 392–402.

Tan, C. C., 1935b. Identification of the salivary gland chromosomes in *Drosophila pseudoobscura. Proc. Natl. Acad. Sci. U.S.* **21**, 200–202.

Tan, C. C., 1936. Genetic maps of the autosomes in *Drosophila pseudoobscura. Genetics* **21**, 796–807.

Tan, C. C., 1937. The cytological maps of the autosomes in *Drosophila pseudoobscura. Z. Zellforsch. u. mikroskop. Anat.* **26**, 439–461.

Wallace, B., and Dobzhansky, T., 1946. Experiments on sexual isolation in *Drosophila*. VIII. Influence of light on the mating behavior of *Drosophila subobscura, D. persimilis* and *D. pseudoobscura. Proc. Natl. Acad. Sci. U.S.* **32**, 226–234.

Weidmann, U., 1951. Ueber den systematischen Wert von Balzhandlungen bei *Drosophila. Rev. suisse zool.* **58**, 502–511.

Wheeler, M. R., 1949. Taxonomic studies on the Drosophilidae. *Univ. Texas Publ.* **4920**, 157–195.

Zollinger, E., 1950. Ein strukturell homozygoter Stamm von *D. subobscura* aus einer Wildpopulation. *Arch. Julius Klaus-Stift. Vererbungsforsch. Sozialanthropol. Rassenhyg.* **25**, 33–35.

Chromosomal Polymorphism in the Diptera

A. Brito da Cunha

*Departamento de Biologia Geral, Faculdade de Filosofia,
Ciências e Letras da Universidade de São Paulo, Brasil*

I. Introduction

According to Ford's definition (1953), "Polymorphism is the occurrence together in the same environment of two or more discontinuous forms of a species in such proportions as the rarest of them cannot be maintained merely by recurrent mutation." The phenomenon of polymorphism has been studied by many biologists in recent times. The reason for such an interest in the analysis of polymorphic populations is due to the fact that their study shows the interplay of evolutionary factors in the maintenance and the improvement of their adaptation to the environment.

The development of polymorphic populations is very important at the population level as well as at the individual level. In a heterogeneous environment, a uniform population may exploit efficiently only few ecological niches. A polymorphic population, having many adaptively different genotypes, may be able to utilize many ecological opportunities and to exploit the environment much more successfully than a homogeneous population. A polymorphic population, being genetically very plastic, is also more able to respond to temporal changes of the environ-

ment than a homogeneous population. The development of polymorphism
through natural selection is one of the ways that a population may im-
prove its capacity to utilize the environment and to survive through temporal changes of it (da Cunha, Burla, and Dobzhansky, 1950).

The adaptedness of populations of cross-fertilizing species has been
shown to be based mainly on the high adaptive values of heterozygous
individuals rather than on those of the homozygotes (Crow, 1948;
Dobzhansky, 1951; Wallace et al., 1953). Polymorphism is, therefore, one
of the methods whereby populations become adapted to their environments. The adaptive values of individuals in populations depend upon
the maintenance of a steady state in their biology despite changes in
environment. The capacity of maintaining a steady state, or in other
words the degree of homeostasis, in variable environments varies from
individual to individual. It is genotypically conditioned, since recent work
has shown that heterozygous individuals usually have a better homeostasis than homozygous ones (Robertson and Reeve, 1952; Dobzhansky
and Wallace, 1953). Polymorphism is a mechanism that promotes heterozygosity and it is, therefore, related to the maintenance of homeostasis.

The phenomenon of polymorphism is widespread; its understanding
has progressed very much recently, thanks to the work of many biologists
using a large variety of organisms. A large share of the progress is due to
the work on genetics of natural populations of Drosophila. The object
of this chapter is to review the work on Drosophila and other genera of
Diptera bearing on the problem of polymorphism. We shall be concerned
mainly with the quantitative aspects of the problem, since an excellent
recent review of the qualitative side may be found in Patterson and
Stone (1952).

II. Phenotypic Polymorphism in Drosophila

Striking phenotypic polymorphism is very rare in the genus Drosophila. The only genetically analyzed cases are those of D. polymorpha,
D. montium, and D. rufa. The phenotypic variability of D. polymorpha
was first noticed by Dobzhansky and Pavan (1943) and later analyzed
genetically by da Cunha (1949). D. polymorpha presents three types of
abdominal color patterns described as the dark, the light, and the intermediate types. Crossing experiments have shown that the variability is
caused by a single pair of alleles, the dark and the light types being
homozygous (EE) and (ee) respectively, and the intermediate type being
heterozygous (Ee). The ratios obtained in the F_2 and in backcrosses made
in the laboratory have indicated a differential mortality favoring the
heterozygotes.

Experimental populations with known frequencies of the genes E and *e* have been prepared. In all cases, the frequencies of the genes have been observed to change with time, and equilibria were obtained at frequencies about 64% of *E* and 36% of *e*. Mathematical analysis of the changes in the artificial populations gave an adaptive value of 0.56 and 0.23 for the homozygotes (*EE*) and (*ee*), respectively, the adaptive value of the heterozygote being taken as unity. Thus, in the laboratory experiments the heterozygote *Ee* is clearly superior to both homozygotes. The situation is different in natural populations.

Many natural populations of *D. polymorpha* have been studied in Brazil. All of them are polymorphic. The gene frequencies vary from population to population, but *E* is always more frequent than *e*. The frequencies of *E* range from 82% to 61%. In a given population the gene frequencies may change from time to time. The available data do not permit, however, a decision on whether the changes are cyclic or not. The data obtained in the natural populations have disclosed that the homozygotes are in excess and the heterozygotes are deficient compared to what is expected according to the binomial square rule. In natural populations, in contrast to what happens in laboratory conditions, a differential mortality in favor of the homozygotes occurs. The heterozygotes must nevertheless be supposed to have some advantages, which give them a superiority over the homozygotes in adaptive value. Otherwise it would be difficult to account for the maintenance of the polymorphism in extensive territories. *D. polymorpha* is also variable chromosomically. Several inversions have been found in its populations, but no correlation exists between the genes which determine the abdominal patterns and the different inversions (da Cunha, 1953a).

D. neocardini, which, like *D. polymorpha*, belongs to the *cardini* group of the subgenus Drosophila, is also phenotypically variable in the abdominal pigmentation pattern. But, while all populations of *D. polymorpha* are polymorphic, those of *D. neocardini* are monomorphic. The abdominal pattern is, however, different in the northern and in the southern Brazilian populations (da Cunha, 1955).

D. montium populations are also polymorphic with respect to the pigmentation of the abdominal tergites. Its variability was described by Pavan and da Cunha (1947) and genetically analyzed by Freire-Maia (1949). Two pigmentation forms have been distinguished, a light and a dark one. The pigmentation patterns are determined by two alleles, the allele which determines the dark pigmentation being dominant. The polymorphism in *D. montium* is balanced. The heterozygote (dark) has a higher adaptive value, and the light homozygote is superior to the dark homozygote. All the populations of *D. montium* studied in Brazil are polymorphic (Freire-Maia, 1949).

D. rufa is a very close relative of *D. montium*, and their variabilities are very similar. The females may have the two last abdominal tergites black or light. Oshima (1952) studied the genetic basis of the two pigmentation types, finding that the dark females may be homozygotes *DD* or heterozygotes *Dd*, and are always clearly distinguishable from the homozygous light type, *dd*. Oshima prepared artificial populations with 50% of each allele, and found that the frequencies changed until an equilibrium was obtained at 60–65% of dark flies. The result seems to indicate that heterozygotes *Dd* have the highest adaptive value and the dark homozygote *DD* the lowest, as in *D. montium*.

Morphological polymorphism has also been reported in *D. auraria* by Moriwaki and coworkers (1952) but no genetic data are yet available. All these cases of polymorphism are clearly adaptive and balanced. Nothing is, however, known about the physiological differences between the various types. The morphological differences found are probably of no adaptive importance by themselves. Physiological differences correlated with the types of pigmentation are certainly the factors responsible for the adaptive differences.

III. Types of Chromosomal Variants and Their Biological Consequences

If major morphological polymorphism is rare in the genus Drosophila, chromosomal polymorphism is very common. Populations of most species studied are chromosomically variable. The commonest type of chromosomal variability is due to inverted sections. Translocations are found but are very rare.

It is of great interest for the understanding of the development and maintenance of the chromosomal polymorphism in natural populations to know the meiotic behavior of the chromosomal aberrations. Stone and Thomas (1935), Beadle and Sturtevant (1935), and Sturtevant and Beadle (1936) have made in *D. melanogaster* a very detailed study of meiosis in flies heterozygous for chromosomal inversions. They have found that, in flies heterozygous for paracentric inversions (inversions in which the centromere is not included), single crossovers inside the inverted sections do occur, but chromosomes produced by such crossovers are not detected in the crosses. Such chromosomes would have deficiencies and duplications and would cause death of the zygotes. However, no change in the fertility of the heterozygotes was found. These results have led Beadle and Sturtevant (1935) to suppose that "It seems probable that . . . for the case of inversions that do not include the locus of the spindle attachment and for other chromosome aberrations in which crossing-over gives rise to chromatids with two spindle attachments, and where the conditions of meiosis are such that (a) the meiotic spindles are oriented so that the reduced nuclei lies approximately on a single straight line, and (b) only one of the terminal nuclei functions in further development."

This hypothesis based on the genetic data was cytologically confirmed by Carson (1946). Carson studied meiosis in the eggs of *Sciara impatiens* heterozygous for a long X chromosome inversion. He observed that non-crossover chromatids are segregated in the terminal nuclei, one of which gives the egg nucleus. The dicentric chromatid produced by crossing-over is stretched at the first meiotic division, forming a bridge from pole to pole of the spindle. The mechanical disabilities of the dicentric chromatids assure that a normal, noncrossover, chromatid goes to the terminal nucleus. Inversions were discovered by Sturtevant in 1926 through the suppression of crossing-over in inversion heterozygotes (Sturtevant, 1926, 1931).

It will be shown later that the biological importance of inversions in nature is due to their capacity of suppressing effective crossing-over. To be retained in natural populations an inversion must (1) prevent recombination, and (2) not cause appreciable reduction of fertility in the heterozygotes.

Pericentric inversions are not expected to be common in nature because chiasmata within the inverted section lead to the formation of deficient and duplicated chromatids, and also no selective elimination of the chromatids occurs at meiosis in the female. Pericentric inversions may be retained in natural populations only if: (1) The occurrence of chiasmata inside the inverted region is infrequent, as it seems to be the case with the pericentric inversions found in the natural populations of *D. robusta* (Carson, personal communication). (2) The pericentric inversion is associated with an overlapping inversion. In this case, deficiencies and duplications will result if the chiasma occurs in the loop with the centromere, but bridge and fragment will result from a crossing within the loop without the centromere. Overlapping inversions, therefore, reduce the disabilities of pericentric inversions. This is what happens with the pericentric inversion described by Miller (1939) in *D. algonquin*. Pericentric inversions occur also in natural populations of *D. ananassae* (Freire-Maia, 1952b) but their behavior is not yet studied.

Translocations are rare in natural populations of animals because they lead to the production of unbalanced gametes. However, translocations have been recorded in natural populations of *D. ananassae* (Dobzhansky and Dreyfus, 1943; Freire-Maia, 1953).

The effects of inversions on the recombination system are not restricted to the reduction of recombination in the inverted section.

Heterozygous inversions may strongly reduce the frequency of recombinations in the rest of the chromosome. Schultz and Redfield (1930, 1951), Steinberg (1936, 1937), and Steinberg and Fraser (1944) have made a detailed analysis of the effects of heterozygous inversions on the recombination in nonhomologous chromosomes in *D. melanogaster*. In general, the suppression of recombination by a heterozygous inversion increases the recombination in nonhomologous chromosomes. The size of the section involved in the inversion is important for the increase of recombination in nonhomologous chromosomes. The larger the inverted section of a chromosome, the higher will be the increase of recombination in other chromosomes. In general, chromosomal regions which normally have a lower incidence of crossing-over are the regions which present a higher increase of recombination.

These findings, made originally in *D. melanogaster*, were confirmed in several other species. MacKnight (1937) studied the recombination in the X chromosome of *D. pseudoobscura* × *D. persimilis* hybrids. He found that heterozygous autosomal inversions increase the recombination in the X chromosome. Levine and Dickinson (1952) obtained similar results in *D. pseudoobscura*, studying the effects of heterozygous inversions of the third chromosome on the recombination in the X chromosome. Komai and Takaku (1940, 1942) found in *D. virilis* that two X chromosome inversions, when heterozygous, have a strong effect increasing the recombination frequencies in the autosomes, and even in the terminal region of the X chromosome itself. As in *D. melanogaster*, they found that, in *D. virilis*, the higher the suppression of crossing-over in the inverted section, the larger will be the increase of chiasmata frequency elsewhere. Dobzhansky and Epling (1948) found that, in third chromosomes of *D. pseudoobscura*, inversion heterozygosis prevents recombination not only in the inverted region itself but also in the region between the centromere and the inversion, and between the inversion and the tip of the chromosome. This is a situation different from that in *D. virilis* but similar to what was found for some X chromosome inversions of *D. melanogaster* by Sturtevant and Beadle (1936).

Carson (1953) has made a detailed study of interchromosomal effects of heterozygous inversions in *D. robusta*. His data are in agreement with those obtained in *D. melanogaster*, *D. virilis*, and *D. pseudoobscura*. An increase of about 30 times the normal frequency of recombination was found in some instances. *D. robusta* inversions of about similar sizes and in the same chromosome may have different power in their interchromosomal effects. In *D. robusta* the interchromosomal effects depend not only on the structural change due to the inversion, but also on the genic content of the inverted section. This agrees with the findings of

Steinberg and Fraser (1944) and Schultz and Redfield (1951) in *D. melanogaster* that factors other than the length of the inversion and its positions are important in the interchromosomal effects. The mechanisms by which these interchromosomal effects are produced are so far unknown.

According to Carson (1953), "The interplay of intrachromosomal suppression and interchromosomal intensification of crossing-over indicates that inversions do not greatly reduce the total frequency of exchanges. On the other hand, crossovers appear to be shunted principally into sections of the chromosome set which are not involved in inversions." He then makes the suggestion that "in this way the species may exploit the advantages of adaptive chromosomal polymorphism and at the same time retain evolutionary plasticity through a high degree of recombination in structurally homozygous chromosome sections."

IV. PRODUCTION AND LOCALIZATION OF CHROMOSOMAL VARIANTS

The mechanisms of the origin of chromosomal aberrations in nature are not well understood. Hinton, Ives, and Evans (1952) have shown that in *D. melanogaster* the chromosome breakability may be under genic control. A total of 13 chromosome aberrations have been detected in a strain of *D. melanogaster* having the gene *hi*, which produces a high mutation rate. The analysis of the chromosomal aberrations showed that the breaks did not occur at random. Twelve of the thirteen aberrations had one of the breaks in the proximal heterochromatin. The mutant gene *hi* seems to induce a high breakability in the heterochromatic regions.

The work on the X-ray induction of chromosomal aberrations suggests, however, that the occurrence of breaks is, in general, proportional to the mitotic chromosome length. If the breaks are studied in salivary gland chromosomes, it will appear that they are much more common in the heterochromatin than in the euchromatin due to the shortening of the heterochromatic regions [see Lea (1946) and Kaufmann (1948) for reviews of this subject]. The results obtained with the induction of breaks by chemical mutagens seem to be in agreement with those from the X-ray work (Fahmy and Bird, 1953).

A comparison of natural and induced chromosome aberrations was made by Helfer (1941) in *D. pseudoobscura*. He found that all the chromosomes are equally breakable by X-rays, the frequency of breaks being proportional to the chromosome length. No region of accumulation of breaks was found. The analysis of 12 inversions produced by the irradiation in the third chromosome showed that they were different from the natural occurring ones. Out of 73 induced breaks in the third chromosome, 10 were in the heterochromatin, but all the 38 breaks, which produced the natural occurring aberrations, are in the euchromatic portions of the chromosome. The fact that all chromosome regions are equally breakable indicates that: (1) the repeated occurrence of the same aberration is very improbable, and (2) chromosomal aberrations found in nature should be distributed among all the chromosomes in proportion to their length.

As expected, in some Drosophila species the inversions are evenly distributed among all the chromosomes. *Drosophila willistoni*, the most variable species so far studied, has 42 described inversions (da Cunha, Burla, and Dobzhansky, 1950; da Cunha and Dobzhansky, 1954; Townsend, 1952), 15 being in the third, 13 in the second, and 14 in the X chromosome.

D. paulistorum, a sibling of *D. willistoni*, has 15 inversions in the third chromosome, 10 in the second, and 9 in the X chromosome (Dobzhansky, Burla, and da Cunha, 1950). In *D. willistoni*, as in *D. paulistorum*, there is no particular chromosome region where the breaks are appreciably more common. *D. robusta* has 6 inversions in the X, 5 in the second, and 2 in the third (Carson and Stalker, 1947); *D. azteca* has 3 inversions in the X, 5 in the second, and 4 in the third (Dobzhansky and Sokolov, 1939); *D. algonquin* has 1 inversion in the X, 3 in the A, 4 in the B, and 2 in the C (Miller, 1939); *D. sturtevanti* (Knapp, 1956) has 6 inversions in the X, 5 in the second, and 7 in the third. These are good examples of Drosophila species with many inversions distributed more or less equally among all the chromosomes.

However, in some other species the chromosomal variability is concentrated in a single chromosome. *D. pseudoobscura* has 15 inversions in the third chromosome, 2 in the second, 1 in the fourth, and 3 in the X (Dobzhansky, 1944, 1951); *D. persimilis* has 10 inversions in the third chromosome, 2 in the second, and 1 in the X (Dobzhansky, 1944, 1951); *D. athabasca* has 16 inversions in C, 2 in E, 1 in B, and 4 in the X (Novitski, 1946); *D. melanica* has 16 inversions in the second chromosome, 4 in the X, and 2 in the fourth (Ward, 1952); *D. nebulosa* has 11 inversions in the third chromosome and 1 in the X (Pavan, 1946; da Cunha, Brncic, and Salzano, 1953); *D. guaramunu* has 25 inversions in the fourth chromosome, 1 in the second, 2 in the third, and 3 in the fifth (Brncic, 1953; Salzano, 1954, 1955). These are some cases in which the inversions are concentrated predominantly in a single chromosome. The natural populations of certain other species are, however, free of inversions. This is the case in *D. repleta* (Wharton, 1942), *D. meridiana* and *D. bifurca* (Warters, 1944), and *D. virilis* (Patterson, Stone, and Griffen, 1940; Warters, 1944).

Experimental data indicate that all chromosomes are equally breakable and, therefore, that inversions should arise equally frequently in all the chromosomes, as is the case in *D. willistoni, D. paulistorum, D. robusta*, and others. The cases of species with inversions mainly in one chromosome and of species with no inversions at all show that, if in ersions appear equally in all chromosomes, their survival values may vary from chromosome to chromosome. Differences in the behavior of the chromosomes in regard to the inversions may be found even in closely related species, such as *D. willistoni* and *D. nebulosa*, and *D. pseudoobscura* and *D. azteca*.

Novitski (1946) contended that the presence of an inversion makes the appearance of a new inversion close to it in a chromosome more probable. The regions where the inversions begin and end are probably under stress in the pairing of inversion heterozygotes. Pairing of the inverted section leaves the two ends of the inversion unpaired and the stress in this unsynapsed region may make its breaking more probable than breaks in other chromosomes. However, there is as yet no good explanation of why the pattern of the distribution of inversion in different species of Drosophila is so strikingly different. The distribution of the heterochromatin may be involved here. As said above, Helfer (1941) found that about 15% of the X-ray induced breaks in *D. pseudoobscura* were in the heterochromatin. However, not a single one of the 38 breakage points in the natural occurring inversions is in the heterochromatin. Inversions with the breakage point in the heterochromatin seem to have a low survival value.

V. CHROMOSOMAL POLYMORPHISM IN *Drosophila pseudoobscura*

Drosophila pseudoobscura is the organism whose populations genetics is by far the best known. Most natural populations of *D. pseudoobscura* are polymorphic with regard to the gene arrangement. As stated above, the third chromosome is the most variable and 15 inversions have been described. The other chromosomes are less variable and, apart from the three inversions which constitute the "sex ratio" arrangement in the X chromosome, the two inversions known in the second chromosome, and the one in the fourth, are very rare. The gene arrangements of *D. pseudoobscura* have been described and analyzed by Dobzhansky and Sturtevant (1938) and by Dobzhansky (1944). Since the third chromosome inversions are related to each other by overlapping sections, it was possible to make a phylogenetic tree showing the relation of all the inversions.

D. pseudoobscura is a species of the eastern coast of North America, and its distribution area tends from British Columbia to Guatemala and from the Pacific coast to Texas. Samples have been analyzed from most of the regions in this very large area. A very detailed analysis of the samples has been presented by Dobzhansky (1944). With few exceptions, natural populations contain two or more different gene arrangements in the third chromosome. Some gene arrangements are endemic and others have very large distribution areas. The gene arrangement Arrowhead, for example, is found in most of the distribution area of the species with exception of southern Mexico and of Guatemala. San Jacinto and Hidalgo, on the other hand, have very restricted distributions.

Any population may be characterized by the frequencies of the gene arrangements in its gene pool. Even geographically very close populations may differ in their chromosomal composition. Dobzhansky and Queal (1938) studied the gene arrangements in the isolated mountains in the Death Valley region. Three gene arrangements, Arrowhead (AR), Standard (ST), and Chiricahua (CH) were present in these populations, but their frequencies varied from population to population. Koller (1939) obtained similar results studying the gene arrangements in populations living in different canyons of one mountain range, the Panamint Mountains (west of Death Valley). Every canyon had a characteristic composition with respect to the relative frequencies of the gene arrangements. In the Death Valley region no geographic regularity was found in the variation. A population of a mountain range may be more similar to a remote than to a close population. In the Panamint mountain range, populations of adjacent canyons tend, however, to be more similar than populations of remote ones.

Dobzhansky (1943, 1947a) found striking differences between three populations only 10–15 miles apart on Mount San Jacinto in Southern California. In the three localities, Keen Camp, Pinon Flats, and Andreas Canyon, the frequencies of the gene arrangement ST were 33.7, 40.7, and 57.6 respectively, and of CH 38.0, 29.1, and 15.3 respectively.

When a large area is considered, a cline may be found in the gene arrangement frequencies. For example, the frequency of ST is about 50% on the Pacific coast and decreases gradually eastward, disappearing in New Mexico. Another gene arrangement, AR rises from about 20% on the Pacific coast to 100% in southwestern Colorado, and again drops to about 20% in southern Texas. A third gene arrangement, Pikes Peak (PP), appears in Arizona with very low frequencies, and attains the maximum frequencies in Texas. The gene arrangement "sex ratio" presents another very clear cline. Its frequency is greatest in southern New Mexico and Arizona, where it represents 33% of all X chromosomes. From this region, in any direction, the frequency of "sex ratio" decreases gradually to near zero in Oregon, Montana, Wyoming, South Dakota, Nebraska, northern Utah, and Guatemala (Dobzhansky, 1944). In most geographic regions the changes in the frequencies of the gene arrangements are gradual. However, in some places the changes are more abrupt. One place of this kind is the Sierra Nevada mountain range. From the western to the eastern foothills of the Sierra Nevada there is a very sharp decrease in the frequency of ST and a sharp increase of AR. The existence of regions with such sharp changes can be used for the delimitation of geographic races. Dobzhansky (1948a) has recognized seven major races in *D. pseudoobscura:* (1) Pacific coast race, (2) Great Basin race, (3) Great Plains race, (4) North Mexican race, (5) Central Mexican race, (6) Northeast Mexican race, and (7) Michoacan-Guatemala race. These races are separated by nonuniformities of the clines, determined by geographical or ecological barriers.

Inside each of the major races, many minor races may be distinguished. Besides the gene arrangement variability in the third and in the X chromosomes, the Y chromosome varies in size and shape. Five types of Y chromosome have been recognized in *D. pseudoobscura*, according to the size and position of the centromere. Deficiencies, duplications, and inversions are probably involved in the differentiation of the Y chromosome. As the Y chromosome cannot be studied in the salivary gland cells, its study is very laborious and the data available are much less extensive than that for the third chromosome. An analysis of the frequencies of the five types of Y chromosome was, nevertheless, made in several populations. There is some parallelism between the distribution of the third chromosome gene arrangements and the Y chromosome types. The distribution of the Y chromosome types is in agreement with the races as delimited on the basis of the frequencies of the third chromosome arrangements (Dobzhansky, 1935, 1937, 1944; Dobzhansky and Sturtevant, 1938).

For a long time it was thought that chromosomal inversions were neutral traits. However, facts were obtained that showed clearly that chromosomal inversions have adaptive values. Systematic analysis of several populations of *D. pseudoobscura* in California has disclosed the existence of temporal changes in the frequencies of the different chromosomal types (Dobzhansky, 1943, 1947a, 1948b, 1952; Koller, 1939). Dobzhansky (1943, 1947a) published the results of six years of periodic collecting in three localities on Mount San Jacinto, Andreas Canyon, Pinon Flats, and Keen Camp. In these localities ST, AR, and CH are the commonest gene arrangements. An altitudinal gradient was found in the frequencies of ST and CH. ST is more common in the lower locality, Andreas Canyon, where its frequency is 57.6%, than in Keen Camp, the higher locality (31%). The intermediate locality has 41% of ST. The gene arrangement CH presents an inverse gradient, with the minimum (15.3%) at Andreas and the maximum (39.8%) at Keen.

At Andreas and at Pinon Flats, it was found that the inversion frequencies varied from month to month, and the yearly collections showed that the variation is cyclic and seasonal. The frequencies of ST decrease from March (52%) to June (28%) and increase from then on. CH is most frequent in early summer (39.5%) and decreases in the fall and winter (20%). AR varies less strikingly than ST and CH, but seems to be more frequent in the spring. At Keen Camp the seasonal fluctuations are not as clear as in the two other localities. However, while at Andreas and Pinon the gene arrangement frequencies were fairly uniform every year, at Keen Camp there was observed a continuous increase in the frequency of ST (28% in 1939 to 50% in 1946) and a decrease of AR (from 30% in 1939 to 15% in 1946) (Dobzhansky, 1947a).

The gene arrangement "sex ratio" in the X chromosome shows a behavior similar to that of the third chromosome CH. At Andreas and at Pinon, the frequency of "sex ratio" increases in the late spring to attain a maximum in June–July and then decreases. At Keen Camp no significant changes occur in the concentration of "sex ratio."

The populations of the Sierra Nevada showed variations similar to those on Mount San Jacinto (Dobzhansky, 1948b). As on San Jacinto, ST, AR, and CH are the commonest gene arrangements in the Sierra Nevada. An altitudinal gradient was also found, but in the Sierra Nevada ST and AR, and not ST and CH as on San Jacinto, are the gene arrangements that show the clearest variation. At an altitude of 260 meters, ST has a frequency of 45.9% and AR 24.8%. The frequency of ST drops and that of AR increases with the altitude. At the timber line (3,200 meters), ST has a frequency of 10% and AR 50%. The variation of CH is small. Collections made at monthly intervals disclosed a cyclic seasonal variation in the frequencies of ST and AR. The frequency of ST rises during the breeding season and that of AR decreases. No change was observed in the lowest locality, Jacksonville (260 meters). The changes are very clear at Lost Claim (910 meters), Mather (1,220 meters), and Aspen (1,900 meters). In the higher localities the breeding season was too short and the number of flies too small to make good observations.

In the Mather population a directional change was also found (Dobzhansky, 1952). The changes observed from month to month were seasonal, but superimposed on these cyclic changes was a gradual increase in the frequencies of AR and decrease of ST. This trend was observed from 1945 to 1950. In 1951 the trend was reversed. These cyclic seasonal changes as well as the altitudinal gradients indicate clearly that the chromosomal inversions have adaptive values. A given gene arrangement is selected in the populations according to the physiological proper- ties of its carriers and the predominant ecological conditions of the environment.

When the ecological change is gradual, a cline is produced in the gene arrangement frequencies, as in the case of the altitudinal changes. When the environmental conditions suffer periodic and cyclic modifications, the populations show seasonal fluctuations in their chromosomal constitution. The changes at Keen Camp and at Mather for a period longer than a year could be correlated with gradual, continuous changes in the environment. At Keen Camp the change in the environment may have been due to forest fires. At Mather there was an abnormally low amount of precipitation during the period in which the chromosomal changes were observed. The local differentiation of the populations found by Koller (1939), Dobzhansky and Queal (1938), and Dobzhansky (1939, 1943, 1947a) are certainly due to different selections in the localities which they studied.

The chromosomal polymorphism of D. pseudoobscura is clearly of the balanced type. The chromosomal types undergo changes in their frequencies but one type never supplants the others. The plasticity of the population is always maintained. This is possible only because the heterozygotes have adaptive values higher than the homozygotes. D. pseudoobscura populations are in a state of continuous flux, which serves to keep the population always adapted to the environmental conditions.

A direct proof that chromosomal arrangements perform adaptive functions, and that natural selection controls their frequencies in natural populations, was given by Dobzhansky and Levene (1948). They collected females inseminated in nature and permitted them to lay eggs. The larvae were raised under optimal conditions to prevent differential mortality. The proportions of larvae homozygous and heterozygous for the several third chromosome gene arrangements present in the populations were studied. No significant departures from what was expected based on the Hardy-Weinberg rule was found in the proportions of homozygotes and heterozygotes. Next, samples of adult flies were taken in nature. The males were crossed to females of known chromosomal composition. The study of the F_1 larvae gave the chromosomal constitution of the male used in the cross. By this method it was found that, among the adult flies, there was a significant deviation from the Hardy-Weinberg equilibrium in the proportions of the homozygotes and the heterozygotes. The heterozygotes were, in general, more frequent and the homozygotes were less frequent than expected.

The fact that, in the egg samples, the homozygotes and the heterozygotes were in the proportions expected on the basis of the Hardy-Weinberg rule, while in the adult flies they were not, shows that differential mortality occurred between the egg and the adult stages. The excess of heterozygotes in the adult sample indicates that differential mortality favors the heterozygotes. These facts are a clear proof that: (1) chromosomal gene arrangements are an adaptive trait; (2) the heterozygotes are usually superior to both homozygotes; and (3) the changes observed in the natural populations are due to natural selection.

A great advance in the study of polymorphism was made by the introduction of methods that permitted simulation in the laboratory populations of some of the changes observed in natural populations. This was possible due to the use of "population cages." L'Heritier and Teissier (1933) introduced the so-called "population cages" for the study of behavior of mutants in laboratory populations of *D. melanogaster*. The culture medium in the population cages is placed in small jars which are inserted in the cage or removed from it at desired intervals. This method permits a continuous maintenance of a population of thousands of flies in more or less uniform conditions.

A population with known genetic composition is placed in the cage, and changes in its composition studied by taking samples of adult flies, or of eggs, and studying the chromosomes in the salivary glands. The egg samples are placed in culture bottles, in which optimal conditions are maintained. The salivary glands of the larvae are prepared by the aceto-orcein method and their chromosomes are determined. Dobzhansky (Wright and Dobzhansky, 1946) applied the population cage technique for the study of the behavior of different chromosomal arrangements in populations. Dobzhansky (Wright and Dobzhansky, 1946) took several strains homozygous for the gene arrangements ST, AR, CH, Tree Line (TL), and Santa Cruz (SC). All the strains were taken from flies collected in the same locality, Pinon Flats (Mount San Jacinto, California). It is possible to arrange the original experimental populations with any desired composition.

As an example, the experiments number 38 and 44 (Dobzhansky, 1948c) may be considered. The population in experiment 38 had the initial composition of 83.8% AR and 12.29% CH, and the cage was kept at 25°C. The frequency of AR decreased gradually and that of CH increased. After about 5 months, the population had its composition stabilized at about 75% of AR and 25% of CH. In experiment 44, the initial frequencies were 29.3% of AR and 70.7% of CH. The frequency of AR rose and that of CH decreased until an equilibrium was attained in about six months with 75% AR and 25% CH. Those two experiments are typical of what happens in experimental populations when flies derived from the same locality and having different gene arrangements in their third chromosomes are put together and maintained at 25°C. Whatever may be the initial frequencies in the populations, the concentrations of the gene arrangements change until an equilibrium point is attained. In a given environment the equilibrium point will always be the same for the same gene arrangements from the same localities.

Those experiments showed clearly that under experimental conditions (population cages kept at 25°C, with corn meal-molasses medium and Fleischmann's yeast as food), the heterozygotes for chromosomal inversions are heterotic. The heterozygotes have adaptive values higher than both homozygotes. The heterosis was found every time the flies came from the same locality, Keen Camp or Pinon Flats on Mount San Jacinto, or Mather in the Sierra Nevada. The only exception were the ST/TL heterozygotes from Mather. In populations with ST and TL from Mather, TL was eliminated. TL reaches an equilibrium, however, in populations in which AR is present, because the hybrid AR/TL is heterotic (Dobzhansky, 1948c).

Wright (Wright and Dobzhansky, 1946) devised a method by which, knowing the rate of change in the chromosomal frequencies per unit time measured in generations, it is possible to estimate the adaptive values of the chromosomal types involved. The adaptive values of the chromosomal types may then be compared in flies of different geographic origins (Dobzhansky, 1948c). It has been found that the same chromosomal type derived from different localities may have different adaptive values. In flies from Pinon Flats, homozygotes AR have an adaptive value much superior to that of CH homozygotes but AR homozygotes from Mather are only a little superior to CH homozygotes from the same locality. The homozygous ST are much superior to the AR homozygotes from Pinon Flats but fairly similar to those from Mather.

When population cage experiments are made at low temperatures 16.5°C, the results are very different from those obtained at 25°C. At 16.5°C no changes occur in the cages. Populations with any frequencies of gene arrangements are stable at 16.5°C. At a low temperature no difference exists between the adaptive value of the heterozygotes and the homozygotes.

Dobzhansky (1947b) made a comparison in artificial populations of the frequencies of gene arrangements in samples of eggs and in samples of adult flies taken from the same population. In the egg samples the homozygotes and heterozygotes appear in the proportions expected by the Hardy-Weinberg rule, but among the adults the heterozygotes are always in excess. In artificial populations, as in natural populations, there is differential mortality in favor of the heterozygotes. The degree of differential mortality was found to be sufficient to account for the selective changes observed in the experimental populations. However, differential mortality is not the only important component of adaptive value. Fertility, fecundity, longevity, etc., may also be involved in the selective processes.

These experiments constitute another proof that the chromosomal variability in natural populations is controlled by natural selection.

Experiments similar to those described above were also made using chromosomes of different geographical origins in the same experimental populations. Dobzhansky (1950) crossed several homozygous CH strains from Pinon Flats with several homozygous AR strains from Mexico. A large number of hybrids was put in a population cage and left to lay eggs. The F_1 adults were crossed with AR/AR flies and their third chromosome constitution was determined. If the three types of F_1, AR/AR, AR/CH, and CH/CH, had the same viabilities the proportions should be 25% AR/AR, 50% AR/CH, and 25% CH/CH. A large deviation from the 1:2:1 ratio was, however, observed. The homozygotes AR/AR had a viability higher than that of the heterozygotes, and these latter higher than the homozygote CH/CH. Therefore, no heterosis was present when the heterozygotes had their third chromosomes from different geographic origins. This phenomenon was observed using several combinations of ST, AR, and CH chromosomes from Pinon Flats, with ST, AR, and CH from Mather and CH from Mexico.

However, the viability is only one of the elements which determine the adaptive value. To have a complete idea of the adaptive value, it is necessary to leave the population in the cage for several generations to follow the changes that may occur. This was done, and in most of the cages it was found that the heterozygotes were not heterotic and that one of the gene arrangements tended to be eliminated. Two populations were especially interesting because the adaptive values, as determined by the populational changes, were ST/AR > ST/ST > AR/AR while the viabilities were the reverse. This shows that the adaptive value of a gene type is not necessarily proportional to its survival value at all developmental stages.

Inversion heterozygotes, in which the two chromosomes are from the same geographic origin, are in general heterotic, but inversion heterozygotes formed by chromosomes of different geographic origins are not necessarily heterotic. Dobzhansky and Levene (1951) presented some experimental data of the greatest importance for understanding of the development of heterosis. They studied hybrids between strains of $D.$ $pseudoobscura$ from California and Mexico, and measured, in population cages, the relative viabilities of the homozygotes and heterozygotes produced by the hybrids ST^c/CH^M and by AR^c/CH^M. The viabilities were found to be CH^M/CH^M, 0.98 ± 0.25; ST^c/CH^M, 1; ST^c/ST^c 1.87 ± 0.39 in one population; and CH^M/CH^M, 1.10 ± 0.35; AR^c/CH^M, 1; AR^c/AR^c, 1.91 ± 0.51 in the other population. The viability of the heterozygotes was in the first case inferior to that of one homozygote and in the second, inferior to both homozygotes.

Dobzhansky and Levene then started two population cages, one (No. 66) with a ST^c/CH^M population and the other (No. 67) with AR^c/CH^M. In both cages the first generations showed a rapid decrease in the frequency of CH^M. However, after some time there was less of a decrease in CH^M, and finally an equilibrium was reached at about 35% of CH^M in cage 66 and at about 25% in cage 67. The flies from cage 66 were removed. Homozygous strains CH^M and ST^c were selected from them. Hybrids CH^M/ST^c were produced and the viabilities of the homozygotes and heterozygotes obtained from them were tested. The relative viabilities after the selection in the cage were CH^M/CH^M, 0.53 ± 0.11; ST^c/ST^c, 0.78 ± 0.14.

The viabilities were evidently changed after selection in the cage and the heterozygotes became heterotic. A mathematical analysis of the population changes has shown that during the experiment there was a change in the adaptive values. The heterozygotes had improved in their relative adaptive value. This improvement was caused evidently by natural selection working on the gene recombinations produced during the experiment.

Experiments on artificial populations in which there are two types of third chromosome, but in which all the chromosomes are similar in geographical origin, are repeatable. On the other hand, the outcome of experiments with chromosomes of different origin are variable. Large differences may be found between experiments which began with the same initial composition. Experiments like No. 66 and No. 67 were repeated with results which varied widely. Heterosis was produced in only one of the four replicate experiments (Dobzhansky and Pavlovsky, 1953).

Within a population, the different third chromosomes are coadapted in such a way that the heterozygotes have an adaptive value higher than that of the homozygotes. This heterosis is not due to the inversion itself. If the heterosis were due to position effects in the inversion, it would be present every time the same two unlike gene arrangements were together, even if they came from different geographic populations. In reality, heterosis is due to coadaptation of the genic contents of different gene arrangements, as shown by Dobzhansky, and also to the coadaptation of the inversion contents with the rest of the genotype (Brncic, 1954; L. Levine, in press).

Dobzhansky's and Levene's (1951) experiments show how coadaptation may arise. The hybrids between different populations are highly heterozygous. Their progenies are very variable due to the segregation of the genic differences. When, among all the recombinants, a heterotic combination is produced, it is picked up and improved by natural selection. The appearance of such heterotic combinations depends on chance. This is the reason why the appearance of heterosis in populations with chromosomes of mixed geographic regions does not necessarily occur in every experimental population. This is also the reason why experimental production of heterosis cannot be reproduced in every experiment.

Harmonic coadaption of the genes within a population exists not only for genes inside the inverted sections but for all genes of the genome. Vetukhiv (1953) selected homozygous AR/AR strains from several localities in California, Utah, and Colorado. He measured the viabilities of the intrapopulational and interpopulational hybrids and of their offspring. He obtained 58.4% and 60.6% survival in the intrapopulational hybrids and 69.4% and 71% in the interpopulational hybrids in the same environment. The F_2 produced from the intrapopulational hybrids gave the same viabilities as F_1, namely 55.4% and 62.1%. However the F_2 offspring of the F_1 interpopulational hybrids gave a significantly lower viability value than the F_1, namely 47.5% and 50.4%. The explanation for the F_2 breakdown in the interpopulational hybrids is that "the genotype of each local population or race represents an integrated adaptive system, the different parts of which are naturally adjusted or coadapted by natural selection. Such systems are broken down by recombination in hybrids."

Very little is known about the physiological differences conditioned by the several gene arrangements in *D. pseudoobscura*. However, in this respect, as in many others, *D. pseudoobscura* is the best known species of Drosophila. Wright and Dobzhansky (1946) and others showed that the physiological effects of the inversions depend, among other things, on the temperature used. Heterosis is present in *D. pseudoobscura* at 25°C, but, at 16.5°C, the homozygotes are equal to the heterozygotes in their adaptive value. The most complete study of physiological differences conditioned by a gene arrangement is that of Wallace (1948) on the X chromosome "sex-ratio" gene arrangement. The "sex ratio" condition is determined by a gene, or genes, localized in a triple inversion of the X chromosome. At meiosis in the males with the "sex ratio" factor, the Y chromosome is lost. The "sex ratio" X chromosome is four-parted at diakinesis, and every one of the four cells produced by the meiotic process receives an X chromosome. The "sex ratio" X chromosome, therefore, has an advantage over the normal X chromosomes. Whereas only half of the spermatozoids receive an X chromosome in normal meiosis, in the meiosis of a "sex ratio" male, all the spermatozoids, without any fertility decrease, receive an X.

This advantage of the "sex ratio" should lead to an increase of its frequency until there is complete homozygosis for it. However, the frequency of the "sex ratio" is stabilized in natural populations. The seasonal changes observed in the frequency of "sex ratio" give evidence that the factor effective in its control is natural selection. Wallace studied experimental populations with "sex ratio" and Standard X chromosomes. In the populations maintained at 25°C, "sex ratio" was eliminated, but an equilibrium was obtained at 16.5°C. Wallace was able to study several factors of importance in the determination of the adaptive value such as larval competition, longevity, fecundity, sexual activity, "sex ratio," and egg hatchability. Knowing the performance of the several genotypes, ST/SR, SR/SR, and ST/ST, in these respects, Wallace was able to calculate the overall adaptive value of the genotypes. The SR males are superior to ST males at 16.5°C but inferior at 25°C. The SR/ST females are superior to both homozygotes at 25°C and at 16.5°C. The adaptive value of SR/SR is close to zero at 25°C. These results explain why SR is eliminated from experimental populations at 25°C but is retained at 16.5°C. The most interesting of Wallace's results is the comparison of the values of the different genotypes for several factors of adaptive importance.

A genotype may be superior to others in one respect but inferior in others. For example, at 16.5°C, SR males are superior to ST males in longevity (1.113) but inferior in larval competition (0.74) and in sexual activity (0.878 or 0.846), the values for ST males being taken as unity. The values for the several adaptive factors are very much changed by temperature. For example, the value of SR/SR in larval competition was 0.152 at 25°C and 0.622 at 16.5°C in comparison with SR/ST taken as unit. A gene arrangement, therefore, affects many adaptive characters and its effects on different characters may not be correlated. The adaptive value has many components which are to some degree independent.

Heuts (1947, 1948) studied the effects of humidity on the viability of pupae and on the viability and the longevity of adults of several chromosomal combinations in *D. pseudoobscura* from Pinon Flats. When the pupae develop at 70–75% relative humidity the AR/AR adults have a higher longevity than ST/ST and CH/CH at any humidity. However, if pupae develop at 100% relative humidity, the longevity of CH/CH adults is superior. The adult flies are also sensitive to temperature. At 28–30°C the relative longevities are ST/ST > ST/CH > CH/CH, but at low temperature, 0–4°C, the values were ST/CH > ST/ST > CH/CH. If the experiments on the longevity of the adults were performed at 25°C and the flies were fed for 24-hour periods 3 times a week, the longevities were ST/ST = ST/CH > CH/CH. The CH/CH larvae are inviable at 28–30°C, and ST/ST survive much better than ST/CH. Heuts' data show clearly that the environmental factors studied affect differentially the different combinations of third chromosomes. Levine (1952) confirmed and extended Heuts' findings.

Spassky (1951) tested the effects of temperature and moisture content of the medium on the viability of chromosomal types in a very elegant way. He selected AR, ST, and CH homozygous strains from Pinon Flats and crossed them to a laboratory strain with the gene Lobe (lethal when homozygous). He observed the relative frequencies of the homozygotes for the gene arrangement and the heterozygotes for Lobe in the next generation, and used them as a measure of the viability of homozygotes. He raised the flies in dry and in normal food media at a low temperature (16.5°C) and at room temperature (25°C). Significant differences were found between the viabilities of the different gene arrangements and also for the same gene arrangement in different conditions. It is very interesting that CH/CH has a higher viability at the high temperature and in dry food, and AR/AR at the cooler temperature and in humid media.

The effects of nutritional variables on the adaptive values of chromosomal types of *D. pseudoobscura* were studied by da Cunha (1951). Experimental populations containing flies with CH and ST chromosomes were maintained in population cages and fed on different yeasts and bacteria. The yeasts and bacteria used were obtained from the crops of flies captured in nature at Mather. The flies used in these experiments were derived also from Mather strains. The behavior of ST and CH varied from cage to cage according to the food used. With some yeasts, the equilibrium frequency was found to be at 70% of ST, with other yeasts at 75% or 80%. Heterosis was present but the relative adaptive values of the three types ST/ST, ST/CH, and CH/CH were different according to the food used. With still other yeasts no heterosis existed, the homozygote ST/ST being superior to ST/CH and to CH/CH.

These results show that the genes carried by chromosomes with different gene arrangements are important in the adaptation of the flies to different types of nutrition. Conversely, the types of food predominant in a given region may be important in determining the chromosomal composition of the Drosophila populations which inhibit this region. It is interesting in this connection to note that Drosophila flies have food preferences, being to some extent able to choose by smell the yeasts that they will feed upon (da Cunha, Dobzhansky, and Sokoloff, 1951; Dobzhansky and da Cunha, 1954).

VI. Chromosomal Polymorphism in *Drosophila persimilis*

D. persimilis (Dobzhansky and Epling, 1944) is a sibling species of *D. pseudoobscura*, which for a long time was referred to as Race B of *D. pseudoobscura*. *D. persimilis* is less well known than *D. pseudoobscura*, but some interesting differences occur between the populations of the two species. The distribution area of *D. persimilis* extends from British Columbia to California, and from the Pacific to the Cascades and the

Sierra Nevada mountains. In California, *D. persimilis* is restricted to the coast and to the higher mountains of the interior. The San Joaquin and the Sacramento valleys of California make the interchange between the populations of the coast and of the mountains difficult. Due to this barrier the populations of the interior and the coastal populations are clearly differentiated. A north-south transect of the coastal region shows a cline in the frequencies of the Klamath (KL) and Mendocino (MD) gene arrangements. The frequencies of KL decrease and those of MD increase from north to south. The gene arrangement Standard (ST) becomes also more frequent southward. A north-south transect in the interior (Cascades-Sierra Nevada) shows KL again decreasing from north to south, but the gene arrangement which has a large increase along this cline is not MD (as on the coast) but Whitney (WT). ST is, as on the coast, more frequent in the South than in the North.

The Y chromosome is also variable and three types are known. Type I (unequal armed V) is most widespread. Type II (equal armed V) has high frequencies around Puget Sound, and Type III (unequal armed V) has high frequency in the Sierra Nevada and the southern coast ranges.

Dobzhansky (1948b) studied the populations of *D. persimilis* in several localities in the Sierra Nevada. This study on the frequencies of the gene arrangements includes data from samples obtained at different seasons of the year for three years. In contrast to what was found in *D. pseudoobscura*, during the same time, no seasonal variations in the gene arrangement frequencies were found. However, as in *D. pseudoobscura*, an altitudinal gradient is present in *D. persimilis*. The frequency of the gene arrangement WT rises gradually from 60% at Jacksonville (elevation 260 meters) to 90.15% at the timber line (3,200 meters). Other gene arrangements decrease, ST from 10% to 6%, KL from 11.67% to 2.27%, and MD from 18.33% to 1.52%. It is interesting that localities far apart in horizontal distance have the same gene arrangements frequencies if they are at the same altitude, while localities close together have large differences if they are at different altitudes.

During the period 1945–1950, there was a steady increase in the frequency of the gene arrangement WT in various localities studied in the Sierra Nevada (Dobzhansky, 1952). After 1950 the concentration of WT went down. These frequency changes are parallel to those of the gene arrangement AR of *D. pseudoobscura* found in the populations of the same region and at the same time. They may be correlated with drought.

Spiess (1950) studied the behavior of *D. persimilis* gene arrangements in experimental populations, using at the same time populations with two different arrangements. At 25°C the different combinations of gene arrangements had more or less similar adaptive values. Accordingly, the frequencies remained stable or changed slowly. In the populations maintained at 16.5°C heterosis was, however, always present. This is another very remarkable difference between *D. persimilis* and *D. pseudoobscura*. The fact that heterosis is present in *D. persimilis* populations at 16.5°C and in *D. pseudoobscura* at 25°C is most probably correlated with the ecological conditions in which the two species live. *D. persimilis* is a species of colder habitats and *D. pseudoobscura* of warmer habitats. Heterosis is present in both species at the temperature closer to that at which the genes involved in the process were selected.

Spiess and coworkers (1952) made a study of the physiological properties of different gene arrangements in *D. persimilis*, analyzing the egg laying capacity, longevity, wing beat frequency, and wing dimensions. The heterozygotes WT/KL showed an egg-laying capacity higher than that of the homozygotes and also had a superior longevity. For the wing beats frequency and wing dimensions, there exist significant differences among the flies with different third chromosome combinations, but there is no clear evidence of heterotic effects for these characters. Another interesting fact in the data on *D. persimilis* populations is that the differences between this species and *D. pseudoobscura* are correlated with ecological dissimilarities between the two species. These differences are clearly adaptive.

VII. CHROMOSOMAL POLYMORPHISM IN *Drosophila robusta*

Drosophila robusta is a species restricted to the deciduous forests of the eastern United States. Its distribution area is correlated with the presence of *Ulmus americanus* on the fermented sap of which the flies breed and feed. The chromosomes of *D. robusta* are very variable. A total of at least 20 gene arrangements are known, and their geographical distribution as well as their frequencies in natural population have been described by Carson and Stalker (1947, 1948, 1949, and unpublished data) and by Levitan (1951a). Very clear north-south gradients were found in the frequencies of many gene arrangements. For example, in the left arm of the X chromosome the arrangement XL-1 is present in 100% of the chromosomes in Wisconsin, 47.7% in Iowa, 14.7% in Missouri, and 0% from Kentucky southward. The arrangement XL and XL-2 show the reverse gradient. In the left arm of the second chromosome, the arrangement 2L-3 occurs in 96% of all second chromosomes in Wisconsin, 30% in Iowa, and 0% from Missouri southward. The distributions of 14 different and widespread gene arrangements were studied, and all of them showed geographic gradients.

It is interesting to note that localities very far apart but at about the same latitude, as Mount Vernon (Iowa) and Wooster (Ohio), have populations with similar compositions. As Carson and Stalker (1947) say, " . . . the post-Pleistocene spread of *D. robusta* may be conceived as involving a gradual spreading of the flies into new area, carrying with them pre-existing gene sequences from the pool of arrangements in Pleistocene refugia. As the spread proceded, selection of heterozygotes could result in the fixation of the gene arrangements frequencies in the different areas at various equilibria, depending on the type of genes trapped in the arrangement and the pressure of different ecological selective factors."

Especially interesting in *D. robusta* is the pericentric inversion 3L-R. The frequency of this gene arrangement is as high as 49% in a Wisconsin population. This is totally unexpected for a pericentric inversion. Stalker and Carson (1947) also studied many morphological traits in flies from 22 localities. They found that for the morphological characters a north-south gradient is also present.

The mountain populations of *D. robusta*, as those of *D. pseudoobscura* and *D. persimilis*, show very clear altitudinal gradients in the frequencies of gene arrangements (Stalker and Carson, 1948). This was found in the Great Smoky Mountains in Tennessee. The transect studied extended from an altitude of 300 meters to 1,200 meters, and for a horizontal distance of 29 kilometers. All the gene arrangements, with the exception of those in the left arm of the second chromosome and of the arrangement XR-1, which was too rare, showed altitudinal clines. Most of the gradients are very sharp, for example, 2L-1 (8% to 37%); 2L-3 (66% to 19%), XL (14% to 75%), XL-1 (42% to 6%), XL-2 (44% to 19%), XR (16% to 44%), and XR-2 (84% to 55%). The first percentage given above is for the altitude of 1,220 meters and the second for 300 meters. The altitudinal gradients in *D. robusta* are thus even more striking than those in *D. pseudoobscura* and *D. persimilis*.

Stalker and Carson suggested that the altitudinal cline is due not to an environmental gradient but to mixing of two races or ecotypes. A mountain and a low-level race meeting in a narrow region of hybridization would produce a sharp gradient. A morphological study of the flies from the altitudinal transect was made. Variation similar to that found on the north-south transect was found. In general, populations of higher altitudes are more similar to northern populations. The correlation of the morphological gradient with the chromosomal one indicates that the inversion gradient is responsible for the morphological cline. However, the gene arrangement frequencies at different altitudes do not necessarily parallel those in southern and western populations. The gene contents of the inversions are probably, as in *D. pseudoobscura* and *D. persimilis*, different in different geographical regions.

116   A. BRITO DA CUNHA

Carson and Stalker (1949) recorded periodically the frequencies of the different chromosomal types of D. robusta near St. Louis, Missouri, during a period of three years. Some unidirectional changes as well as changes which were later reversed were found, but no cyclic seasonal fluctuations. However, a clear, seasonal, morphological fluctuation was discovered. During the summer months the populations shifted clearly to a more southern morphology and these fluctuations were cyclic and observable for at least one year (Stalker and Carson, 1949).

Levitan (1951a,b,c) obtained results different from those of Carson and Stalker. He studied a population in New Jersey in which seasonal variation seems to exist at least for one gene arrangement, 2L. What was remarkable in this population is that males and females differed in gene arrangement frequencies. Females had higher frequencies of XL and 2L, and males higher frequencies of XL-1 and 2L-3. The chromosomal type 2L is more common in spring in males (44.9%) than in females (25%), but in the fall it is more abundant in females (50%) than in males (34.3%). Seasonal changes were also found in Virginia, where the fluctuations are significant for several chromosomal types. However, the seasonal changes were in general more significant among the males than among the females. The situation concerning seasonal fluctuations is, therefore, very different in the several populations studied. In some populations there is no seasonal fluctuation at all, as in Missouri, while in others seasonal changes occur.

The chromosomal composition of egg and adult samples from natural populations was studied (Levitan, 1951a). No significant deviations from the expectation according to the Hardy-Weinberg rule were found. However, there is some indication of excess of homozygotes but the differences are not significant. Differential mortality between egg and adult stage seems not to be in operation in the D. robusta populations studied.

Levitan (1951a) also studied the behavior of the chromosomal types in population cages. All the inversion heterozygotes studied were heterotic. The chromosomal types were also found to be sensitive to temperature and to humidity. The high sensitivity of the chromosomal combinations of D. robusta to small differences in temperature, in humidity, and probably also in food makes the experiments very variable and hardly repeatable. The pericentric 2L-3 was among the inversions studied, which also gave heterosis in combination with 2L or 2L-1. In D. robusta, as in D. pseudoobscura and D. persimilis, the chromosomal polymorphism is maintained by a heterosis produced by the inversion heterozygosis.

VIII. CHROMOSOMAL POLYMORPHISM IN Drosophila funebris

Drosophila funebris differs from the other species studied because it often lives in environments created or modified by man. The knowledge about the population genetics of *D. funebris* is due mainly to the work of Dubinin and Tiniakov on the Russian populations of this species. *D. funebris* is chromosomally very variable. Eight different gene arrangements were found in the vicinity of Moscow, U.S.S.R. The concentration of the inversion heterozygotes was very different in different parts of the city of Moscow. The heterozygosity was at its maximum in the central part of the city, where the percentage of heterozygotes was 88.54%. From the center to the periphery of the city the heterozygosity decreased gradually to 12.1% at the periphery of the city. In the rural region around Moscow the frequency of heterozygotes was very low, about 1.5%, and in villages at 200–500 kilometers from Moscow no inversions were found. There is, therefore, a very clear cline in the frequency of heterozygotes from a maximum in the center of the city to a minimum in the rural area. High frequencies of heterozygotes were found also in other cities studied, namely, Saratov (53.9%), Ivanovo (37.2%), and Erivan (21.2%).

Low frequencies of heterozygotes occurs in rural areas and in "garden cities," as Alma-Ata (1.48%). Among the several cities studied the frequency of heterozygous inversions is proportional to the degree of their industrialization (Dubinin and Tiniakov, 1946a, 1947a). Collections in Moscow made at monthly intervals disclosed that within the same city the percentage of inversions found varied according to the season. In a region of the city of Moscow the percentage of inversions increased 15 times from May to August and in others the increase was of 1.8 times. In contrast to the city populations, no seasonal change was found in the rural ones (Dubinin and Tiniakov, 1945).

Another correlation of the inversions with the environment is given by studies on the geographic distribution of the gene arrangements. The gene arrangement II-1 is more common in the north and decreases towards the south of Russia. The frequency of II-1 is 80% at Ivanovo, 72% at Moscow, 54% at Michurinsk, 35% at Saratov, and 1.3% at Erivan. The inversion II-2 shows a reverse gradient (Dubinin and Tiniakov, 1946c, 1947a).

Dubinin and Tiniakov (1946c, 1947b) exposed populations of known chromosomal compositions, kept in population cages, to low temperature of −2°C to +3°C. The survivals after 15, 30, 45, and 75 days of treatment were analyzed cytologically. In some experiments the homozygotes were more frequent among the survivals than in the original population. This was the case for the homozygotes for "normal" against the II-1 gene arrangement. In other cases, however, the heterozygotes survived better than the homozygotes, as in the case of the heterozygotes for IV-1. These two experiments are in agreement with the findings in natural populations where the frequency of II-1 increases in the summer and that of IV-1 increases with cold weather.

Another indication of a higher adaptive value of heterozygotes in *D. funebris* was obtained by Dubinin and Tiniakov (1946b). They released 100,000 flies which were homozygous for the II-1 inversion in Kropotovo, near Moscow, where this gene arrangement is rare (0.92%). The introduced gene arrangement spread very rapidly. The data on the gene arrangement frequencies after II-1 was introduced indicated that the heterozygotes were favored by natural selection. The heterozygotes were 13% more frequent than expected according to the Hardy-Weinberg rule.

Little is known about *D. funebris* outside the U.S.S.R. Berrie and Sansome (1948) reported an analysis of a population of *D. funebris* near Manchester, England. In this population, every individual was heterozygous for three small inversions in the fifth chromosome. It was impossible to obtain homozygous strains in the laboratory; the authors believe this to be a case of balanced lethals.

IX. Chromosomal Polymorphism in *Drosophila subobscura*

Drosophila subobscura is the best studied member of the *obscura* group in Europe. The taxonomic situation in the *obscura* species group in Europe is not yet clear and some confusion exists regarding the earlier work. Dubinin, Sokolov, and Tiniakov (1937) studied the chromosomal variability of three species of the *obscura* group, but the classification of the species is uncertain. They found the populations to be chromosomally highly variable. Flies heterozygous for as many as 8 chromosomal aberrations involving 20 breaks were found. In a more recent note about their "*D. obscura* 3," which is probably *D. subobscura*, Sokolov and Dubinin (1941) gave the frequencies of several gene arrangements in the locality of Sochi. The fifth chromosome (the species has five pairs of rod-shaped chromosomes and one pair of dot-shaped) was found to be, with very rare exceptions, always heterozygous for an inversion called B. Other chromosomes also show frequent heterozygosis, the second chromosome, Aa, 66%, the third, Bb, 45%, and the fourth, Aa, 91%. The high frequencies of heterozygous inversions indicates that in *D. subobscura* the heterozygotes are heterotic, as in the other species already discussed.

Philip *et al.* (1944) stated in a preliminary note that in the English populations of *D. subobscura* almost all larvae show inversions in the 5 pairs of rod-shaped chromosomes. The relative viability of homozygotes and heterozygotes for several gene arrangements was explored. In some cases the heterozygotes seemed to be as viable as the homozygotes, and in other cases the heterozygotes were the most viable and fertile types. A strain heterozygous for 3 inversions was inbred, and after 15 generations of inbreeding it was still heterozygous for the 3 inversions. The probability of keeping the 3 heterozygous gene arrangements after 15 generations of inbreeding in the absence of selection is of 1 in 37,000 trials. Strains made homozygous for any of the 3 gene arrangements mentioned were, in general, lost due to their very low adaptive values.

A detailed study of the chromosomal variability of the southwestern European populations of D. subobscura was made by Stumm-Zollinger (1953). Populations from Portugal, France, and Switzerland were studied. A total of 23 inversions were found, 2 in the X chromosome, 1 in the second, 4 in the third, 5 in the fourth and 11 in the fifth. Most of the inversions were found in all the localities studied. Some inversions, always the rare ones, were found only in few places. Probably none of the inversions is endemic and, if sometimes they seem to be so, it is due to their rarity and to the smallness of the samples.

Some of the inversions present a cline in their frequency distribution. The inversions Aldo (13.3% to 48.5%), Ursula (11% to 43.1%), Edda + Eleonore (14.1% to 37%), for example, have their frequencies increased going from east to west (the figures given are the frequencies of Fetan, the easternmost place, and Lisbon in the western extreme). Other inversions showed a more irregular distribution. In four places in Switzerland, namely Küsnacht, Eglisan, Braunwald, and Fetan, periodic collections were made to see whether seasonal variations occur in the gene arrangement frequencies. No significant differences were found. No significant variations independent from the seasons were found either. Only two inversions, Ursula in Küsnacht and Olga in Eglisan, showed some tendency to vary.

Collections made at the same time of the year at different altitudes, Fetan (1750 meters), Braunwald (1300 meters) and Vitznau (440 meters) showed no correlation between the altitude and the gene arrangement frequencies. The degree of polymorphism in the different populations was measured by the mean number of heterozygous inversions per individual. The populations in France (Garonne, Tellay, and Biaz) were found to be the most variable ones, with about 4 heterozygous inversions per male and 4.4 to 4.8 per female. The Swiss populations were the least variable, 2.2 to 2.9 per male and 2.5 to 3.8 inversions per female. The Portugese population studied was intermediate between the French and the Swiss in the degree of variability, the number of heterozygous inversions being 3.4 per male and 4.2 per female. No correlation was found between degree of variability of the populations and the ecological characteristics of the environment where the populations lived.

A preliminary note by Gunson (1952) indicates that the populations of D. subobscura in Scotland are chromosomally very diversified, but unfortunately no numerical data are available.

X. Chromosomal Polymorphism in Neotropical Drosophila

Drosophila willistoni belongs to a group of four sibling species of the *willistoni* group of the subgenus Sophophora. *Drosophila willistoni* is morphologically very hard to distinguish from the three other siblings, *D. paulistorum*, *D. equinoxialis*, and *D. tropicalis*. However, they may be easily differentiated by the salivary gland chromosomes. The metaphase chromosomes are identical; the four species have two pairs of V-shaped chromosomes, one being the sex chromosomes, and one pair of rod-shaped chromosomes. The four siblings are completely isolated reproductively and cannot be crossed at all. The distribution and ecology of the four siblings are also different. *D. willistoni* is found from Florida to Argentina and in this enormous area it may be found in quite different ecological situations. *D. paulistorum* is recorded from northern Brazil to the Tropic of Capricorn, and in this area it does not occur in dry environments. *D. equinoxialis* and *D. tropicalis* are restricted to the Amazon Valley and to central Brazil (Burla *et al.*, 1949; Dobzhansky, Burla, and da Cunha, 1950; Townsend, 1952; da Cunha and Dobzhansky, 1954).

The chromosomal variability of *D. willistoni* has been the object of intensive study (da Cunha, Burla, and Dobzhansky, 1950; Townsend, 1952; da Cunha and Dobzhansky, 1954). *D. willistoni* is the most variable species known. A total of 42 different inversions distributed evenly among the three chromosomes is known. Most of the inversions are short and recombination between them permits formation of an enormous number of chromosomal types.

Some of the inversions in *D. willistoni*, like IIL-A, IIL-E, IIL-F, III-A, III-H, and III-J, have the widest known distribution area for a chromosomal variant, being present in the populations from Florida and Cuba to southern Brazil and Argentina. Other inversions have less extensive distributions. Endemic inversions are very rare, only IIL-G, III-K, III-Al, and III-N being known.

The frequencies of the gene arrangements in populations indicate the existence of many geographic races. Some of the races, like the "Bahia race" are rather sharply delimited. The inversion III-A, which in heterozygous state is very common everywhere, is very rare or absent in the region of Bahia and Espirito Santo. The same inversion III-A is again rare on the Island of Marajó, but on this island the rest of the chromosomal composition of the populations is quite different from the "Bahia race."

Repeated collections of *D. willistoni* were made only in Mogi das Cruzes, Vila Atlântica, Piraçununga, and Belém do Pará. Most of the inversions did not show any significant variation among the several samples. Only XR-D and III-A + B at Mogi, III-H and III-L + M at Piraçununga, and III-F and IIL-A + B at Belém showed significant fluctuations. The data do not permit a decision on whether the variations are seasonal and cyclic. It is interesting to note that the climate in Belém is remarkably uniform, and the variations observed must, therefore, be due to changes in biotic factors, like fruit seasons.

Some inversions were found in heterozygous state with frequencies higher than 50%. These inversions are clearly heterotic. It is interesting to notice that two of these inversions are localized in the X chromosome. Since males are always homozygous for X chromosome genes, the X chromosome inversions are heterotic only in females. The heterosis in the X chromosome inversions is, therefore, due to genes with "sex-*limited*" effects (da Cunha, 1953b).

The degree of variability of the populations was measured by the mean number of heterozygous inversions per individual. The least variable population had a mean of about 1 heterozygous inversion per individual female and the most variable had a mean of about 9 per female. The most variable populations, those of Goyaz and of Western Bahia in Brazil, with a mean of 9 to 7.5 heterozygous inversions per female, are only about 500 kilometers distant from the least variable population which is in Central Bahia with a mean of 1 inversion per female. At Rio Branco, in the northernmost part of Brazil, the frequency of heterozygous inversions changes from a mean of about 4.8 per female to a mean of about 2.7 within a distance of only 60 kilometers. The main factors in the determination of the variability of the populations are ecological factors.

The degree of variability of the populations has a very definite relation with the ecology of the region which the flies inhabit. Populations living in ecologically rich environments are more variable than populations living in ecologically poor environments. In regions of savanna plus rain forest, the degree of variability is 9.4 heterozygous inversions per female, but in a desert (caatinga) the degree of variability is only 0.8 heterozygous inversions per female. In ecologically similar regions, even when very far apart, the populations tend to have the same amount of variability. Thus, the variability of populations living in the savanna is similar in Piraçununga (in southern Brazil) and in Rio Branco or Amapá (in the northernmost part of Brazil).

Where the species reaches geographical or ecological limits of its tolerance, the variability of its populations is decreased. Close to the southern limits of distribution of *D. willistoni* as well as at its northern limits (Townsend, 1952), the degree of variability is low, about 1.9 heterozygous inversions per female.

An attempt to explain these findings was made by da Cunha, Burla, and Dobzhansky (1950) and Dobzhansky, Burla, and da Cunha (1950). These authors advanced a hypothesis according to which, other things being equal, the degree of polymorphism of a population is positively correlated with the number of ecological niches exploited by the population. Levene (1953) has studied mathematically some aspects of this hypothesis showing that it is compatible with the principles of mathematical genetics. New data on the variability of natural populations of *D. willistoni* were obtained by da Cunha and Dobzhansky (1954) in order to put the hypothesis to a further test. Collections were made in ecologically critical regions of Brazil. Based on ecological data available, predictions were made of the results to be obtained. In all cases but three, the predictions were fairly accurate. The three samples the results of which disagreed with predictions were from one ecological region inhabited by an unexpectedly uniform race, the "Bahia race."

However, the results of the sampling of 39 regions out of 42 (including Townsend's data for Florida, 1952) ecological regions is in very good agreement with the hypothesis. Da Cunha and Dobzhansky (1954), following suggestions of Danserau (1952), attempted to estimate the variability of the environment in quasi-quantitative terms. The environments were classified according to several biologically important factors such as types of flora, types of climate, degrees of competition, and frequency of species. The types of flora and climate were graded according to their relative variability. The degrees of competition and the relative frequencies of the species were graded according to their probable importance in determining the share of the environment occupied by the species. Every habitat then had a score that was the sum of the grades given to the several factors. The details of this evaluation of the environment may be found in da Cunha and Dobzhansky (1954). When the amounts of chromosomal variability of the populations were plotted against the scores of environmental diversity, a fairly good correlation was obtained.

D. nebulosa, a species which also belongs to the *willistoni* group, presents a pattern of chromosomal variability in many ways similar to that found in *D. willistoni* (da Cunha, Brncic, and Salzano, 1953). A total of 10 different inversions have been found in 10 South American populations studied. All the inversions are localized in the third chromosome. The variability of the populations varied between 2.36 $\pm$ 0.19 heterozygous inversions per individual to 0.86 $\pm$ 0.08. In *D. nebulosa*, as in *D. willistoni*, populations living in ecologically poor regions, as in the desert-like caatinga, are much less variable than populations living in ecologically richer places. The populations living at the margin of the distribution area of *D. nebulosa* show a small amount of variability. The data on

D. nebulosa are much less extensive than those on *D. willistoni*, but they show that the pattern of variability seems to be determined in the same way in both species.

Comparative study of the chromosomal variability in closely related species disclosed also another relation between the variability and the ecology of the species (Dobzhansky, Burla, and da Cunha, 1950). As stated above, *D. willistoni* and its siblings *D. paulistorum*, *D. tropicalis*, and *D. equinoxialis* have different distribution areas and different ecologies. *D. willistoni* has the wider distribution (from Florida to Argentina), *D. paulistorum* is the next, extending from northern South America to the Tropic of Capricorn, and *D. equinoxialis* and *D. tropicalis* are restricted to the Amazon region and central Brazil. Within its distribution area, *D. willistoni* is found in all kinds of habitats, while *D. paulistorum*, *D. tropicalis*, and *D. equinoxialis* are restricted to humid rainforests.

The chromosomes of *D. willistoni* are the most variable, 42 different inversions having being known. *D. paulistorum* is the second with 34 inversions, followed by *D. tropicalis* and *D. equinoxialis* with 4 inversions each. The mean number of heterozygous inversions per individual female in the populations varied in *D. willistoni* from 0.80 to 9.4, in *D. paulistorum* from 0.6 to 1.8, in *D. tropicalis* it is about 0.14, and in *D. equinoxialis* it is 0.11.

These data clearly show that species with larger geographical distributions and with broader ecological versatility are more variable than closely related but geographically or ecologically restricted species. Da Cunha, Brncic, and Salzano (1953) made a comparative study of the variation in closely related neotropical species, *D. polymorpha* and *D. cardinoides*, and in *D. guaramunu* and *D. griseolineata*, which are also closely related. *D. polymorpha* and *D. guaramunu* have larger geographical distributions and are ecologically more versatile than their relatives *D. cardinoides* and *D. griseolineata*. The numbers of inversions found in natural populations of these four species are about 6 in *D. polymorpha* and 3 in *D. cardinoides*, 16 in *D. guaramunu*, and 5 in *D. griseolineata*. The mean number of the heterozygous inversions per individual varied in *D. polymorpha* from 0.54 to 1.82 (in females), in *D. cardinoides* from 0 to 0.16, in *D. guaramunu* from 1.6 to 3.2, in *D. griseolineata* from 0.01 to 0.47.

Quantitative data on chromosomal variability is also available for some cosmopolitan species associated with man (Freire-Maia, 1952a,b, 1953; Freire-Maia, Zanardini, and Freire-Maia, 1953). *D. ananassae* was found to be the most variable among such "weedy" species. A total of 15 paracentric and 5 pericentric inversions, 2 translocations, 1 deficiency,

1 transposition, and several duplications have been recorded by Freire-Maia. One reciprocal translocation was previously described by Dobzhansky and Dreyfus (1943) also from a Brazilian population of *D. ananassae*. The mean number of heterozygous inversion per individual in the several populations of *D. ananassae* studied varied from 1.2 to 1.7, the mean in this total data being 1.34.

The next most variable domestic species is *D. melanogaster* with 10 known inversions and a mean of 0.61 heterozygous inversions per individual. *Drosophila immigrans* and *D. montium* have 1 inversion each and the average number of heterozygous inversions are 0.23 and 0.11, respectively. *D. hydei* has 2 inversions but the average number of inversions is very low, 0.04. No inversions were found in the populations of *D. simulans*.

D. simulans, *D. immigrans*, *D. melanogaster*, and *D. hydei* are the commonest domestic species in Brazil, *D. simulans* being by far the most abundant. *D. ananassae* is abundant in some places but its distribution is more erratic. *D. montium* is very restricted geographically. It seems that the chromosomal variability of domestic species, with the exception of *D. funebris*, is not in accord with the rule established for wild species. However, the history of species associated with man makes such species a special case. Before any generalizations are made concerning domestic species, their ecology must be studied. One of the possibilities is that a species like *D. simulans* is adapted to occupy few but very widespread ecological niches, while a species like *D. ananassae* is able to exploit many different, but rarely found, niches.

XI. Chromosomal Polymorphism in Diptera Other than Drosophila

Chromosomal polymorphism of the type studied in the natural populations of *Drosophila* was also found in other Diptera with good polytene chromosomes, namely in *Chironomus*, *Liriomyza*, *Anopheles*, and *Sciara*. Bauer (1936) and Philip (1942) studied natural populations of several species of *Chironomus*, finding chromosomal inversions in some species, such as *C. riparius* and *C. dorsalis*, but no chromosomal variability in other species, like *C. thummi*. Philip (1942) found four inversions in two populations of *C. dorsalis*, and five inversions in one population of *C. riparius*, in England. The inversions found in the English population of *C. riparius* were the same as found by Bauer (1936) in northern Germany.

Within the populations of *C. dorsalis* the different types of chromosomes are distributed at random. The two populations studied differ significantly in the frequency of one of the inversions. In the two *C. dorsalis* populations, the homozygotes and the heterozygotes were found in proportions expected on the assumption of random mating. No difference of viability was found between the homozygotes and heterozygotes. The German population of *C. riparius* studied by Bauer and the English one studied by Philip differed significantly in the frequencies of three out of the five inversions found. In the German population there was a significant excess of heterozygotes, and in the English an excess of heterozygotes was also observed, but it was not significant. There is, therefore, an indication that the heterozygotes are favored in *C. riparius*.

Populations of *Chironomus* in China have also been studied (Hsu and Liu, 1948). Three populations living within 11 kilometers were studied and six different gene arrangements were found in an unclassified species of *Chironomus*. Two of the gene arrangements were specially interesting. One of them is a tandem paracentric inversion which was probably originated by four breaks produced at the same time. This inversion shows that complex rearrangements may be produced in a single step. The other interesting condition is the alteration of chromosome morphology. One homozygote for the rearrangement has a clear "bulb" and the other has no "bulb." In the heterozygotes the "bulb" is present only in half of the chromosome. The other four gene arrangements are simple paracentric inversions. The data for the three Chinese populations indicate that the different chromosomal types are combined at random and that the populations are at equilibrium. However, the equilibrium points for the inversions are different in the three localities and are probably due to different environmental conditions.

More recent data on chromosomal variability in *Chironomus* were obtained by Beermann (1952) and Acton (unpublished data). Beermann (1952) was able to produce hybrids between *Camptochironomus tentans* and *C. pallidivittatus*. Both species have four pairs of chromosomes and they differ by many chromosomal rearrangements. The hybrids are fully viable and the chiasmata are produced normally, giving recombinations between chromosomes with different gene arrangements for which the hybrids are heterozygous. Numerical data concerning the intraspecific variability are not given by Beermann, but the variability is certainly very high. Beermann indicates the presence of eight simple and one complex inversions frequent in *C. tentans* and six simple and one complex frequent in *C. pallidivittatus*. Acton (unpublished data) has made a detailed analysis of natural populations of several species of Chironomus in England, and he found much variability in the populations of *C. dorsalis*, *C. tentans*, and *C. singulatus*.

In Drosophila, inversions are protected against the adaptively undesirable results of a crossing-over within the inverted section by (1) the mechanism of meiosis which always makes a noncrossover chromatid stay in the egg nucleus; (2) absence of crossing-over in males. The chromosomes with inverted sections probably behave in the female meiosis of other Diptera in the same way as they do in *Drosophila* (Carson, 1946). The main problem concerning the maintenance of inversions in Diptera, which, like *Chironomus*, have crossing-over in both sexes, is therefore how the inverted chromosomes behave in the male meiosis.

Philip (1942) calculated that if crossing-over occurred regularly within the inverted sections, in a *Chironomus* male with 4 inversions and having a reduction of the spermatozoa number to $\frac{1}{16}$, only 20–30 spermatozoa per egg would be produced.

Cytological studies of meiosis made by Philip in *Chironomus dorsalis* and *C. riparius*, both having inversions, showed that no chiasmata are formed within the inversions. Therefore, it seems that, in organisms with crossing-over in the male, only inversions protected by a localization of chiasmata may survive. Why, then, should an inversion be useful in a region where crossing-over normally does not occur? The answer is, probably, that the localization of chiasmata is not absolute, and the inversions prevent crossing-over in the regions where they occur.

Populations of the Agromyzid, *Liriomyza urophorina*, analyzed by Mainx (1951) proved to be chromosomally very polymorphic. Larvae of this fly live on flower buds of *Lilium martagon*, apparently being ecologically very specialized. *Liriomyza* has only one generation per year. There were 6 kinds of inversions found in a total of 842 larvae examined from 8 Austrian populations. Within a population, the homozygotes and heterozygotes were found in the proportions demanded by the Hardy-Weinberg rule.

Inversion frequencies differ among the populations studied. Two populations in the Vienna woods, only 1 kilometer apart, were significantly different in the frequencies of 2 gene arrangements. In *Liriomyza* such differences between very close populations are possibly due to the low-flying capacity of the adult flies. The 3 more widespread inversions are more common in heterozygous conditions in Hollenburg, and the frequencies of heterozygotes decrease from that region in a roughly uniform cline. The rather wide distribution area of the inversions and the high frequencies with which they were found in heterozygous conditions indicate that their distribution is regulated by natural selection. However, no correlation was found between the presence of any of the inversions and any ecological factor.

The studies of Frizzi (1952 and earlier) on *Anopheles* disclosed that the chromosomes of different species differ by inverted sections. However, no polymorphism was found within populations of the same species. However, studying *Anopheles maculipennis messeae*, Frizzi (1952) found that *messeae* differs from *A. m. typicius*, *A. m. subalpinus* and *A. m. melanoon* by an inversion in the X chromosome. Heterozygous X chromosomes were found in nature but always with a frequency very much lower than expected from the frequencies of homozygotes. Mating of the flies is clearly not random with regard to the X chromosome types. The two types of X chromosomes are correlated with ecological and morphological differences. *Anopheles* probably has no mechanism protecting it from the unfavorable effects of crossing-over within the inversions, and for this reason the populations are homogeneous for gene arrangements.

Remarkable differences exist between the chromosomal variability in the genus Sciara and in the other Diptera. Metz (1938, 1941, 1947) found that the commonest differences between chromosomes within and between species are very small deficiencies or duplications. In *Sciara ocellaris*, the species more thoroughly studied by Metz, a total of 17 minute deficiencies and duplications were found. Some strains of *S. coprophila* and *S. impatiens* also showed such small chromosomal differences. Both duplications and deficiencies occur within the species or interspecific hybrids, such as in *S. ocellaris* × *S. reynoldsi* (Metz and Lawrence, 1948). Rohm (1947) found one inversion, and a two-band deficiency in the C chromosome of *S. ocellaris*, but found no intraspecific variation in *S. reynoldsi*.

An extensive study of natural chromosomal variability in the genus Sciara was made by Carson (1944) in *S. impatiens*. In the natural populations of *S. impatiens*, which has 7 chromosomes in the males and 8 in the females, Carson found not only 13 small "deficiencies or duplications" but also 12 inversions. The inversions are very frequent in the natural populations of *S. impatiens*, frequencies as high as 25–60% being very common. Only in exceptional cases were larvae structurally homozygous in all chromosomes found. The inversions are evenly distributed among the four chromosomes. The "small differences" (presumably small deficiencies and duplications) are also very widespread in the populations. The frequencies of heterozygotes for such variations were found to be: td-1A, 4.1%; td-2A, 33.3%; 3-16A, 71.3%; td-1B, 28.6%; td-2B, 87%; td-1aC, 1.9%; td-1bC, 9.4%; and td-2C, 28.1%.

McCarthy (1945) made a study of the occurrence of "repeats," of inversions, and of deficiencies and duplications in strains of eight species of *Sciara*. This study showed that (1) four of the eight species have "repeats" in the X chromosome, of which four are single and two are double, (2) five of the eight species show chromosome inversions, and (3) six of the eight species show "small differences" between homologues in the salivary gland chromosome banding which are seemingly characteristic of the genus.

Population genetics of *Sciara* is very little known. The chromosome inversions in *Sciara* most probably play the same biological role as in *Drosophila*. The abundance of duplications suggests that in *Sciara* increases of the genic materials are very common occurrences.

XII. CONCLUSION

Chromosomal inversions present in natural populations of Diptera have been shown to be heterotic in heterozygous conditions in all cases in which tests have been made. Even in cases in which no tests have been carried out, there are good indications that the inversions are important in the adaptedness of their carriers. The adaptive significance of the chromosomal inversions is due to the complexes of genes which they hold together. The function of the inversions is to tie together adaptive gene combinations.

The heterosis produced by chromosomal inversions develops through natural selection by means of formation of coadapted gene combinations. Since the heterozygotes have adaptive values higher than the homozygotes, the populations become genetically variable and acquire a high degree of ecological plasticity.

The frequencies of the gene arrangements vary from population to population in accord with the environmental conditions in which the populations live. The populations are always kept adapted to their environments, and always preserve a high plasticity which enables them to respond adaptively to normal environmental changes.

The adaptive plasticity of polymorphic population is important not only for adjustment to ecological changes produced in time but also for mastering the ecological diversity in space. The more polymorphic a population the higher its capacity to exploit the many ecological niches offered by nature.

Robertson and Reeve (1952) and Dobzhansky and Wallace (1953) have shown that homeostasis is connected with heterozygosity. Heterozygous flies have a higher capacity of maintaining their physiological processes constant despite environmental changes than more homozygous individuals. A sufficient degree of homeostasis is certainly one of the factors which produce the heterosis in inversion heterozygotes. Homeostasis is particularly important in very heterogeneous environments, and it is exactly in this type of environment that chromosomal polymorphism is highly developed. As shown by the work of Dobzhansky and his colleagues in *D. pseudoobscura*, by Crow (1948) in corn, and more recently by Wallace and collaborators in *D. melanogaster*, selection within populations "favors particular heterozygotes and thereby builds up selected series of alleles at all (or at least many) loci—the particular alleles at any locus being determined in each population by those present at all other loci" (Wallace et al., 1953).

Since natural selection favors heterozygotes, and since the adaptive values of genes is a relative matter, a large store of variability is always maintained in natural populations. The maintenance of this variability is, of course, possible without chromosomal inversions. However, chromosomal inversions, by holding many genes together, permit the formation of more complex coadapted genic systems, the existence of which would be impossible within a single gene arrangement. The chromosomal inversions permit a genic organization at a higher level which would be impossible otherwise.

XIII. ADDENDUM

Several papers on the subject of this review were published after its writing. We intend to present in this addendum a list of the new papers and their main conclusions.

Mizuno (1952) has reported the finding of morphological polymorphism in Japanese populations of *Drosophila nigromaculata*. Three color patterns of the abdominal tergites were found in the populations studied. The color patterns are sensitive to temperature and humidity and can be modified by these factors. Mizuno has also studied cytologically samples of populations of several species and found inversions in *D. nigromaculata* and in *D. immigrans* and no chromosomal variability in *D. virilis*, *D. funebris*, and *D. auraria*.

Wallace (1953) has presented a very interesting hypothesis to explain the coexistence of some inversions and the exclusion of others in natural populations. The adaptive value of the inversions, being due to the coadapted genic combinations which they tie together, will be decreased if any transfer of genes will occur between the inverted sequences. That is what would happen if three overlapping inversions, called triads by Wallace, coexisted in the same population. Serial transfer of genes from one arrangement to another would be produced by crossing-over in the triads, disrupting the coadapted genic combinations. Therefore, within a population only two members of a triad should be expected to be present with high frequencies. That is what really happens in the populations of *D. pseudoobscura* analyzed by Wallace. However, the data from populations of *D. robusta* do not support Wallace's hypothesis (Levitan, Carson, and Stalker, 1954).

Carson (1955) has devised a most useful index of crossing-over for Drosophila populations. The purpose of the index is to measure the evolutionary flexibility of the populations. "The index is an expression of the percent of the total haploid euchromatic chromosome length of the chromosomes of an individual in which free crossing-over may occur.

The index is prepared by measuring the euchromatic length of the entire polytene chromosome complement and equating this to 100. The length of the chromosome segments in which crossing-over is blocked is then measured in per cent of the total. The total blocked length is subtracted from 100, leaving the per cent of the total in which free crossing-over occurs. A chromosome segment is arbitrarily considered to be 'blocked' if crossing-over occurs there in the formation of no more than 1% of the gametes." "In the preparation of the index, all of the chromosome section located within a segment heterozygous for an inversion is considered to be blocked to crossing-over. Although it is known that inversions suppress crossing-over in sections of chromosome adjacent to them, this suppression has not been taken in account, as there is little basis as yet for accurately estimating it." The indices of free recombinations were very low in the center of the distribution area of *D. robusta*, in accord with the results obtained in the Missouri Ozarks, West Virginia and eastern Tennessee populations. Marginal populations in Wisconsin-Minnesota and in Georgia-Alabama have the highest mean percentages of free crossing-over, while intermediate populations have lower intermediate indices. These data are in accord with the findings of da Cunha and Dobzhansky (1954) and da Cunha, Burla, and Dobzhansky (1950) in *D. willistoni* whose marginal populations have less chromosomal polymorphism than the populations living in central and ecologically more diversified areas. "These correlations are interpreted to mean that central populations are genetically more specialized, many genes being effectively tied up in nonrecombining coadapted groups. Marginal populations, on the other hand, tend to be structurally homozygous and have a greater free recombination. Marginal populations are thus genetically more flexible in the sense of capacity for immediate evolutionary adjustment to new conditions. This is possible because of their greater potentiality for adjustment through extensive recombination of polygenes" (Carson, 1955).

New data on interchromosomal effects of inversions on crossing-over were obtained by Levine and Levine (1954). They studied in *D. pseudoobscura* the effects of third chromosome inversions on the incidence of crossing-over in the region *y-sn-v* of the X chromosome. The inversions analyzed were ST, CH, and AR. Homozygosis for CH and for AR caused higher increase in the incidence of crossing-over in the X chromosome than homozygosis for ST. Heterozygosis for some inversions increased the rate of recombination but for others it had no effect. They concluded that: "there is a genotypic control of crossing-over in the X chromosome by III chromosome genes. The control may be mediated either through contributions made to crossing-over by genes in a particular III chromosome in a given inversion combination, or through genetic interactions between the two chromosomes of the combination."

Dobzhansky and Spassky (1954) studied the effects of different nutrients, i.e., species of yeasts, on the adaptive values of chromosomal inversions in *D. pseudoobscura*. Their results, although different in details, confirmed the findings of da Cunha (1951) that the adaptive values of the inversions vary according with the food used.

Epling, Mitchell, and Mattoni (1953) studied changes in the frequencies of inversions in natural and in artificial populations of *D. pseudoobscura* and concluded that: "those changes may be substantially determined by factors internal within the population rather than being simple responses of the inversions to the external environment."

Spiess (1954), continuing his studies of the physiological properties of gene arrangements carriers in *D. persimilis*, has found interesting differences in egg-laying capacities of flies with different gene arrangements. There are only slight differences in egg-laying capacity between homozygotes WT/WT and ST/ST. However, heterozygotes produced by ST/ST females have, in the first 10 days, a laying rate about half of that of hybrids produced by WT/WT females. There is, therefore, a cytoplasmic influence on the fecundity of the heterozygotes WT/ST.

J. and S. Maynard Smith (1954) studied the relative viabilities of inversion homozygotes and heterozygotes as well as their rates of development in *D. subobscura*. They found that in the five stocks studied the heterozygotes have higher viabilities and a more rapid development than the homozygotes. They also found that for different temperatures the heterozygotes have a better homeostasis in regard to the eclosion time.

More data on the chromosomal variability of tropical species of Drosophila was presented by Carson (1954) and Salzano (1954, 1955). Carson (1954) studied the variability of the two sibling species *D. bocainensis* and *D. parabocainensis*. While *D. bocainensis* is very variable, with a minimum of 13 different inversions localized mainly in the third chromosome, *D. parabocainensis* has only 4. However, the number of samples examined was too small to give a good idea of their variability. *D. bocainensis* in the populations well sampled had a mean of 0.3 to 0.6 heterozygous inversions per female in the X chromosome and a mean of 3.4 to 4.1 heterozygous inversions per individual in the autosomes. *D. bocainensis* and *D. parabocainensis* are well isolated in nature, intercrossings having never been found where they occur sympatrically. However, they cross easily in the laboratory and their hybrids are heterozygous for 13 to 26 inversions. The hybrids are perfectly fertile with the exception of the F_1 males produced by *D. bocainensis* mothers. Salzano (1954, 1955) has found 12 new inversions in *D. guaramunu*. The total number of inversions in this species is now 31, of which 25 are in the fourth chromosome. The species closely related to it, *D. griseolineata*, has only 5 inversions. *D. griseolineata* is ecologically less versatile than *D. guaramunu*. A hybrid larva was obtained between the two species and the greater divergence in chromosomal structure was found in the fourth and in the fifth chromosomes which are also the most variable within the parental species.

Mainx, Kunze, and Koske (1953) presented new data on *Chironomus dorsalis* where they found 5 inversions. The inversions were in 3 chromosomes and combined at random. Their frequencies were calculated.

XIV. ACKNOWLEDGMENTS

The author is very grateful to Prof. Th. Dobzhansky for reading the manuscript and making many helpful suggestions. He is also indebted to Miss Therezinha de M. Ungaretti and Mrs. Marta E. Breuer for their aid and interest.

XV. REFERENCES

Bauer, H., 1936. Beiträge zur vergleichenden Morphologie der Speicheldrusen chromosomen. *Zool. Jahrb.* **56**, 239–276.

Beadle, G. W., and Sturtevant, A. H., 1935. X chromosome inversions and meiosis in *Drosophila melanogaster. Proc. Natl. Acad. Sci. U.S.* **21**, 384–390.

Beermann, W., 1952. Chromosomen polymorphismus und Bastardierung Zweier Chironomus-Arten. *Verhandl. deut. Zool. Ges.* **1952**, 290–295.

Berrie, G. K., and Sansome, F. W., 1948. Wild population studies; *Drosophila funebris* near Manchester. *J. Genet.* **49**, 151–152.

Brncic, D., 1953. Chromosomal variation in natural populations of *Drosophila guaramunú. Z. indukt. Abstamm. u.-Vererbungsl.* **85**, 1–11.

Brncic, D., 1954. Heterosis and the integration of the genotype in geographic populations of *Drosophila pseudoobscura. Genetics* **39**, 77–88.

Burla, H., da Cunha, A. B., Cordeiro, A. R., Dobzhansky, T., Malogolowkin, C., and Pavan, C., 1949. The *willistoni* group of sibling species of *Drosophila. Evolution* **3**, 300–314.

Carson, H. L., 1944. An analysis of natural chromosome variability in *Sciara impatiens* Johansen. *J. Morphol.* **75**, 11–59.

Carson, H. L., 1946. The selective elimination of inversion dicentric chromatids during meiosis in the eggs of *Sciara impatiens. Genetics* **31**, 95–113.

Carson, H. L., 1953. The effects of inversions on crossing-over in *Drosophila robusta. Genetics* **38**, 168–186.

Carson, H. L., 1954. Interfertile sibling species in the *willistoni* group of *Drosophila. Evolution* **8**, 148–165.

Carson, H. L., 1955. Variation in genetic recombination in natural populations. *J. Cellular Comp. Physiol.* **45**, Suppl. in press.

Carson, H. L., and Stalker, H. D., 1947. Gene arrangements in natural populations of *Drosophila robusta. Evolution* **1**, 113–133.

Carson, H. L., and Stalker, H. D., 1949. Seasonal variation in gene arrangement frequencies over a three-year period in *Drosophila robusta* Sturtevant. *Evolution* **3**, 322–329.

Crow, J. F., 1948. Alternative hypotheses of hybrid vigor. *Genetics* **33**, 477–487.

da Cunha, A. B., 1949. Genetic analysis of the polymorphism of color pattern in *Drosophila polymorpha*. *Evolution* **3**, 239–251.

da Cunha, A. B., 1951. Modification of the adaptive values of chromosomal types in *Drosophila pseudoobscura* by nutritional variables. *Evolution* **5**, 395–404.

da Cunha, A. B., 1953a. A further analysis of the polymorphism of *Drosophila polymorpha*. *Nature* **171**, 887.

da Cunha, A. B., 1953b. Chromosomal inversions with sex-limited effects. *Nature* **172**, 815.

da Cunha, A. B. 1955. Sôbre duas raças de *Drosophila neocardini* Streisinger. *Rev. Brasil. Biol.* **15**, 117–125.

da Cunha, A. B., Brncic, D., and Salzano, F. M., 1953. A comparative study of chromosomal polymorphism in certain South American species of *Drosophila*. *Heredity* **7**, 193–202.

da Cunha, A. B., Burla, H., and Dobzhansky, T., 1950. Adaptive chromosomal polymorphism in *Drosophila willistoni*. *Evolution* **4**, 212–235.

da Cunha, A. B., and Dobzhansky, T., 1954. A further study of chromosomal polymorphism in *Drosophila willistoni* in its relation to the environment. *Evolution* **8**, 119–134.

da Cunha, A. B., Dobzhansky, T., and Sokoloff, A., 1951. On food preferences of sympatric species of *Drosophila*. *Evolution* **5**, 97–101.

Dansereau, P., 1952. The varieties of evolutionary opportunity. *Rev. Can. Biol.* **11**, 305–388.

Dobzhansky, T., 1935. The Y chromosome of *Drosophila pseudoobscura*. *Genetics* **20**, 366–376.

Dobzhansky, T., 1937. Further data on the variation of the Y chromosome in *Drosophila pseudoobscura*. *Genetics* **22**, 340–346.

Dobzhansky, T., 1939. Microgeographic variation in *Drosophila pseudoobscura*. *Proc. Natl. Acad. Sci. U.S.* **25**, 311–314.

Dobzhansky, T., 1943. Genetics of natural populations. IX. Temporal changes in the composition of populations of *Drosophila pseudoobscura*. *Genetics* **28**, 162–186.

Dobzhansky, T., 1944. Chromosomal races in *Drosophila pseudoobscura* and *Drosophila persimilis*. *Carnegie Inst. Wash. Publ.* **554**, 47–144.

Dobzhansky, T., 1947a. A directional change in the genetic constitution of a natural population of *Drosophila pseudoobscura*. *Heredity* **1**, 53–64.

Dobzhansky, T., 1947b. Genetics of natural populations. XIV. A response of certain gene arrangements in the third chromosome of *Drosophila pseudoobscura* to natural selection. *Genetics* **32**, 142–160.

Dobzhansky, T., 1948a. Chromosomal variation in populations of *Drosophila pseudoobscura* which inhabit Northern Mexico. *Am. Naturalist* **82**, 97–106.

Dobzhansky, T., 1948b. Genetics of natural populations. XVI. Altitudinal and seasonal changes produced by natural selection in certain populations of *Drosophila pseudoobscura* and *Drosophila persimilis*. *Genetics* **33**, 158–176.

Dobzhansky, T., 1948c. Genetics of natural populations. XVIII. Experiments on chromosomes of *Drosophila pseudoobscura* from different geographic regions. *Genetics* **33**, 588–602.

Dobzhansky, T., 1950. Genetics of natural populations. XIX. Origin of heterosis through natural selection in populations of *Drosophila pseudoobscura*. *Genetics* **35**, 288–302.

Dobzhansky, T., 1951. "Genetics and the Origin of Species," 3rd rev. ed., 364 pp. Columbia Univ. Press, New York.

Dobzhansky, T., 1952. Genetics of natural populations. XX. Changes induced by drought in *Drosophila pseudoobscura* and *Drosophila persimilis*. *Evolution* **6**, 234–243.

Dobzhansky, T., Burla, H., and da Cunha, A. B., 1950. A comparative study of chromosomal polymorphism in sibling species of the *willistoni* group of *Drosophila*. *Am. Naturalist* **84**, 229–246.

Dobzhansky, T., and da Cunha, A. B., 1954. Differentiation of nutritional preferences in Brazilian species of *Drosophila*. *Ecology* **36**, 34–39.

Dobzhansky, T., and Dreyfus, A., 1943. Chromosomal aberrations in Brazilian *Drosophila ananassae*. *Proc. Natl. Acad. Sci. U.S.* **29**, 301–305.

Dobzhansky, T., and Epling, C., 1948. The suppression of crossing-over in inversion heterozygotes of *Drosophila pseudoobscura*. *Proc. Natl. Acad. Sci. U.S.* **34**, 137–141.

Dobzhansky, T., and Levene, H., 1948. Genetics of natural populations. XVII. Proof of operation of natural selection in wild populations of *Drosophila pseudoobscura*. *Genetics* **33**, 537–547.

Dobzhansky, T., and Levene, H., 1951. Development of heterosis through natural selection in experimental populations of *Drosophila pseudoobscura*. *Am. Naturalist* **85**, 247–264.

Dobzhansky, T., and Pavan, C., 1943. Studies on Brazilian species of *Drosophila*. *Univ. São Paulo Fac. Filosof. Ciênc. e Letras* Bol. No. **36**, pp. 7–72.

Dobzhansky, T., and Pavlovsky, O., 1953. Indeterminate outcome of certain experiments on *Drosophila* populations. *Evolution* **7**, 198–210.

Dobzhansky, T., and Queal, M. L., 1938. Genetics of natural populations. I. Chromosome variation in populations of *Drosophila pseudoobscura* inhabiting isolated mountain ranges. *Genetics* **23**, 239–251.

Dobzhansky, T., and Sokolov, D., 1939. Structure and variation of the chromosomes in *Drosophila azteca*. *J. Heredity* **30**, 3–19.

Dobzhansky, T., and Spassky, N., 1954. Environmental modification of heterosis in *Drosophila pseudoobscura*. *Proc. Natl. Acad. Sci. U.S.* **40**, 407–415.

Dobzhansky, T., and Sturtevant, A. H., 1938. Inversions in the chromosomes of *Drosophila pseudoobscura*. *Genetics* **23**, 28–64.

Dobzhansky, T., and Wallace, B., 1953. The genetics of homeostasis in Drosophila, *Proc. Natl. Acad. Sci. U.S.* **39**, 162–171.

Dubinin, N. P., and Tiniakov, G. G., 1945. Seasonal cycles and the concentration of inversions in populations of *Drosophila funebris*. *Am. Naturalist* **79**, 570–572.

Dubinin, N. P., and Tiniakov, G. G., 1946a. Structural chromosome variability in urban and rural populations of *Drosophila funebris*. *Am. Naturalist* **80**, 393–396.

Dubinin, N. P., and Tiniakov, G. G., 1946b. Inversion gradients and natural selection in ecological races of *Drosophila funebris*. *Genetics* **31**, 537–545.

Dubinin, N. P., and Tiniakov, G. G., 1946c. Natural selection and chromosomal variability in populations of *Drosophila funebris*. *J. Heredity* **37**, 39–44.

Dubinin, N. P., and Tiniakov, G. G., 1947a. Inversion gradients and selection in ecological races of *Drosophila funebris*. *Am. Naturalist* **81**, 148–153.

Dubinin, N. P., and Tiniakov, G. G., 1947b. Natural selection in experiments with population inversions. *J. Genet.* **48**, 11–15.

Dubinin, N. P., Sokolov, N. N., and Tiniakov, G. G., 1937. Intraspecific chromosome variability. *Biol. Zhur.* **6**, 1007–54.

Epling, C., Mitchell, D. F., and Mattoni, R. H. T., 1953. On the role of inversion in wild populations of *Drosophila pseudoobscura*. *Evolution* **7**, 342–365.

Fahmy, O. G., and Bird, M. J., 1953. Chromosome breaks among recessive lethals induced by chemical mutagens in *Drosophila melanogaster*, Symposium on chromosome breakage. *Heredity Suppl.* **6**, 149–159.

Ford, E. B., 1953. The genetics of polymorphism in the Lepidoptera. *Advances in Genet.* **5**, 43–87.

Freire-Maia, N., 1949. Balanced polymorphism in *Drosophila montium. Evolution* **3**, 98.

Freire-Maia, N., 1952a. Chromosomal variation in Brazilian domestic species of Drosophila. *Drosophila Information Service* **26**, 100.

Freire-Maia, N., 1952b. Pericentric inversions in Brazilian populations of *D. ananassae. Drosophila Information Service* **26**, 100–101.

Freire-Maia, N., 1953. *in* "Evolução dos seres vivos," edited by Centro de Estudos de Historia Natural, Curitiba, pp. 46–125.

Freire-Maia, N., Zanardini, I. F., and Freire-Maia, A., 1953. Chromosome variation in *Drosophila immigrans. Dusenia* **4**, 303–311.

Frizzi, G., 1952. Nuovi contributi e prospettive di ricerca nel gruppo *Anopheles maculipennis* in allo studio del dimorfismo cromosomico (ordinamento ad X invertito e tipico) nel *messeae., Symposia Genetica* **3**, 231–265.

Gunson, M., 1952. Local chromosomal races of *D. subobscura. Drosophila Information Service* **26**, 104.

Helfer, R. G., 1941. A comparison of X-ray induced and naturally occurring chromosomal variations in *Drosophila pseudoobscura. Genetics* **24**, 278–301.

Heuts, J., 1947. Influence of humidity on the survival of different chromosomal types in *Drosophila pseudoobscura. Proc. Natl. Acad. Sci. U.S.* **33**, 210–213.

Heuts, J., 1948. Adaptive properties of carriers of certain gene arrangements in *Drosophila pseudobscura. Heredity* **2**, 63–75.

Hinton, T., Ives, P. T., and Evans, A. T., 1952. Changing the gene order and number in natural populations. *Evolution* **6**, 19–28.

Hsu, T. C., and Liu, T. T., 1948. Microgeographic analysis of chromosomal variation in a Chinese species of Chironomus (Diptera). *Evolution* **2**, 49–57.

Kaufmann, B. P., 1948. Radiation induced chromosome aberrations. *Brookhaven Conf. Rept.* BNL-C-4: 27–35.

Knapp, E. P., 1956. Polimorfismo cromossômico em populações naturais de *Drosophila sturtevanti* Duda. *Univ. São Paulo Fac. Filosof. Ciênc. e Letras Bol.* in press.

Koller, P. C., 1939. Genetics of natural populations. III. Gene arrangements in populations of *Drosophila pseudoobscura* from contiguous localities. *Genetics* **24**, 22–33.

Komai, T., and Takaku, T., 1940. Two independent inversions in the X-chromosome of *Drosophila virilis* and their effects on crossing-over and disjunction. *Cytologia Tokyo* **2**, 245–260.

Komai, T., and Takaku, T., 1942. On the effect of the X-Chromosome inversions on crossing-over in *Drosophila virilis. Cytologia Tokyo* **12**, 357–365.

Kunze, E., 1953. Artunterschiede im Bau der Riesenchromosomen in der Gattung *Simulium* Latr. *Österr. zool. Z.* **4**, (1/2), 23–32.

Lea, D. E., 1946. "Actions of Radiations on Living Cells," 402 pp. Macmillan, New York.

Levene, H., 1953. Genetic equilibrium when more than one ecological niche is available. *Am. Naturalist* **87**, 331–333.

Levine, R. P., 1952. Adaptive response of some third chromosome types of *Drosophila pseudoobscura. Evolution* **6**, 216–233.

Levine, R. P., and Dickinson, J. I., 1952. The modification of recombination by naturally occurring inversions in *Drosophila pseudoobscura. Genetics* **37**, 599.

Levine, R. P., and Levine, E. E., 1954. The genotypic control of crossing-over in *Drosophila pseudoobscura*. *Genetics* **39**, 677–691.

Levitan, M., 1951a. Experiments on chromosomal variability in *D. robusta. Genetics* **36**, 285–305.

Levitan, M., 1951b. Selective differences between males and females in *Drosophila robusta. Am. Naturalist* **85**, 385–388.

Levitan, M., 1951c. Response of the chromosomal variability in *D. robusta* to seasonal factors in a Southwest Virginia wood (Abstr.). *Records Genet. Soc. Amer.* **20**, 109–110.

Levitan, M., Carson, H. L., and Stalker, H. D., 1954. Triads of overlapping inversions in *Drosophila robusta. Am. Naturalist* **88**, 113–114.

L'Heritier, P., and Teissier, G., 1933. Étude d'une population de Drosophiles en équilibre. *Compt. rend.* **198**, 770–772.

McCarthy, M., 1945. Chromosome studies on eight species of Sciara (Diptera) with special reference to chromosome changes of evolutionary significance. *Am. Naturalist* **79**, 104–121, 228–245.

MacKnight, R. H., 1937. Crossing-over in the sex chromosome of racial hybrids of *Drosophila pseudoobscura. Genetics* **22**, 249–256.

Mainx, F., 1951. Die Verbreitung von Chromosomen dislocationen in natürlichen Populationen von *Liriomyza urophorina* Mik. *Chromosoma* **4**, 521–534.

Mainx, F., Koske, T., and Smital, G., 1953. Untersuchungen über die chromosomale Struktur europäischer Vertreter der *Drosophila obscura* Gruppe. *Z. Vererbungsl.* **85**, 354–372.

Mainx, F., Kunze, E., and Koske, T., 1953. Cytologische untersuchungen an Lunzer Chironomiden. *Österr. zool. Z.* **4**, (1/2), 33–44.

Maynard Smith, J., and Maynard Smith, S., 1954. Genetics and cytology of *Drosophila subobscura*. VIII. Heterozygosity, viability, and rate of development. *J. Genet.* **52**, 152–164.

Metz, C. W., 1938. Observations on evolutionary changes in the chromosomes of Sciara (Diptera). *Carnegie Inst. Wash. Publ.* **501**, 275–294.

Metz, C. W., 1941. Species hybrids, evolutionary changes and the mechanism of chromosome rearrangement in Sciara. *Proc. 7th Intern. Congr. Genet.* 215–218.

Metz, C. W., 1947. Duplication of chromosome parts as a factor in evolution. *Am. Naturalist* **81**, 81–103.

Metz, C. W., and Lawrence, E. G., 1938. Preliminary observations on Sciara hybrids between *S. ocellaris* and *S. reynoldsi. J. Heredity* **29**, 179–186.

Miller, D. D., 1939. Structure and variation of the chromosomes in *Drosophila algonquin. Genetics* **24**, 699–708.

Mizuno, T., 1952. A note on the genetical survey of *Drosophila* in Hokkaido. *Japanese Coordinating Committee for Research in Genetics* Vol. 3, pp. 51–55.

Moriwaki, D., Okada, T., and Kurokawa, H., 1952. Two types of *D. auraria. Drosophila Information Service* **26**, 112.

Novitski, E., 1946. Chromosome variation in *Drosophila athabasca. Genetics* **31** 508–524.

Oshima, C., 1952. Genetic analysis of the dimorphism of color pattern in *D. rufa. Drosophila Information Service* **26**, 116.

Patterson, J. T., and Stone, W. S., 1952. "Evolution in the Genus Drosophila," 610 pp. Macmillan, New York.

Patterson, J. T., Stone, W. S., and Griffen, A. B., 1940. Evolution of the virilis group in *Drosophila. Univ. Texas Publ.* **4032**, 218–250.

Pavan, C., 1946. Chromosomal variation in *Drosophila nebulosa. Genetics* **31**, 546–557.

Pavan, C., and da Cunha, A. B., 1947. Especies brasileiras de Drosophila. *Univ. São Paulo Fac. Filosof. Ciênc. e Letras* Bol. No. **86**, 3–46.

Philip, U., 1942. An analysis of chromosomal polymorphism in two species of Chironomus. *J. Genet.* **44**, 129–142.

Philip, U., Rendel, J. M., Spurway, H., and Haldane, J. B. S., 1944. Genetics and karyology of *Drosophila subobscura*. *Nature* **154**, 260–262.

Robertson, F. W., and Reeve, E. C. R., 1952. Heterozygosity, environmental variation, and heterosis. *Nature* **170**, 296.

Rohm, P. B., 1947. A study of evolutionary chromosome changes in Sciara (Diptera), chromosome C in the salivary gland cell of *Sciara ocellaris* and *Sciara reynoldsi*. *Am. Naturalist* **81**, 5–29.

Salzano, F. M., 1954. Chromosomal relations in two species of Drosophila. *Am. Naturalist* **88**, 399–405.

Salzano, F. M., 1955. Chromosomal polymorphism in two species of the *guarani* group of Drosophila. *Chromosoma* in press.

Schultz, J., and Redfield, H., 1930. The constitution of the germinal material in relation to heredity. *Yearbook Carnegie Inst. Wash.* **29**, 352–359.

Schultz, J., and Redfield, H., 1951. Interchromosomal effects on crossing-over in Drosophila. *Cold Spring Harbor Symposia Quant. Biol.* **16**, 175–197.

Sokolov, N. N., and Dubinin, N. P., 1941. Permanent heterozygosity in *Drosophila*. *Drosophila Information Service* **15**, 39–40.

Spassky, B., 1951. Effect of temperature and moisture content of the nutrient medium on the viability of chromosomal types in *Drosophila pseudoobscura*. *Am. Naturalist* **85**, 177–180.

Spiess, E. B., 1950. Experimental populations of *D. persimilis* from an altitudinal transect of the Sierra Nevada. *Evolution* **4**, 14–33.

Spiess, E. B., 1954. Physiological properties of gene arrangement carriers in *Drosophila persimilis* III. Cytoplasmic influence on fecundity of arrangement heterozygotes. *Evolution* **8**, 29–32.

Spiess, E. B., Ketchel, M., and Kinne, B. P., 1952. Physiological properties of gene arrangement carriers in *Drosophila persimilis*. I. Egg-laying capacity and longevity of adults. *Evolution* **6**, 208–215.

Spiess, E. B., Terrile, B. A., and Blumenheim, U., 1952. Physiological properties of gene arrangement carriers in *Drosophila persimilis* II. Wing-beat frequency and wing dimensions. *Evolution* **6**, 421–427.

Stalker, H. D., and Carson, H. L., 1947. Morphological variation in natural populations of *Drosophila robusta* Sturtevant. *Evolution* **1**, 237–248.

Stalker, H. D., and Carson, H. L., 1948. An altitudinal transect of *Drosophila robusta* Sturtevant. *Evolution* **2**, 295–305.

Stalker, H. D., and Carson, H. L., 1949. Seasonal variation in the morphology of *Drosophila robusta* Sturtevant. *Evolution* **3**, 330–343.

Steinberg, A. G., 1936. The effect of autosomal inversion on crossing-over in the X chromosome of *Drosophila melanogaster*. *Genetics* **21**, 615–624.

Steinberg, A. G., 1937. Relation between chromosome size and effects of inversion on crossing-over in *D. melanogaster*. *Proc. Natl. Acad. Sci. U.S.* **23**, 54–56.

Steinberg, A. G., and Fraser, F. C., 1944. Studies on the effect of X-chromosome inversions on crossing-over in the third chromosome of *Drosophila melanogaster*. *Genetics* **29**, 83–103.

Stone, W., and Thomas, I., 1935. Crossover and disjunctional properties of X chromosome inversion in *Drosophila melanogaster*. *Genetics* **17**, 170–184.

Stumm-Zollinger, E., 1953. Vergleichende untersuchung über die inversionshäufigkeit bei *Drosophila subobscura* in populationen der Schweiz und Südwesteuropas. *Z. indukt. Abstamm.-u. Vererbungsl.* **85**, 382–407.

Sturtevant, A. H., 1926. A crossover reducer in *Drosophila melanogaster* due to inversion of a section of the third chromosome. *Biol. Zentr.* **46**, 697–702.

Sturtevant, A. H., 1931. Known and probable inverted sections of the autosomes of *Drosophila melanogaster. Carnegie Inst. Wash. Publ.* **42**, 1–27.

Sturtevant, A. H., and Beadle, G. W., 1936. The relations of inversions in the X-chromosome of *Drosophila melanogaster* to *crossing-over* and disjunction. *Genetics* **21**, 554–604.

Townsend, J. I., 1952. Genetics of marginal populations of *Drosophila willistoni. Evolution* **6**, 428–442.

Vetukhiv, M., 1953. Viability of hybrids between local populations of *Drosophila pseudoobscura. Proc. Natl. Acad. Sci. U.S.* **39**, 30–34.

Wallace, B., 1948. Studies on "sex-ratio" in *Drosophila pseudoobscura* I. Selection and "sex ratio." *Evolution* **2**, 189–217.

Wallace, B., 1953. On coadaptation in *Drosophila. Am. Naturalist* **87**, 343–358.

Wallace, B., King, J. C., Madden, C. V., Kaufmann, B., and McGunnigle, E. C., 1953. An analysis of variability arising through recombination. *Genetics* **38**, 272–307.

Ward, C. L., 1952. Chromosome variation in *Drosophila melanica. Univ. Texas Publ.* **5204**, 137–157.

Warters, M., 1944. Chromosomal aberrations in wild populations of *Drosophila. Univ. Texas Publ.* **4445**, 129–174.

Wharton, L. T., 1942. Analysis of the *repleta* group of *Drosophila. Univ. Texas Publ.* **4228**, 23–52.

White, M. J. D., 1954. "Animal Cytology and Evolution," 2nd rev. ed. Cambridge Univ. Press, London.

Wright, S., and Dobzhansky, T., 1946. Genetics of natural populations. XII. Experimental reproduction of some of the changes caused by natural selection in certain populations of *Drosophila pseudoobscura. Genetics* **31**, 125–156.

Abnormal Combinations of Nuclear and Cytoplasmic Systems in Frogs and Toads

JOHN A. MOORE

Department of Zoology, Barnard College and Columbia University, New York, New York

I. INTRODUCTION

The gametes of Amphibia offer unusual advantages for experiments combining nuclei and cytoplasm in various ways. Recent technical advances have provided easy methods for securing ova and sperm, and the gametes can be subjected to a variety of experimental conditions. Cross fertilizations can be performed with ease. There are techniques for accomplishing an astonishing amount of chromosome juggling. The embryonic stages can be reared with little difficulty under laboratory conditions. The adults of many species are common and widely distributed. Every continent, except Antarctica, has a rich Salientian fauna and the Caudata are common in the Holarctic area.

Two Orders of Amphibia, the Caudata (or Urodela, including salamanders, newts, etc.) and Salientia (or Anura, including frogs, toads, etc.) have been used extensively for hybridization and related types of experimentation. These two Orders probably have been separate phylogenetic lines since the close of the Paleozoic, or for approximately 200 million years. In spite of this long time interval after their presumed common ancestor, the embryos of the Caudata and Salientia have much in common. This similarity applies not only to features of normal development but to the physiological processes studied by the techniques of experimental embryology as well.

The early work on hybridization and related phenomena was done almost entirely on European species. Some of the results were summarized by P. Hertwig (1936) and more recently by Montalenti (1938a). During this period and later, Baltzer and his co-workers used the techniques of experimental embryology to study the development of Urodele hybrids and other types of embryos with abnormal combinations of nuclear and cytoplasmic systems. This has resulted in a most important body of data relating to the effects of various chromosome combinations in development. The results are well known and the reviews of Baltzer (1940, 1950, 1952), Fankhauser (1945, 1952), and Gallien (1953) may be consulted. The recent genetic and cytogenetic work on the interrelation of European newts is reviewed by Spurway (1953).

The scope of the present review is hybridization, androgenesis, gynogenesis, parthenogenesis, and related phenomena in the Salientia. The period covered will begin with 1938, the year of Montalenti's review, and extend to the present. First, a summary will be made of the types of nuclear-cytoplasmic combinations that are possible. Second, some of the biological problems that are studied with these techniques will be discussed.

The various crosses that have been performed since Montalenti's (1938a) list, are given in Table 1. This is essentially a summary of crosses of non-European species since little work has been done on European frog hybrids in the period covered by my report. Furthermore, when Montalenti published his summary there was only one study of non-European forms (apart from a few crosses of European and non-European species).

Two new combinations of European species, which are not listed by Montalenti (1938a), have been made since 1938. These are the reciprocal hybrids of *Rana esculenta* and *Rana ridibunda* (Mandeville and Spurway, 1949). New information is available for some of the European crosses listed by Montalenti. These are *Bufo vulgaris* ♀ × *Bufo viridis* ♂ (Montalenti, 1938b; Perri, 1946, 1949), *Rana arvalis* ♀ × *Rana fusca* ♂ (Cukierzys, 1937; Dürken, 1938), *Rana esculenta* ♀ × *Rana fusca* ♂ (Brachet, 1945, 1954), *Bufo vulgaris* ♀ × *Rana fusca* ♂ (Fedorova,

TABLE 1
Crosses among Salientia

Female	Male	Stage reached	References
Pelobatidae			
Scaphiopus couchi	S. hammondi	Neurula	Blair, 1947
Scaphiopus hammondi	S. couchi	Yolk plug	Blair, 1947
Bufonidae			
Bufo cognatus	B. punctatus	Adult	Blair, unpubl.
Bufo compactilis	B. terrestris americanus	Neurula	Blair, unpubl.
Bufo compactilis	B. w. woodhousei	Neurula	Blair, unpubl.
Bufo m. microscaphus	B. boreas halophilus	Adult	Blair, unpubl.
Bufo m. microscaphus	B. microscaphus californicus	Adult	Blair, unpubl.
Bufo m. microscaphus	B. compactilis	Adult	Blair, unpubl.
Bufo m. microscaphus	B. punctatus	Adult	Blair, unpubl.
Bufo m. microscaphus	B. w. woodhousei	Adult	Blair, unpubl.
Bufo microscaphus californicus	B. compactilis	Adult	Blair, unpubl.
Bufo microscaphus californicus	B. m. microscaphus	Adult	Blair, unpubl.
Bufo microscaphus californicus	B. w. woodhousei	Adult	Blair, unpubl.
Bufo punctatus	B. boreas halophilus	Adult	Blair, unpubl.
Bufo punctatus	B. cognatus	Adult? (killed as larvae)	Blair, unpubl.
Bufo punctatus	B. compactilis	Gastrula or later	Blair, unpubl.
Bufo punctatus	B. m. microscaphus	Gastrula or later	Blair, unpubl.
Bufo punctatus	B. w. woodhousei	Gastrula or later	Blair, unpubl.
Bufo raddei	B. asiaticus	Adult	Chen-Chao-Hsi, 1940
Bufo t. terrestris	B. terrestris americanus	Adult	Blair, 1941a
Bufo t. terrestris	B. woodhousei fowleri	Adult	Blair, 1941a
Bufo t. terrestris	B. valliceps	Adult	Blair, 1941a
Bufo terrestris americanus	B. b. boreas	Adult	Blair, unpubl.
Bufo terrestris americanus	B. cognatus	Adult	Blair, unpubl.
Bufo terrestris americanus	B. woodhousei fowleri	Adult	Blair, 1941a; Volpe, 1952
Bufo terrestris americanus	B. woodhousei hemiophrys	Adult	Blair, unpubl.
Bufo terrestris americanus	B. t. terrestris	Adult	Blair, 1941a
Bufo terrestris americanus	B. w. woodhousei	Adult	Blair, 1941a

TABLE 1. *(Continued)*

Female	Male	Stage reached	References
Bufo w. woodhousei	*B. terrestris americanus*	Adult (fertile)	Blair, 1941a, 1946
Bufo w. woodhousei	*B. b. boreas*	Adult	Blair, unpubl.
Bufo w. woodhousei	*B. microscaphus californicus*	Adult	Blair, unpubl.
Bufo w. woodhousei	*B. woodhousei fowleri*	Adult	Blair, 1941a
Bufo w. woodhousei	*B. m. microscaphus*	Adult	Blair, unpubl.
Bufo w. woodhousei	*B. t. terrestris*	Adult	Blair, unpubl.
Bufo woodhousei fowleri	*B. terrestis americanus*	Adult (fertile)	Blair, 1941a; Volpe, 1952
Bufo woodhousei fowleri	*B. cognatus*	Adult	Blair, unpubl.
Bufo woodhousei fowleri	*B. marinus*	Gastrula or later	Blair, unpubl.
Bufo woodhousei fowleri	*B. t. terrestris*	Adult	Blair, unpubl.
Bufo woodhousei fowleri	*B. valliceps*	Adult	Blair, unpubl.
Bufo woodhousei fowleri	*B. w. woodhousei*	Adult	Blair, 1941a
Leptodactylidae			
Crinia signifera	*C. haswelli*	Larva (diploid)	Moore and Moore, unpubl.
Crinia signifera	*C. insignifera*	Most die as larvae / Few to adult	Moore, 1954
Crinia signifera	*C. rosea*	No cleavage	Moore and Moore, unpubl.
Crinia signifera	*C. tasmaniensis*	Haploid larva	Moore, 1954
Crinia signifera	*Adelotus brevis*	Late blastula	Moore and Moore, unpubl.
Crinia signifera	*Hyla ewingii*	Haploid larva	Moore and Moore, unpubl.
Crinia signifera	*Hyla phyllochroa*	Neurula	Moore and Moore, unpubl.
Crinia signifera	*Limnodynastes peronii*	Haploid larva	Moore and Moore, unpubl.
Crinia signifera	*Pseudophryne australis*	Haploid larva	Moore and Moore, unpubl.
Limnodynastes peronii	*L. dorsalis*	Larva (Stage 17)	Moore and Moore, unpubl.
Limnodynastes peronii	*Adelotus brevis*	Stage 12	Moore and Moore, unpubl.

TABLE 1. (*Continued*)

Female	Male	Stage reached	References
Limnodynastes peronii	Crinia signifera	No development	Moore and Moore, unpubl.
Limnodynastes peronii	Heleioporus pictus	Gastrula	Moore and Moore, unpubl.
Limnodynastes peronii	Lechriodus fletcheri	Neurula	Moore and Moore, unpubl.
Limnodynastes peronii	Pseudophryne australis	No development	Moore and Moore, unpubl.
Limnodynastes tasmaniensis	L. peronii	Adult	Moore and Moore, unpubl.
Hylidae			
Acris gryllus crepitans	Pseudacris clarki	Gastrula or later	Blair, unpubl.
Acris gryllus crepitans	Pseudacris streckeri	Gastrula or later	Blair, unpubl.
Hyla aurea	H. adelaidensis	Larva (diploid)	Moore and Moore, unpubl.
Hyla aurea	H. bicolor	Neurula	Moore and Moore, unpubl.
Hyla aurea	H. phyllochroa	Haploid larva	Moore and Moore, unpubl.
Hyla aurea	H. raniformis	Haploid larva	Moore, 1954
Hyla crucifer	Pseudacris brachyphona	Gastrula or later	Blair, unpubl.
Hyla crucifer	Pseudacris t. triseriata	Gastrula or later	Blair, 1941b
Hyla versicolor	H. crucifer	Larva	Blair, unpubl.
Hyla versicolor	H. gratiosa	Adult	Blair, unpubl.
Hyla versicolor	Acris gryllus crepitans	Gastrula or later	Blair, unpubl.
Hyla versicolor	Pseudacris clarki	Adult	Blair, unpubl.
Hyla versicolor	Pseudacris streckeri	Adult	Blair, unpubl.
Hyla versicolor	Pseudacris nigrita triseriata	Larva	Blair, unpubl.
Pseudacris brachyphona	P. streckeri	Gastrula or later	Blair, unpubl.
Pseudocris brachyphona	P. t. triseriata	Gastrula or later	Blair, unpubl.
Pseudacris brachyphona	Hyla crucifer	Gastrula or later	Blair, unpubl.
Pseudacris clarki	P. t. triseriata	Larva	Blair, unpubl.
Pseudacris nigrita triseriata	P. brachyphona	Gastrula or later	Blair, unpubl.
Pseudacris nigrita triseriata	P. streckeri	Larva	Blair, unpubl.

TABLE 1. (*Continued*)

Female	Male	Stage reached	References
Pseudacris nigrita triseriata	*Hyla crucifer*	Adult	Blair, 1941b
Pseudacris nigrita triseriata	*Scaphiopus h. holbrookii*	Gynogenetic haploids	Ting and Price, 1950; Ting, 1951
Pseudacris streckeri	*P. clarki*	Larva	Blair, unpubl.
Pseudacris streckeri	*P. t. triseriata*	Adult.	Blair, unpubl.
Pseudacris streckeri	*Hyla versicolor*	Gastrula or later	Blair, unpubl.
Microhylidae			
Microhyla c. carolinensis	*M. carolinensis olivacea*	Larva	Blair, 1950
Microhyla carolinensis olivacea	*M. c. carolinensis*	Larva	Blair, 1950
Ranidae			
Rana areolata	*R. catesbeiana*	Gastrula	Moore, 1949a
Rana aerolata	*R. clamitans*	Gastrula	Moore, 1949a
Rana areolata	*R. palustris*	Adult	Moore, 1949a
Rana areolata	*R. pipiens*	Adult	Moore, 1949a
Rana areolata	*R. sylvatica*	Gastrula	Moore, 1949a
Rana catesbeiana	*R. areolata*	Gastrula	Moore, 1949a
Rana catesbeiana	*R. clamitans*	Gastrula	Moore, 1949a
Rana catesbeiana	*R. palustris*	Gastrula	Moore, 1949a
Rana catesbeiana	*R. pipiens*	Gastrula	Moore, 1941a, 1949a
Rana catesbeiana	*R. sylvatica*	Gastrula	Moore, 1949a
Rana clamitans	*R. capito*	No cleavage	Moore, 1949a
Rana clamitans	*R. catesbeiana*	No cleavage	Moore, 1941a, 1949a
Rana clamitans	*R. heckscheri*	No cleavage	Moore, 1941a, 1949a
Rana clamitans	*R. palustris*	No cleavage	Moore, 1941a, 1949a
Rana clamitans	*R. pipiens*	No cleavage	Moore, 1941a, 1949a
Rana clamitans	*R. septentrionalis*	No cleavage	Moore, 1941a, 1949a
Rana clamitans	*R. sylvatica*	No cleavage	Moore, 1941a, 1949a
Rana esculenta	*R. ridibunda*	Adult	Mandeville and Spurway, 1949
Rana fukiensis	*R. nigromaculata*	Adult	Ting, 1939, 1948
Rana japonica	*R. tagoi*	Gastrula	Kawamura, 1950
Rana japonica	*R. temporaria*	Adult	Kawamura, 1942, 1943
Rana japonica	*R. temporaria orna- tiventris*	Adult (sterile)	Kawamura, 1950 and 1952

TABLE 1. *(Continued)*

Female	Male	Stage reached	References
Rana nigromaculata	*R. plancyi*	Adult (?fertile)	Ting, 1939, 1948
Rana. n. nigro-maculata	*R. n. brevipoda*	Adult (partially fertile)	Moriya, 1951; Sambuchi, 1952
Rana nigromaculata brevipoda	*R. n. nigromaculata*	Adult (partially fertile)	Moriya, 1951
Rana palustris	*R. areolata*	Adult	Moore, 1949a
Rana palustris	*R. catesbeiana*	Gastrula	Moore, 1949a
Rana palustris	*R. clamitans*	Gastrula	Moore, 1949a
Rana palustris	*R. pipiens*	Adult	Rugh, 1935a; Moore, 1941a, 1943, 1946c, and 1949a
Rana palustris	*R. sylvatica*	Gastrula	Moore, 1941a, 1949a
Rana pipiens	*R. areolata*	Adult	Moore, 1943, 1949a
Rana pipiens	*R. capito*	Adult	Moore, 1949a; Ting, 1951
Rana pipiens	*R. catesbeiana*	Gastrula	Rugh and Exner, 1940; Moore, 1941a, 1949a; Briggs, 1947, 1952; Briggs, Green, and King, 1951; Briggs and King, 1952
Rana pipiens	*R. clamitans*	Gastrula	Moore, 1949a; Ting, 1951; Healy, 1952
Rana pipiens	*R. grylio*	Gastrula	Moore, 1949a
Rana pipiens	*R. palmipes*	Gastrula	Moore, unpubl.
Rana pipiens	*R. palustris*	Adult	Moore, 1941a, 1943, 1946c, and 1949a
Rana pipiens	*R. septentrionalis*	Gastrula	Moore, 1949a
Rana pipiens	*R. sylvatica*	Gastrula	Moore, 1941a, 1946a, 1947b, 1948, 1949a; Jaeger, 1945; Barth, 1946; Barth and Jaeger, 1947; Gregg, 1948; Ting, 1951; Sze, 1953; Mezger-Freed,1953

TABLE 1. (*Continued*)

Female	Male	Stage reached	References
Rana pipiens	R. temporaria	Gastrula	Moore, 1951
Rana pipiens	R. virgatipes	Gastrula	Moore, 1949a
Rana pipiens	Scaphiopus h. holbrookii	Gynogenetic haploids	Ting and Price, 1950; Ting, 1951
Rana plancyi	R. nigromaculata	Adult (?fertile)	Ting, 1939, 1948
Rana ridibunda	R. esculenta	Adult	Mandeville and Spurway, 1949
Rana septentrionalis	R. catesbeiana	Tailbud, few adults	Moore, 1949a
Rana septentrionalis	R. clamitans	Gastrula	Moore, 1941a, 1949a
Rana septentrionalis	R. palustris	Tailbud	Moore, 1949a
Rana septentrionalis	R. pipiens	Tailbud	Moore, 1941a, 1949a
Rana sylvatica	R. areolata	Gastrula	Moore, 1949a
Rana sylvatica	R. catesbeiana	Gastrula	Moore, 1941a, 1949a
Rana sylvatica	R. clamitans	Gastrula	Moore, 1949a
Rana sylvatica	R. palustris	Gastrula	Moore, 1941a, 1949a
Rana sylvatica	R. pipiens	Gastrula	Moore, 1941a, 1949a
Rana sylvatica	R. temporaria	Late blastula	Moore, 1951
Rana tagoi	R. japonica	Tailbud	Kawamura, 1950
Rana tagoi	R. temporaria ornativentris	Tailbud	Kawamura, 1950
Rana temporaria	R. sylvatica	No cleavage	Moore, 1951

1951; Brachet, 1954), and *Rana temporaria* ♀ ✕ *Bufo bufo* ♂ (Ahrenfeldt, 1952).

Data for many of the crosses of Table 1 have not been published. Blair has performed a tremendous number of crosses, largely with Bufo. When the final details are available, this will be the most comprehensive set of data of hybridization of the species of a single genus. Much of this work has been reported in lectures and Blair has consented to the publication of the results of his crosses. It should be mentioned that in the last few years many of the American toads formerly thought to be species have now been reduced to subspecies. Nevertheless, I have listed all of Blair's crosses in the table of interspecific crosses irrespective of the taxonomic status of the individuals involved. The names used are those of the last official checklist (Schmidt, 1953).

A second group of unpublished results are those of Moore and Moore on Australian species. Many of these are intergeneric combinations that result in gynogenetic embryos and not true hybrids.

Crosses that are clearly of an intraspecific nature are not included in Table 1. They are discussed at the end of Section II, 2.

II. Possible Combinations of Nuclei and Cytoplasm

For simplicity's sake we can consider that a zygote at the beginning of development consists of three parts: (1) a cytoplasm formed under the influence of the genes of the female parent, (2) a haploid set of chromosomes of the female parent, and (3) a haploid set of chromosomes of the male parent. The various combinations of these entities are listed in Table 2. These will be considered in order of the listing and with the same reference numbers and letters.

TABLE 2

Possible Combinations of Nuclei and Cytoplasm*

Type of embryo	♀ cyto-plasm	♀ hap-loid chromo-some sets	♂ hap-loid chromo-some sets	Method of production
1. Normal diploid	A	1 A	1 A	Normal fertilization
2. Diploid hybrid	A	1 A	1 B	Cross fertilization
3. Gynogenetic haploid	A	1 A	O	a. Cross fertilization b. Chemical treatment of sperm c. Radiation of sperm d. Parthenogenetic stimulation
4. Gynogenetic diploids and polyploids	A	2 or 2 + A	O	Parthenogenetic stimulation
5. Gynogenetic "hybrids"	A	1 or 2 B	O	Enucleation of ovum and implantation of foreign maternal nucleus
6. Androgenetic haploid	A	O	1 A	a. Radiation destruction of ♀ nucleus in fertilized ovum b. Removal of ♀ nucleus from fertilized ovum
7. Androgenetic haploid hybrid	A	O	1 B	Removal of ♀ nucleus after fertilization with foreign sperm
8. Achromosomal embryos	A	O	O	Removal of ♀ nucleus after fertilization with inactivated or foreign sperm
9. Triploid	A	2 A	A	Temperature shock treatment of fertilized ova
10. Triploid hybrids	A	2 A	1 B	Temperature shock treatment of fertilized ova

* "A" and "B" are different species.

Many of the abnormal combinations of nuclei and cytoplasm seem to occur under natural conditions but their frequency is very low. Nearly all of them can be produced with ease by experimental means.

1. *Normal Diploids*

In this section a brief survey will be made of the gametes and the methods of obtaining them. This will give a basis for the discussion of the results of combining nuclei and cytoplasm.

In those parts of the temperate zones with sufficient moisture, most Salientia have definite breeding seasons that are correlated with environmental temperature. In dry regions and in the tropics, the period of breeding usually is correlated with the rainy season. It is generally not necessary to rely on the breeding season for gametes. Normal ova and sperm can be obtained by artificial means from individuals with mature gonads.

The now standard techniques for obtaining ova and sperm were perfected about 20 years ago by Rugh (1934, 1935a,b, 1937). Reference should also be made to Robinson and Hill (1940), Hill and Robinson (1941), Waring, Landgrebe, and Neill (1941), and to the long bibliography in Rugh (1948). Ovulation is stimulated by the injection of frog anterior pituitary glands. Functional sperm are secured by cutting up the testes in water. The ova are squeezed from the female into the sperm suspension and sperm penetration occurs at once. The simplicity of these techniques is responsible for the large amount of experimental work that has been done with Salientian gametes since the mid-1930's.

Recent studies on gametes and their formation include: polar bodies in *Rana pipiens* (Rugh and Railey, 1948) ovulation *in vitro* (Ryan and Grant, 1940; Samartino and Rugh, 1945; Nadamitsu, 1953), overripeness of eggs (Zimmerman and Rugh, 1941; Briggs, 1941; Briggs and Berrill, 1941; Allison, 1953; Witschi, 1952), maturation of the ova (Tchou-Su, 1948b,c), maturation induced by osmotic effects (Tchou-Su, 1948a, 1950), oögenesis (Kemp, 1953; Wittek, 1952; Guyenot and Danon, 1953), time relations in ovulation (Wright, 1950), fertilization in relation to meiotic stage (Tchou-Su and Hsi, 1942), seasonal and hormonal induced changes in the testes (Biesinger and Miller, 1952).

Embryonic development is conveniently described in terms of Pollister's stages for *Rana sylvatica* (Pollister and Moore, 1937). These stages can be used for nearly all species of frogs and toads. They have been modified slightly for *Rana pipiens* (Shumway, 1940, 1942). Larval and metamorphic stages in *Rana pipiens* have been described by Taylor and Kollros (1946). Pollister's stages have been modified for *Xenopus laevis* (Weisz, 1945) and *Hyla regilla* (Eakin, 1947). Similar stages have been described for *Discoglossus pictus* (Gallien and Houillon, 1951) and *Rana fusca* (Kopsch, 1952).

The preparation of amphibian gametes and embryonic tissues for microscopic examination has always been a problem. For many purposes Smith's fixative followed by Feulgen and Light Green staining is very satisfactory (B. C. Moore and Ryan, 1940). Gregg and Puckett (1943) have suggested a new fixative. Slater and Dornfeld (1939) and Ting (1950) have proposed new staining methods.

When the ova are shed normally, or obtained experimentally from the uterus, the first polar body has been given off and the nucleus is in the metaphase of the second meiotic division. The second polar body is normally given off after fertilization. Tchou-Su and Hsi (1942) described an exceptional case in Bufo. They obtained uterine ova in all stages of maturation after pituitary injection. Those ova with intact germinal vesicles were not penetrated by sperm. When the germinal vesicle began to break down polyspermy occurred. Polyspermy was noted at all stages up to the metaphase of the second meiotic division. In the fully mature ova only a single sperm enters, in contrast to the situation in some Urodeles.

Wickbom (1945, 1949a,b) has made a comparative study of amphibian chromosomes and, in the last citation, listed the haploid chromosome numbers for many species of Anura. The smallest number is 11, which is found in Bufo. Hyla has 12 and Rana 13. The highest number, 18, is found in Xenopus. Bushnell, Bushnell, and Parker (1939) find $N = 12$ for 3 species of Hyla and $N = 11$ for 2 species of Acris.

Some of our more cherished beliefs regarding the constancy of chromosome numbers have been shaken by Green's (1953) discovery that the mesenchyme cells of a normal *Rana pipiens* embryo are not diploid, as we would expect, but haploid. In an extension of this work Green and Freed (1954) have reported that the haploid mesenchyme cells contain the same amount of DNA as diploid epidermal cells.

2. *Diploid Hybrids (Including Intraspecific Crosses)*

When cross fertilizations are attempted between different species of amphibia, a variety of results are obtained (Table 1). In some instances, such as those involving *Rana clamitans* ova, there is no development. The reason for this is not known, but it is possible that the foreign sperm is unable to penetrate the jelly surrounding the ova.

In 91 % of the crosses listed some development is obtained. If development begins at all, it proceeds at least as far as the late blastula or late gastrula stage. This result is obtained in 21 % of the crosses.

Another class, comprising 19%, fail in late gastrula, neurula, and tailbud stages.

Still another category, representing 9%, includes the embryos that reach an early larval stage. They usually hatch and have the main organ systems developed. Some of these exhibit a characteristic set of abnormalities such as reduced eyes, truncated bodies, and crooked tails. In those cases where these have been studied cytologically, it is found that the embryos are not hybrids at all but gynogenetic haploids. The role of the sperm has been limited to activation of the ovum and its nucleus fails to play the usual part in development. It is generally possible to recognize these haploids by their external appearance. A study of chromosomes in the tail tip will establish the point beyond doubt.

Of the crosses listed, 42% form normal tadpoles or reach the adult stage. Metamorphosis is generally looked upon as a "crisis" in development, but it is my belief that it represents no special crisis for hybrids. If a normal or reasonably normal tadpole is produced, it should be able to transform into a young adult. Failure to do so is more probably due to difficulties in raising the animals than to their hybrid constitution. For example, Blair believes that many of his Hylidae crosses, which develop to the tadpole stage but not beyond, would give adults with improved rearing conditions.

It is laborious to raise transformed frogs to the stage where sexual maturity can be tested. As a result many investigators terminate their experiments after the tadpoles have transformed into young frogs. A few investigators, with more patience than others, have raised hybrids to the stage of fully grown animals and have attempted backcrosses with the parent species.

Blair (1941a) tested the fertility of males of the *Bufo w. woodhousei* ♀ × *Bufo terrestris americanus* ♂ cross. These were backcrossed to *americanus* females. "Some developmental abnormalities were present, but the majority of tadpoles seemed normal." A number of these backcross tadpoles were carried through metamorphosis. Blair (1946) kept one *Bufo w. woodhousei* ♀ × *Bufo terrestris americanus* ♂ hybrid for a period of 6 years.

Ting (1948) found that the fully grown hybrids of *Rana nigromaculata* × *Rana plancyi* differed from the parents in many ways. In some characteristics they resembled one or the other parent, in others they were intermediate, and in still others they were neither intermediate nor like either parent. A cross was made between one of the F_1 males and a female *R. nigromaculata*. Some of the backcross embryos reached the frog stage. They were similar in appearance to the F_1 hybrids.

Kawamura (1950) raised hybrid males of the cross *Rana japonica*

♀ × *Rana temporaria ornativentris* ♂ to maturity. Secondary sex characters were well developed. The sperm were abnormal in shape and were immobile when placed in water. Meiosis was abnormal and most spermatocytes "seemed to degenerate after the first maturation division." Sterility was established by attempted backcrosses with *Rana japonica* females.

Moriya (1951) has crossed two frogs that he regards as subspecies, namely, *Rana n. nigromaculata* and *R. n. brevipoda*. These two forms differ markedly in coloration, size, body proportions, egg size and color, speed of embryonic development, temperature tolerance, and breeding season. They are sympatric in portions of their ranges, but apparently show no evidence of intergradation. On the basis of these observations, it seems clear that the two forms are species and not subspecies. Reciprocal crosses were made and some of the F_1 of each cross were raised to sexual maturity. Females of the parent species were crossed with F_1 male hybrids and the F_1 female hybrids were crossed with males of the parent species. "Eggs of *nigromaculata* were fertilized with spermatozoa of hybrid males with conspicuous difficulty in contrast with facility in crossing *brevipoda* ♀ × hybrid ♂. Although the hybrids used in crossing experiments were few in number and moreover some difficulty was met with in the crossing, it was certain that both sexes of the reciprocal hybrids were more or less fertile."

Crosses among individuals of the same species, but coming from different geographical regions, have been made with *Rana pipiens* (Moore, 1941b, 1946b, 1947a, 1950; Porter, 1941a,b, 1942; Ting, 1951; Volpe, 1954).

The *Rana pipiens* situation is both interesting and complex. This species ranges over most of North America and consists of a great number of local populations that can be distinguished on the basis of pigmentation and other characters (Moore, 1944). Some authors have used subspecific names, the more important being *pipiens* and *sphenocephala*. I have not felt that the situation is clarified by using subspecific names. A large number of crosses have been made and the results fall into a pattern. When eggs of northern individuals are fertilized with sperm of southern individuals, the embryos develop abnormally. The main defects are enlarged head structures and a defective circulatory system. The reciprocal crosses give embryos with small heads. The extremely defective ones lack eyes, olfactory organs, and a mouth. The degree of abnormality becomes progressively greater as the north-south distance between the parent populations increases. Localities close to one another show no defects. Crosses between Vermont and Florida or ·between Vermont and north east Mexico may result in 100% mortality (Moore, 1949b). These results are correlated in a rough way with the environmental temperatures of the regions from which the individuals come. The greater the temperature differences between the two regions the greater the defects in the hybrids. It is clearly not a matter of mere distance since Vermont × Colorado crosses result in normal embryos and even individuals from Vermont and the cooler mountain regions of Costa Rica can be crossed and normal embryos are obtained.

Porter (1941a,b, 1942) has found that androgenesis results in an exaggeration of the defects found in the diploid hybrids. The diploid combination of a cold region egg and a warm region sperm produces a large-headed embryo. In the androgenetic combination of an enucleated cold region egg and a warm region sperm, the head is even larger.

Some intraspecific crosses have demonstrated the presence of simple Mendelian factors in wild populations of frogs. A form originally described as "*Rana burnsi*" was shown to differ from ordinary *Rana pipiens* by a single dominant gene (Moore, 1942, 1943). Baker (1951) has made a biochemical study of this mutant. Moriya (1952) has reported a similar situation in *Rana nigromaculata*, Lantz (1947) one for *Discoglossus pictus*, and Moriwaki (1953) one for *Rana linnocharis*.

3. *Gynogenetic Haploids*

A variety of techniques are available for stimulating an ovum to develop without the inclusion of paternal chromosomes in the embryo's nuclei.

a. *Cross fertilization.* In some crosses fertilization of ova with sperm of a different species results in gynogenetic development. This is a frequent occurrence in crosses between Australian species (Table 1). Ting and Price (1950) and Ting (1951) have reported this in the cross *Rana pipiens* ♀ × *Scaphiopus h. holbrookii* ♂ and *Pseudacris nigrita triseriata* ♀ × *Scaphiopus h. holbrookii* ♂. The sperm head enters the eggs and "lies along the first cleavage spindle, but does not fuse with the female pronucleus. It is eliminated after the first division."

The expected haploid chromosome number is not always obtained in these crosses. Many years ago G. and P. Hertwig (1920) crossed *Rana esculenta* ♀ × *Bufo viridis* ♂. In this combination the sperm nucleus degenerates once it is in the egg. Nevertheless, the embryos were diploid. This was a peculiarity of the individual female, which was producing diploid eggs. The controls, *Rana esculenta* ♀ × *Rana esculenta* ♂, were triploids.

b. *Chemical treatment of sperm.* Chemical substances have been employed to inactivate the sperm nucleus without affecting the ability of the sperm to initiate development. For many years it has been known that

acriflavine has this effect. Briggs (1952) tested this, together with toluidine blue, methylene blue, thionine, and pyronin in *Rana pipiens*. All
"were found to inactivate the sperm nucleus without damaging appreciably the extranuclear parts." Toluidine blue was studied in detail. If
sperm were placed in a dye concentration of 2×10^{-7} M at pH 8.1 for
different lengths of time, the following was observed. A 7-minute exposure
gave 7% normal diploids, 91% abnormal embryos, and 2% haploids.
A 40-minute exposure gave 3% abnormal embryos and 97% haploids.
These results are explained in terms of degree of inactivation. A 7-minute
exposure does not entirely inactivate the sperm nucleus. As a result, an
abnormal or unbalanced set of male chromosomes becomes part of the
embryo's nucleus. This leads to pronounced postgastrula defects. Longer
exposure results in complete inactivation of the sperm nucleus, and, as a
result, none of the paternal chromosomes play a part in development.

The pH of the solution was found to be important for inactivation.
With a dye concentration of 5×10^{-6} M and an exposure time of 10
minutes, the per cent haploids obtained at pH 6.1, 7.1, and 7.9 were 3,
39, and 91, respectively. It was computed that the amount of dye needed
to inactivate the nucleus, but not the extranuclear structures, of a single
sperm was 4×10^6 molecules.

Toluidine blue fails to inactivate sperm kept in the dark. The dye
enters the sperm head in the dark but does not have any effect until the
sperm are brought into light. This finding of the effect of light was a confirmation of previous work of Drebinger (1951).

c. *Radiation of sperm.* Early workers in the field knew of the effects
of radium and X-rays on sperm inactivation. Rugh (1939, 1954) has
studied the effect of radiations on *Rana pipiens* sperm. He exposed sperm
to doses varying from 15 r to 50,000 r and then used these to fertilize
ova. Up to 10,000 r there was a gradual decrease in the per cent of embryos that reached the hatching stage. Various defects were noticed but
these were always in stages in later rather than early gastrula. At doses
greater than 10,000 r, the per cent that reached hatching increased with
increasing doses. At 50,000 r, the percentage hatching was nearly as high
as in the nonirradiated controls but the embryos showed characteristic
defects associated with haploidy. No data on chromosome counts were
given by Rugh, but the probable explanation is in terms of degree of
damage. At doses up to 10,000 r, the X-rays may be thought of as resulting in progressively greater chromosomal injury yet not preventing the
formation of a zygote nucleus. The embryological defects would be the
result of chromosome unbalance and aberration. The highest doses could
be thought of as inactivating the nucleus of the sperm but not its activating power. The 50,000-r series would consist largely of gynogenetic

haploids. Similar work by earlier workers indicates that this explanation is correct.

Henshaw (1943) performed a similar experiment and observed the same general result. There is some doubt that this is a real confirmation of Rugh's work since some of the photographs he gives appear to be the same as those in Rugh's paper. Both might be describing the same data.

Rugh and Exner (1940) performed a similar experiment using *Rana pipiens* ova and *Rana catesbeiana* sperm (see also Briggs, Green, and King, 1951). The hybrids in this cross develop to the beginning of gastrulation and then stop. If the *catesbeiana* sperm are given 66,000 r, 97.2% gastrulated and developed into embryos with the haploid syndrome.

There is a close parallel between the effects of X-rays and dyes on sperm. Increasing amounts result in increasing nuclear defects until a point is reached where the sperm will activate the ovum but cannot enter into a zygote nucleus. The resulting embryo is a gynogenetic haploid.

d. *Parthenogenetic stimulation.* Gynogenetic haploid development can be initiated, under certain conditions, by pricking ova with a glass needle. The method frequently used by the early workers in this field was to smear ova with frog blood and then prick them. The pricking, in itself, seems to be of little or no importance. The stimulus to parthenogenetic development comes from some material pushed into the ovum by the needle. This material has been called the "second factor" and more recently the "cleavage-initiating substances" (Shaver, 1949, 1953). Shaver has made a study of this material by injecting tiny quantities of various test materials into unfertilized ova of *Rana pipiens* and *Rana fusca* and noting whether or not parthenogenetic development resulted. His most active preparations were those containing large granules (mitochondria), although smaller granules (microsomes) were not without effect. The "second factor" is widely distributed in adult frog tissues, and very potent samples were obtained from mammalian and avian sources as well. The "second factor" is nearly absent from the cleavage and early blastula stages of frog embryos. There is a rapid increase in it during the late blastula and early gastrula stages. Injection of the large granules of embryos of these stages results in 45% of the ova developing at least to the blastula stage. In postneurula stages there is a rapid decline in the "second factor."

Briggs and King (1953) have found that injection of the "second factor" into enucleated ova (second maturation spindle removed) is not a sufficient stimulus for cleavage.

Zorzoli and Rugh (1941) have reported that a higher percentage of "overripe" *Rana pipiens* ova cleave after pricking than was noted in unaged controls. Tokunaga (1949) obtained some albino tadpoles and frogs, after parthenogenetic stimulation, and made a study of their endocrine glands. Harding (1949) has reported that parthenogenesis is less frequent if eggs are pricked after being smeared with heparinated blood than when untreated blood is used. Rostand (1951a,b) has studied parthenogenesis in *Bufo* and *Xenopus*.

The technique of pricking or injecting ova with various materials is not a very reliable one for obtaining gynogenetic haploid embryos. In most cases the per cent of developing embryos obtained is quite small and it is impossible to give a uniform stimulus to all of the embryos used. The use of sperm of a foreign species that will merely activate the ovum, or the technique of inactivating the sperm nucleus by X-rays or dyes, are much better methods for obtaining gynogenetic haploids.

The chief purpose of the pricking or injecting method for future work would seem to be in studying the nature of the "second factor" in parthenogenetic stimulation.

4. *Gynogenetic Diploids and Polyploids*

In Parmenter's (1933, 1940, 1952) and Kawamura's (1939a,b,c, 1940, 1949) experiments on parthenogenetic development in *Rana pipiens*, *Rana palustris*, *Rana fusca*, and *Rana nigromaculata*, not all of the embryos have been the expected haploids. Parmenter (1952) has summarized the data and reports "47.9% are haploids, 21.4% are diploid, 21.2% are triploid, and 9.5% have various other chromosome numbers." This variability presents interesting problems of the manner that chromosome numbers greater than haploid are achieved.

There is good evidence that the increase results from several different methods. In some embryos, it has been observed that the interval between successive cleavages may be double the normal time required. This is interpreted as indicative of a nuclear division without a cell division, resulting in a doubled chromosome number. In other instances, there is evidence that the second polar body may unite with the female pronucleus. The total suppression of the second meiotic division would also result in a diploid ovum. It is known that a small percentage of uterine ova are diploid. Parthenogenetic stimulation of these would, of course, give diploid embryos. The frequency of diploid ova is very small but when one considers the small percentage of parthenogenetically stimulated ova that do develop, this is a factor of some importance. One suggestion for triploid embryos is the fusion of the first polar body with the female pronucleus.

The relation between chromosome number and cleavage delay in parthenogenetic embryos is well shown in Kawamura's (1939a) experiments. Of 198 haploid individuals, 197 had undelayed cleavage and 1 had delayed cleavage. Of 80 diploids, 4 had undelayed and 76 had delayed cleavages. Of 90 triploids, 89 had undelayed and one had delayed cleavages. This excellent paper should be consulted for details of the development of parthenogenetic embryos.

No parthenogenetic haploid has developed beyond the early larval stage. Many gynogenetic diploid and a few gynogenetic triploids have reached the frog stage (Kawamura, 1939c).

A technique of obtaining gynogenetic diploid embryos, which should produce them with higher frequency than parthenogenetic stimulation, is available but seems never to have been used. Ova could be "fertilized" with sperm treated chemically or irradiated to inactivate the nucleus or by sperm of a foreign species that would activate the ova but not contribute chromosomes to the embryo. These ova could then be subjected to temperature shocks to suppress the second maturation division. The result would be diploid gynogenetic embryos.

5. *Gynogenetic Hybrids*

Improbable though it may seem, experimentally and semantically, the possibility of studying gynogenetic "hybrids" is now at hand with the techniques perfected by Porter, Briggs, and others. The second maturation spindle can be removed from unfertilized ova. This results in an enucleated ovum. If now one implants a nucleus from a gynogenetic haploid or diploid of a different species, the resulting combination might be called a gynogenetic hybrid. The hybridization is between the maternal chromosomes of one species and the cytoplasm of another.

Although within the realm of possibility, it seems that this experiment has not been performed.

6. *Androgenetic Haploids*

Androgenetic embryos are those containing only paternal chromosomes. There are two ways of obtaining them.

a. *Destruction of the maternal nucleus.* The first attempts to obtain androgenetic development in the frog depended on the use of radium or X-rays to inactivate the maternal chromosomes. At the time of laying, the first polar body has been formed and the maternal chromosomes are in the metaphase of the second meiotic division. They are located immediately below the egg surface at the center of the animal pole. It is possible to inactivate the maternal chromosomes by radiations and have development with paternal chromosomes alone, but there is no way of preventing concomitant cytoplasmic effects of the radiations. For this reason the method is not satisfactory for the large scale production of androgenetic haploids.

Rollason (1949) has studied the effects of various dosages of X-rays on ova of *Rana pipiens* and has noted the effects on embryonic development. When uterine ova were given even low doses there was an effect on development, and 800 r reduced the percentage of normal larvae obtained to near zero.

b. *Removal of the maternal chromosomes.* The most successful method for obtaining androgenetic haploid embryos in frogs is that perfected by Porter (1939). The second maturation division spindle is removed by pushing a glass needle under it and raising the needle. This forms a tiny exovate containing the spindle. The operation is performed shortly after fertilization and the resulting embryo develops with the haploid set of paternal chromosomes. Porter reported approximately 90% of the operations are successful in giving haploid embryos, and later workers, such as Briggs and King (1953), have modified the method slightly and obtained nearly 100% haploids.

Porter gives an excellent description of the androgenetic haploid embryo of *Rana pipiens*. The cleavage stages are identical with the diploid controls. In the late blastula stages, it can be seen that the haploids have smaller cells than the diploids. Gastrulation is delayed approximately 1 hour (at 19.4°C) in the haploids, and they are retarded increasingly throughout the rest of their development. Morphological abnormalities are noted in the neurula and later stages. In the haploid, compared to the diploid, the neural plate is shorter, the neural folds are flatter and closer together, the tailbud is smaller, the abdominal region larger, the head smaller, and gill development and circulation retarded. Near the end of their development, the haploids are shortened edematous embryos with swollen abdomens and reduced heads. Internally the haploids show defects in optic cup and lens formation, brain development, otocyst formation, and in the circulatory and digestive systems. Yolk utilization in the haploids is slower than in the normals.

The androgenetic haploid embryos of *Rana palustris* do not develop as far as androgenetic haploids of *Rana pipiens* (A. B. C. Moore, 1950). In general, they show the same defects.

7. *Androgenetic Hybrids*

The removal of the second maturation spindle, and with it all of the maternal chromosomes, from an ovum fertilized with sperm of a different species produces an androgenetic haploid hybrid. This combination affords an opportunity of studying the interaction of the chromosomes of one species with the cytoplasm of another and in a technically easier manner than in the gynogenetic hybrid combination. This technique has been used to produce androgenetic hybrids between different species (A. B. C. Moore, 1950; Ting, 1951; Briggs, Green, and King, 1951; Briggs and King, 1952; Sambuichi, 1952; Moore and Moore, 1953) and between individuals of the same species coming from different geographical regions (Porter, 1941a,b, 1942; Ting, 1951).

A. B. C. Moore used *Rana pipiens* and *Rana palustris* in her experiments. Diploid hybrids of these species develop normally past metamorphosis but no attempt has yet been made to rear the young frogs to sexual maturity. The hybrids are intermediate in physiological and morphological respects. The normality of their development suggests there is little difficulty in the *pipiens* chromosome plus *palustris* chromosome plus *pipiens* (or *palustris*) egg cytoplasm combination collaborating in the sequence of embryological events. The androgenetic hybrid of *pipiens* cytoplasm and *palustris* paternal chromosomes develop to the neural plate stage and then cytolyze. The notochord does not differentiate. The reciprocal androgenetic hybrid, consisting of *palustris* egg cytoplasm and *pipiens* paternal chromosomes, is able to develop somewhat further. The best embryos are very abnormal tadpoles with some differentiation of notochord and neural tissue.

Ting (1951) found the androgenetic hybrid composed of *Rana pipiens* egg cytoplasm and *Rana capito* paternal chromosomes dies at the neural plate stage. The *Rana pipiens* egg cytoplasm plus *Rana sylvatica* paternal chromosomes combination does not develop beyond the late blastula stage (see also Moore and Moore, 1953). The *Rana pipiens* egg cytoplasm plus *Rana clamitans* paternal chromosomes combination also ceases development in the late blastula stage.

Briggs, Green, and King (1951) and Briggs and King (1952) found the combination of *Rana pipiens* egg cytoplasm and *Rana catesbeiana* paternal chromosomes is capable of development only to the late blastula stage.

Sambuichi (1952) has studied androgenetic development in crosses between two forms he considers subspecies, namely *Rana n. nigromaculata* and *R. n. brevipoda*. As has been mentioned before, it is more likely that these are full species and not subspecies. The two types of androgenetic hybrid develop to a surprisingly advanced stage. Many reach gill circulation (stage 20) and several reached the stage of operculum formation (stage 23–24). There are differences in gill and operculum development between *nigromaculata* and *brevipoda*. In one of the crosses where the androgenetic hybrids reach a sufficiently advanced stage, it appears that the paternal nucleus, and not the egg cytoplasm, determined the type of gill and operculum development.

In all of the cases mentioned, there is a good correlation between the behavior of the androgenetic hybrids and the diploid hybrids. When the androgenetic hybrids fail in the late blastula stages, the diploids are incapable of developing beyond an early gastrula stage. When the androgenetic hybrids are able to develop beyond the gastrula stages, the diploid hybrids reach metamorphosis. As a further general statement, it should be mentioned that these interspecific androgenetic hybrids do not develop as well as the gynogenetic or androgenetic haploids formed of a nucleus and cytoplasm of the same species.

Porter (1941a) has described some highly interesting results obtained by androgenetic hybridization of individuals of different geographic populations of *Rana pipiens*. The reciprocal androgenetic hybrids between individuals from Vermont and Pennsylvania showed slight differences. Thus, the Vermont egg cytoplasm with Pennsylvania paternal chromosomes resulted in an embryo with enlarged head structures. The Pennsylvania egg cytoplasm with Vermont paternal chromosomes combination produced an embryo with reduced head structures. These features noted in androgenetic haploid hybrids were exaggerations of differences present in diploid hybrids. In two later papers (Porter, 1941b, 1942), preliminary results of crosses among Vermont, Pennsylvania, Louisiana, and Florida individuals are reported. In general, the more extreme the cross in the geographic sense, the more extreme the defects in the androgenetic haploid hybrids.

Ting (1951) has repeated these experiments and found that the androgenetic hybrid of Vermont cytoplasm and New Jersey (equivalent to Porter's Pennsylvania material) paternal chromosomes develop to the neurula stage and then die. The Vermont cytoplasm and Florida paternal chromosome combination died somewhat earlier. In view of Porter's work this is an unexpected and unexplained finding.

8. *Achromosomal Embryos*

We have seen that it is possible to obtain gynogenetic development by the inactivation of the sperm chromosomes by radiation or chemical means. It is also possible to obtain androgenetic embryos by the removal of the second maturation spindle from a fertilized ovum. It is possible to combine both of these methods and study the development of an embryo without maternal or paternal chromosomes.

Briggs, Green, and King (1951) obtained achromosomal embryos by removing the second maturation spindle from ova that had been fertilized with irradiated sperm. Approximately 100% of the embryos cleaved, although at a retarded rate, and produced abnormal mid and late blastulae. In nearly every case, the area of cleavage was restricted to the animal hemisphere. The partial blastulae are formed in 24–36 hours after which there is no further development. Cytological examination showed that some of the cells contained Feulgen positive fragments. Cleavage occurred equally well in cells with or without these fragments. There was some evidence that cells with Feulgen positive fragments survived a little longer than those without any. Transplants of achromosomal tissue to normal diploid embryos did not aid the differentiation of the transplants.

This experiment was extended by using sperm treated with toluidine blue. When a dose just sufficient for inactivation of the nucleus was employed, results similar to those obtained with X-ray inactivated sperm, were produced. With a greater exposure to the dye, the achromosomal embryos were arrested in the early cleavage stages. These "results suggest that the dye first inactivates the sperm nucleus, leaving the rest of the sperm cell relatively unaffected so that it may function by itself to provide a division center for the egg, which then develops into a partial blastula. As the dye treatment is continued it would appear that the extranuclear parts of the sperm may be affected in such a way that the capacity of the sperm to form a division center and maintain cleavage in the absence of the egg nucleus is reduced."

Still another method of obtaining achromosomal eggs was by the removal of the second maturation spindle from eggs smeared with blood and pricked to produce parthenogenetic stimulation. No blastulae were formed by this treatment, possibly because of the absence of a division center.

The authors conclude from these experiments that "although cleavage definitely occurs in chromatin-free blastomeres, it appears that the amphibian egg as a whole will not begin to cleave unless it is provided with a cleavage center from the sperm or from the egg nucleus" and further " . . . the initiation of cleavage of the achromosomal frog's egg described in this paper depends primarily upon the presence of the cleavage center provided by the irradiated sperm." This conclusion is made more probable by the finding that enucleated ova (second maturation spindle removed), injected with the "second factor" to produce parthenogenetic stimulation, showed no signs of development (Briggs and King, 1953).

Still another method of obtaining achromosomal embryos has been used by Ting (1951). In the cross *Rana pipiens* ♀ × *Scaphiopus holbrookii* ♂, the sperm enters, but the male pronucleus does not combine with the female pronucleus. Development is gynogenetic. Now if the second maturation spindle is removed from *Rana pipiens* ova fertilized with the *Scaphiopus* sperm, the egg should be without functional chromosomes. A detailed analysis was not made of this case but it appeared that a few irregular cleavages was the maximum possible development and a majority of the eggs did not even begin to cleave.

9. Triploid and Tetraploid Embryos

Triploid embryos are known to occur infrequently in amphibians collected under natural conditions and in those obtained by standard laboratory procedures. The frequency is generally less than 0.5%, a figure suggested by the work of Briggs, Green, and King (1951).

The origin of triploidy is generally assumed to be the fertilization of a diploid ovum with a haploid sperm. This could come about through a failure of the second meiotic division, resulting in the retention of the chromosomes normally eliminated in the second polar body (Parmenter, 1933, 1940). Parmenter (1952) has observed another situation that would also result in triploidy. In the ova of a single female he noticed that some had the diploid number of dyads on the second division spindle. The female pronucleus of these exceptional ova would be diploid and, if fertilized by a haploid sperm, the embryo would be triploid. This situation is known in Bufo as well.

These spontaneous triploids are of interest but their low frequency mitigates against their use. Fortunately, methods of obtaining triploid frog embryos in numbers are now available. These methods are modifications of ones previously developed for urodele material.

Kawamura (1941) produced triploidy by placing embryos of *Rana nigromaculata* at near zero temperatures shortly after fertilization. They were left at the low temperatures for 4 hours or more. Many triploids were found but the effectiveness of the method was difficult to evaluate since approximately a third of one of the control series were triploids. The triploids were raised to the adult stage. No differences between diploids and triploids were noted. Nearly all of the triploids were males and some of these were raised to sexual maturity and crossed with normal females (Kawamura, 1951). The percentage of developing embryos was low. The best cross gave 29% embryos but, in most, the figure was less than 9%. Development was normal or nearly normal until the late embryonic stages. "Most died of severe edema at the age of 11 to 20 days." The other defects noted were bent tails and defective eyes, heart, and pronephros. Chromosome counts showed considerable variability, but generally the numbers were more or less intermediate between $2N$ and $3N$.

Briggs (1947) finds that triploidy can be induced in *Rana pipiens* embryos by appropriate treatment with supranormal temperature shocks. The best results were obtained by keeping embryos first at 18.1°C and, 20 minutes after fertilization, placing them in water at 37°C for 4 minutes. After this they were returned to 18.1°C. In one experiment, 41% of the eggs that cleaved produced triploids. The per cent of triploids varied considerably from experiment to experiment and in some no triploids were produced. The data strongly suggest that triploidy is due to the suppression of the second meiotic division, resulting in a diploid ovum that was then fertilized with a haploid sperm.

The rate of development as measured by cleavage, growth in length, and time of metamorphosis was the same in the triploids as in the diploid controls. Briggs was unable to find any "developmental abnormalities and no differential mortality attributable to triploidy as such." It was possible to distinguish the triploids from diploids by external appearance.

Triploidy has an unusual effect on sex determination in *Rana pipiens*. Both sexes are present in the tadpole stage but later the females change into males. At the time of metamorphosis all of the animals are males (Humphrey, Briggs, and Fankhauser, 1950).

Muto (1952) used both low and high temperature shocks to produce triploids in *Bufo vulgaris formosus*. Development of the triploids was normal. The sex of 17 animals was determined. Of these 13 were females, 1 was a male, and 3 were undifferentiated. The author suggests that in Bufo the female is the heterogametic sex. If this is so, Bufo has a sex determining mechanism similar to that of at least some urodeles and differing, perhaps, from Rana.

Sato (1952) produced triploids in *Rana limnocharis* by cold treatment. These developed normally to metamorphosis. Up to this time all of the individuals examined, both the triploids and the diploids, were females. This may be an "undifferentiated" species in the sense that the expected sex ratio is not obtained in the early stages and appears late in development, as a result of the sex reversal of some "females" into males.

Kawamura and Tokunaga (1952) produced triploids in *Rana japonica* by cold shock treatment. In this species the diploids have an equal sex ratio at the time of metamorphosis. All of the triploids, however, were males.

Temperature shock treatment has produced a few diploid-tetraploid mosaics in *Rana nigromaculata* (Kawamura and Miyada, 1951) and haploid-triploid mosaics in *Bufo vulgaris formosus* (Muto, 1951).

We have already seen that triploidy occurs in some embryos developing as a result of parthenogenetic stimulation.

Kawamura and Moriwaki (1953) obtained one tetraploid tadpole among a group of triploids that had been produced by cold treatment. This individual reached metamorphosis a little earlier than the diploid and triploid embryos. It died two months after transformation. The authors suggest two possible mechanisms for the formation of this tetraploid frog. One way it could have happened is by the union of a diploid egg and a diploid sperm nucleus. The second way could be through the fertilization of a triploid egg by a normal haploid sperm. The authors suggest that the triploid egg could arise through the fusion of the diploid first polar body with the haploid female pronucleus. This is the first record of a tetraploid frog, but this condition has been observed previously in urodeles.

Some success in inducing polyploidy by colchicine has been reported by Keppel and Dawson (1939), Hsu, Hsiang, and Liu (1949), and Lüscher (1946).

10. *Triploid Hybrids*

Temperature shock treatment to suppress the formation of the second polar body in ova, fertilized with sperm of a foreign species, will result in triploid hybrids. Briggs (1947, footnote p. 263) performed such an experiment but did not report the outcome. Kawamura (1952) seems to be the first to report triploid hybrids in frogs. Eggs of *Rana japonica* were fertilized by sperm of *Rana temporaria ornativentris* and some of the embryos were kept at 0–0.5°C for 16–18 hours. Some of the embryos were triploid as was shown by cytological examination of tail tips. The triploid hybrids were raised to sexual maturity together with some diploid hybrids. The triploid hybrids resembled the diploid hybrids in some respects but in the case of most characters they resembled *Rana japonica* more closely. All of the diploid and triploid hybrids were males. The *Rana japonica* diploid controls were males and females in approximately equal numbers. Meiosis in the triploid males was abnormal.

III. Transplantation of Nuclei

As a climax to a series of important studies on the interrelations of chromosomes and cytoplasm in the early development of the frog, Briggs and his associates have recently developed techniques for transplanting nuclei from older embryos to the enucleated ovum of *Rana pipiens* (Briggs and King, 1952, 1953).

The possibility of nuclear differentiation concomitant with embryonic differentiation, and a causal connection between the two, has long interested embryologists. In the lack of critical evidence, it has generally been assumed that all cells of the body of an animal, such as the frog, are diploid and genetically identical. This does not exclude the possibility of cells in different parts of the body acting differently at the same stage of development or cells in the same part of the body acting differently at different stages of development. Early experiments with ligatured urodele embryos indicated that there was no nuclear differentiation during the early cleavage stages but this technique did not permit a study of the nuclei in older embryos.

Briggs and King enucleated *Rana pipiens* ova by removing the second maturation spindle. Next, a single cell from the animal hemisphere of a blastula was drawn up into a pipette having a bore smaller than the diameter of the cell. This treatment breaks the membrane of the cell. The broken cell, including the nucleus, is then injected into the previously enucleated ovum. The amount of cytoplasm injected into the ovum represents about 1/20,000 of the volume of the ovum. It is assumed that an amount this small would be without effect and so the results can be attributed to the action of the injected nucleus above.

It was found that many of the enucleated ova injected with blastula nuclei would develop as normal diploid embryos, indicating the absence of an irreversible limitation of genetic ability in the late blastula nucleus. Nuclei from the presumptive ectoderm of early gastrulae behaved in the same way. These blastula and gastrula nuclei were from cells that are "undetermined" in the embryological sense and so might be expected to give the observed result. In a more recent report, King and Briggs (1953, 1954a,b) have obtained a small percentage of normal embryos after injecting enucleated ova with nuclei of presumptive notochord and presumptive neural plate cells of late gastrula and neurula stages. These nuclei are from "determined" areas. Endoderm nuclei from neurula and tailbud stages fail to develop normally when transplanted to enucleated ova.

It has been observed that the percentage of normal development decreases with the increasing embryological age of the nuclei used for transplantation. Whether this is the result of increased sensitivity of the nuclei to manipulation, or a change in their ability to provide for complete development, remains to be seen.

This method of transplantation will allow one to determine the time a nucleus can no longer support development, if the effects of injury due to manipulation can be excluded. Whether this method is sensitive enough to detect other kinds of nuclear differentiation remains to be seen. Part of the difficulty lies in the fact that almost any nucleus, even one badly disrupted by X-rays, will allow development to the late blastula stage. It is conceivable, therefore, that a nucleus of some postgastrula stage be differentiated in a highly specific way yet be perfectly capable of supporting development to the late blastula stage if transplanted to an enucleated ovum. It is less easy to see how one could detect specific effects of differentiated nuclei in postblastula stages although one hopes that it will prove possible.

Rostand (1943) has attacked this problem with quite a different technique but one that does not permit unequivocal conclusions.

IV. Embryological Problems

The various types of experimentation so far discussed have been used to provide information in two quite different areas of biology, namely, embryology and evolution. We will discuss some of the problems from the field of embryology first.

1. The Role of the Nucleus in Early Development

This problem can be traced back to an early and naive question, "Which is more important, the nucleus or the cytoplasm?" In more recent years this has become a quest for information on the effects of foreign genes in development.

In many species of animals, and this includes the amphibia, the ovum, at the time of fertilization, is a complex cell and as typical of its species and genotype as is any other cell. Its characteristic structure and chemistry is developed under the influence of the maternal genes. If genes of a different species enter the ovum, as in hybridization, the question can be asked, "When will the foreign genes have their first detectable effect?" The answer, that the first effects were noted at or near the beginning of gastrulation, was given tentatively several generations ago and in the succeeding years all new evidence substantiates this belief. The course of development seems to be fixed throughout the cleavage and blastula stages, as a result, presumably, of the action of the maternal genes during oögenesis. The main evidence for this is as follows, all of it being available from a single species, *Rana pipiens.*

(1) In gynogenetic embryos, development as far as the late blastula stage is essentially the same as in normal diploids. Therefore, the paternal chromosomes are shown not to have an effect on these early stages.

(2) In androgenetic embryos development as far as the late blastula stage is essentially the same as in normal diploids. Therefore, the maternal chromosomes are shown not to have an effect on these early stages.

(3) In androgenetic hybrid embryos, development as far as the late blastula stage is essentially the same as in normal diploids. This is the case no matter whether the androgenetic hybrid is capable of developing only to the late blastula or into a typical haploid larva.

(4) If hybridization is possible, development is essentially the same, as in the diploid controls, at least to the late blastula stages. This is true whether the hybrids are capable of reaching the adult stage or are arrested at or near the beginning of gastrulation.

(5) If sperm which have been irradiated or treated chemically to produce nuclear defects are used to fertilize ova, a series of developmental abnormalities may result. These never appear in the pregastrula stages no matter how severe the postgastrula effects.

(6) Keeping in mind (1) and (2), we might inquire about the possibility of development through the blastula stage in achromosomal embryos. To a certain extent this has been achieved. (This is, of course,

not a necessary deduction from (1) and (2). The fact that paternal chromosomes can be dispensed with if the maternal ones are there, or that the maternal ones can be dispensed with if the paternal ones are there, does not mean that all chromosomes can be dispensed with.) The failure to obtain normal development to the late blastula or early gastrula stage in embryos without chromosomes is probably due more to the absence of a suitable mechanism for cell division than to any immediate genetic effects.

(7) To these observations we should add those of Holtfreter (1943), who noted that some morphogenetic movement, of the type characteristic of normal development, occurs in unfertilized and uncleaved ova.

These observations suggest that the mature ovum of *Rana pipiens* (and perhaps all Salientia) is "determined" with respect to cleavage pattern, tempo of development, and morphology for the embryonic stages up to and including the late blastula (stage 9). This determination is the result of gene action during oögenesis and it cannot be modified by gene action, or the lack of it, during the cleavage and blastula stages. These statements are based on data now available. It is possible that pregastrula effects will be observed some day. A likely way for this to occur would be through the action of foreign genes that affect the division apparatus.

2. The Problem of Arrested Gastrulae

There are a number of nuclear-cytoplasmic systems that develop normally to a late blastula or early gastrula stage and then stop. These include some diploid hybrids, some androgenetic haploid hybrids, and some embryos derived from sperm treated with X-rays or drugs.

It is unlikely that the arrest at gastrulation noted in these various situations is due to the same cause. It is even unlikely that the many hybrids, which are blocked at the beginning of gastrulation, suffer the same defects. This is borne out by the different behavior of the various crosses in this class of hybrids. Even though they cease development as early gastrulae, they show some obvious differences. If, for example, ova of *Rana pipiens* are fertilized by sperm of *Rana sylvatica* or *Rana clamitans*, it is found that the two classes of hybrids are not the same. The pipiens ♀ × *sylvatica* ♂ hybrids form a dorsal lip, and, in a few cases, a small amount of invagination, followed by some slight differentiation, may occur. Most of the embryos remain as early gastrulae but go through a sequence of abnormal stages and cytolyze when the controls are about stage 22. The *pipiens* ♀ × *clamitans* ♂ hybrids have little or no invagination and cytolize when the controls are about stage 14. On the other hand, the *sylvatica* ♀ × *pipiens* ♂ hybrids form a deep blastoporal groove and die when the controls are stage 13. The difference in the behavior of this hybrid and its reciprocal is especially striking.

The *pipiens* ♀ × *sylvatica* ♂ hybrids have been the object of a series of studies. A ponderous description of the sequence of abnormal events in the hybrids that are arrested as early gastrulae and in the few that show further differentiation is given by Moore (1946a). This hybrid combination has a special advantage in embryological studies. Approximately 20 hours (at 20°C) are required for it to realize its developmental potentialities by reaching the early gastrula stage. It then remains alive for an additional 150 hours (more or less) as an arrested gastrula and then cytolizes. This long period of blocked development gives one an opportunity to study the hybrid tissue in a variety of embryological and biochemical ways.

If the competence of the *pipiens* ♀ × *sylvatica* ♂ gastrula ectoderm is tested by transplantation to normal hosts, it is found that the hybrid tissue is capable of doing more than it does when left in place. Its competence is, however, considerably less than that of normal gastrula ectoderm (Moore, 1947b). Tests of inductive ability of the hybrid dorsal lip gives similar results. It does induce more than if left *in situ*, but is less potent than a normal dorsal lip (Moore, 1948). Thus, in two measurable ways, the developmental capabilities of the hybrid tissue are greatly reduced. (Brachet (1945) found what seems to be a more normal capacity for induction in the dorsal lip of *Rana esculenta* ♀ × *Rana fusca* ♂ hybrids.)

It must be kept in mind that the foreign sperm in this hybrid combination is acting as a "poison." Without it the *pipiens* egg cytoplasm plus *pipiens* maternal chromosomes can produce a gynogenetic haploid embryo that reaches a larval stage with all the main organ systems formed. As a result of the presence of *sylvatica* paternal chromosomes, the *pipiens* ovum and maternal chromosomes are unable to realize their full developmental potentialities. This situation could result from a type of competitive inhibition. The *sylvatica* chromosomes are acting in a genetically different cytoplasm and their activity might be using up limited substrates or result in the production of abnormal substances, which would act as competitive metabolites to the normal gene products, or even as poisons. An interpretation along these lines seems necessary when we remember the differences in length of survival between the different types of hybrids, and the fact that these hybrids cytolize when there is still an abundance of yolk in their cells. (It is of interest to note that androgenetic hybrids survive longer in the arrested state than do diploid hybrids (Briggs and King, 1952) in the *pipiens* × *catesbeiana* cross.)

This hypothesis is somewhat strengthened by studies on the androgenetic hybrid composed of an enucleated *pipiens* ovum fertilized by a *sylvatica* sperm. In contrast to the diploid hybrid, the androgenetic hybrid does not form a dorsal lip but remains as an arrested late blastula. If the competence of this presumptive ectoderm is tested, it is found to be zero. Pieces of tissue transplanted to normal embryos remain as undifferentiated groups of late blastula cells (Moore and Moore, 1953).

Barth and his associates have made a number of physiological and biochemical studies on these *pipiens* ♀ × *sylvatica* ♂ hybrids. Barth (1946) found that the rate of O_2 consumption in the hybrids and normals was the same throughout the cleavage and blastula stages. Both groups showed a steady rise until the beginning of gastrulation. After that the normals continued to show a steadily increasing rate of O_2 consumption, but the hybrids continued at the early gastrula rate. The R.Q. for hybrids and normals was the same up to the early gastrula stage. Thereafter the differentiating normals showed a slight drop and the arrested gastrulae a slight rise. Measurements of bound CO_2 in the hybrids and normals showed that both were the same during early stages. At the time the normals were at the end of gastrulation, however, differences between the two groups were apparent, the hybrids having less bound CO_2. Lactic acid production of the arrested gastrulae was lower than in normal gastrulae.

Sze (1953) compared the O_2 consumption of four regions of the animal hemisphere of normals and *pipiens* ♀ × *sylvatica* ♂ hybrids. The stage of development chosen was the early gastrula, when the hybrid rate had fallen below that of the normals. Sze found that respiration of the four regions of the hybrids was lower, by approximately the same amount, than the normals. "This indicates that the respiratory block in the hybrid embryo is not localized" in the morphological sense.

Jaeger (1945) found that the decrease of glycogen in the chorda-mesoderm, which occurs during invagination, is not observed in the chorda-mesoderm of the *pipiens* ♀ × sylvatica ♂ hybrids. The amount of invagination in the hybrids is, of course, slight. It was also found that the decrease did not occur in explanted normal chorda-mesoderm. The decrease is associated with the process of invagination, and so does not occur in the hybrids or in normal tissue that does not invaginate.

Barth and Jaeger (1947) have compared phosphorylation in normal embryos and in the *pipiens* ♀ × *sylvatica* ♂ hybrid. The two types of embryos have the same amounts of adenosinetriphosphate and inorganic phosphate at the early gastrula stage. The hybrids show a greater than normal anaerobic increase in phosphate due, possibly, to the breakdown of some phosphate ester.

Gregg (1948) has studied carbohydrate metabolism in these hybrids. Normal embryos show a nearly constant amount of glycogen up to gastrulation. After this there is a rapid decrease and by stage 20 they have used 44% of their glycogen. The hybrid is probably identical with the normals before gastrulation (there is a suggestion of an earlier than normal utilization of glycogen in the hybrid) and thereafter a slight decline. By the time the normals have reached stage 20, the arrested gastrulae have used only 16% of their glycogen. Gregg reaches the conclusion that "it is almost certain that one of the effects of the *sylvatica* sperm on a *pipiens* egg is the partial blockage of at least one step in the glycolytic chain. But this step might be one involving *both* glycolysis and hydrogen-transport, for instance, the diphosphopyridine nucleotide-catalyzed oxidation of diphosphoglyceraldehyde."

Mezger-Freed (1953) has studied phosphoprotein phosphatase activity in the *pipiens* ♀ × *sylvatica* ♂ hybrids and in normal embryos and concluded that there were no differences between the two for stages 7, 8, 9, and 10. Thereafter, the arrested hybrids show a decrease in activity. The normals also show a decrease in postgastrula stages. A comparison of enzyme activity in various regions of the hybrid and normal gastrula showed slight differences between the two.

Barth and Barth (1954) have summarized this work on hybrids and point out that the biochemical basis of the block to development is not understood. "As far as the problem of relating respiratory metabolism with development goes, we are not in a position as yet to decide whether the block to respiratory metabolism precedes the block to development, or whether development is blocked and as a consequence no further changes in respiratory metabolism occur."

The *Rana pipiens* ♀ × *Rana clamitans* ♂ hybrid is also arrested by the beginning of gastrulation. It differs from the pipiens ♀ × *sylvatica* ♂ hybrid in surviving only a short time after differentiation ceases, cytolysis beginning when the controls are neurulae. Healy (1952) has found that these hybrids do not show a gastrula arrest in rate of O_2 consumption, as in *pipiens* ♀ × *sylvatica* ♂, but the rate continues to rise normally even though development has stopped.

Brachet (1954) has made biochemical studies, especially on nucleic acid metabolism, of the *Rana esculenta* ♀ × *Rana fusca* ♂ and *Bufo vulgaris* ♀ × *Rana fusca* ♂ hybrids. The first cross develops to gastrulation and stops, the second to the late blastula stage. He made numerous and interesting observations but concludes, with Barth and Barth, that it is not possible to explain the developmental block in hybrids in biochemical terms. In general, he found that the hybrids parallel the normals, as long as the former are developing, in O_2 consumption and RNA synthesis. He suggests that the block in development is due to some lack of directed metabolism in the hybrid, associated perhaps with abnormal permeability, defective RNA synthesis, and respiratory metabolism. Brachet's 1947, 1949, and 1952 reviews should be consulted for discussion of protein and nuclear protein synthesis in development.

For the possibility of DNA having a direct effect on embryos, see Mazia (1949) and Thomas *et al.* (1952).

These data on the biochemistry of the arrested hybrid gastrulae support the belief that the ova are determined, as a result of gene action during oögenesis, for development at least to the late blastula and possibly to the early gastrula stage. We have seen before that this is so for morphology and rate of development. The data just presented indicate that it is true for all the physiological and chemical processes studied.

It seems likely that each hybrid cross will have its own biochemical peculiarities. If this is so, they may have an importance in unravelling the chemistry of development similar to that which the many metabolic poisons have had for cellular biochemistry.

3. *The Haploid Syndrome*

The failure of haploids to reach the adult stage is an unexplained phenomenon. The behavior of androgenetic and gynogenetic haploids is similar. Both reach an early larval stage and show a characteristic set of abnormalities, which are known as the haploid syndrome.

Some have held that death is caused by recessive lethal genes that are effective in the haploids, but would be masked by normal alleles in diploids. There is no doubt that recessive lethal genes would result in the death of any haploids possessing them but this can account for only a portion of the mortality.

The arguments against this concept of haploid mortality being caused solely or mainly by lethal genes can be developed as follows:

(1) There is variability in the type of defects and the time of death of the haploids but, considering the life cycle as a whole, this variability is slight.

(2) Thus, if lethal genes were involved, they would have to have their effects at nearly the same time and in nearly the same way.

(3) The frequency of these lethal genes in the population would have to be such that every gamete would possess at least one of them. This is a necessary deduction since no haploid Salientian has ever reached the adult stage.

(4) If lethal genes were this frequent, we might expect an appreciable number of diploid individuals to be homozygous for them. Presumably, these would show the haploid syndrome in spite of their chromosome number.

(5) This is not the case. Frog embryos from natural spawnings or obtained under optimum laboratory conditions show 99–100% normal development. The few that are defective do not exhibit the haploid syndrome.

(6) It must also be remembered that haploids of many different species and genera show nearly the same abnormalities and time of death. It seems unlikely that similar lethal genes would have appeared in all of them.

(7) In embryos that are mosaics of haploid and diploid (or triploid) cells, the haploid cells can differentiate and form adult organs.

One cause for the failure of haploids is to be sought in some relation between the amount of nuclear and cytoplasmic material. An experiment of Briggs (1949) is especially noteworthy in this respect. He observed that the ova in a female *Rana pipiens* were highly variable in size. The largest ova were of a size normal for the species but the smallest ones were approximately half this volume. Androgenetic haploids were made using both large and small ova. In addition, large and small diploid controls were studied. Both types of diploids were normal in their development and differed only in size. The large haploids developed into the usual abnormal embryos and were dead by 18 days. They were not observed to feed. Many of the small haploids were much more normal, were able to feed, and survived as long as 9 months.

In an earlier paper Briggs (1946) showed that the enzyme inhibitor, hexenolactone, had a greater effect on haploids than on diploids.

These results can be understood in terms of gene action. It is assumed that a certain concentration of gene products is necessary to control the development of the amount of material normally present in the ovum. A haploid set of chromosomes does not produce enough of the required gene products but the diploid does. The improved development of the small haploids is due to a smaller than normal amount of cytoplasm that the smaller than normal amount of gene products has to control. The hexenolactone results can be explained along similar lines. A reduction in enzyme activity in the diploids, which presumably produce more than enough enzymes through gene action, is less drastic than a reduction of the already deficient amount in the haploids.

Whatever these necessary gene products are they are capable of passing from cell to cell. Muto (1951) has reported chromosome-number mosaics in *Bufo*. A mosaic that was triploid on one side and haploid on the other reached the adult stage. The haploid tissues did not die and in the presence of the triploid cells were able to form normal adult structures. There are similar observations by others.

Moore and Moore (1953) have reported some incomplete experiments suggesting a lower than normal competence of haploid tissue in *Rana pipiens*.

A more complete discussion of the haploid syndrome will be found in Porter (1939), Briggs (1949), and A. B. C. Moore (1950).

V. EVOLUTIONARY PROBLEMS

1. *Hybridization and Taxonomic Relationships*

It has been realized for many years that there is no simple relation between the ability of two species to form hybrids and their genetic, or more properly their systematic, relationships. There are enough instances where the reciprocal hybrids differ to make us use with care the data of hybridization. It is possible, however, to make these statements for Salientian species:

(1) No two species believed to be remotely related produce hybrids that reach metamorphosis.

(2) If two species are believed to be closely related, they may or may not produce hybrids that reach metamorphosis.

(3) If two species are capable of producing hybrids that reach metamorphosis, there is always other evidence indicating that they are closely related.

Perhaps the greatest difficulty in correlating taxonomic relationships and ability to cross, stems from our inability to express relationships in a precise manner. The best we can do at present is accept the subjective judgment of a "good" taxonomist, realizing all the while that it is just as difficult to recognize a good taxonomist as it is to recognize good taxonomy.

When remotely related species are crossed, a frequent result is gynogenetic embryos. This is a common occurrence when the forms belong to different genera or families. This is not always the case, however. Blair (1941b) crossed *Hyla crucifer* and *Pseudacris triseriata* and found that a few hybrids reached the frog stage. There is some evidence of hybridization in nature between these two species. At first sight these results may seem to be at considerable variance with taxonomy. In this case, however, there is reason to question the current taxonomy. Some authorities felt the two species were cogeneric even before Blair's work was performed.

A paradoxical situation is encountered in crosses between geographical populations of *Rana pipiens* and *Rana palustris*. It has been mentioned before that individuals of *Rana pipiens* from certain well separated localities, such as Vermont and Florida, show considerable hybrid inviability when crossed. These localities are connected with a continuous interbreeding population of *pipiens* so there is no doubt that the Florida and Vermont individuals belong to the same genetic species. In spite of the difficulty in producing hybrids between Vermont and Florida *pipiens*, both will form normal hybrids when crossed with *Rana palustris*. Thus, in respect to the genetics of the early embryos, the intraspecific differences are greater than the interspecific ones. These relationships demonstrate the difficulty in correlating taxonomy and hybridization, and raise interesting questions regarding the selective forces that are responsible for these differences.

In the case of American species, we have interesting group differences between species of the genus Rana and of the genus Bufo. The Ranas appear to be well differentiated species in the taxonomic sense, and the only forms that give normal hybrids that reach the adult stage are in the *pipiens-palustris-areolata-capito* group. In most crosses the hybrids fail at the gastrula stage. The Bufos, on the other hand, are a puzzling group. Differences between the various forms are slight and there is much evidence of intergradation. Their taxonomy is confused, the different forms being species or subspecies, depending on the authority. Correlated with the fact that these are poorly differentiated forms in the taxonomic sense, we find that a high proportion of the crosses give hybrids that reach the adult stage.

There are many reports of crossing of species in nature and the occurrence of individuals believed to be hybrids (Power, 1926; Pickens, 1927; Bragg, 1939; Blair, 1941a,b; Neill, 1949; Orton, 1951; Storm, 1952).

2. *Geographic Races and Hybridization*

It is believed by many that the most common method for the origin of two or more species from a single species is by geographic speciation. Simply stated, the process is as follows. The starting point is a single species occupying an ecologically diverse area. Through the course of time the local populations evolve genotypes that adapt themselves better to their peculiar local environments. This genetic divergence eventually reaches the point where the local populations are different species.

The bulk of the evidence for geographic speciation is morphological and consists of a spectrum of case histories beginning with a morphologically uniform population, passing through species that show progressively greater intraspecific geographic variation, and ending with allopatric species. In these cases, it is assumed that morphological diversity and genetic diversity are developing in a parallel manner. Such an assumption is undoubtedly valid but it is necessary to have the actual genetic data in some instances, especially if we regard species as genetic rather than morphological phenomena.

Perhaps the most interesting stage in this process of geographic speciation is that of a population which appears to be near the borderline between geographic races and full species. There are three such cases in Salientia. The first seems to be as close to the race-species borderline as it is possible to imagine, and the second and third represent early stages in the divergence of closely related species.

Rana pipiens is the first example and some of the data have been mentioned before. If one considered only the data on crosses between individuals of the southeastern United States (or the lowlands of northeastern Mexico) with individuals from the northern tier of states, the conclusion would be that two different species are involved. If, on the other hand, one considers the data on crosses between individuals from more closely situated localities, it is clear that a single species is involved. On one set of data *Rana pipiens* is a single species, on another, two. The parallel data on adaptation suggests that natural selection has chanelled the evolution of the southern populations into a warm adapted race and the northern ones into a cold adapted race. There is even some evidence that these differences are the basis of the defects in the development of the hybrids.

Other data show that a different evolutionary course has been taken by this species in the western United States and the highlands of tropical America. Crosses between Vermont and Colorado, and Vermont and highland Costa Rica give normal embryos. It is probable that the *Rana pipiens* occupying the region beginning with the northern United States and Canada, curving through the Rocky Mountains, and following the highlands to Panama, has not evolved in such a way as to give local population cross inviability.

In *Rana pipiens* of eastern America, the northern and southern individuals behave as though they are different species when crossed. They are however connected by completely intergrading local populations, hence they should be regarded a single species. Two examples, both in Australian frogs, may be thought of as exemplifying the next step in specification (Moore, 1954). In these the terminal members of the distribution behave as different species and there are no connecting populations. The stage of allopatric species has been reached. That it has just been reached is shown by the fact that the terminally distributed populations are so much alike that taxonomists have considered them to be the same species.

Hyla aurea has a disjunct distribution in Australia. Part of the population occurs in the southeast part of the continent and the other part in the southwest. The south-central part of the continent is unsuitable for this form due to aridity. During the Pleistocene there was sufficient moisture for *Hyla aurea* to have a continuous transcontinental distribution. The present day eastern and western frogs are listed as the same species by herpetologists since no morphological differences of the "species-level" magnitude separate them. Cross fertilization experiments, however, show that the two populations are different genetic species. *Crinia signifera* shows the same phenomenon.

In these three cases we have emphasized the development of genetic differences that lead to hybrid inviability. It must be pointed out that the species level of divergence can be reached with no hybrid inviability at any stage of the divergence. For example, *Rana pipiens* and *Rana palustris* are full species and no herpetologist regards them as anything else. Their hybrids are entirely normal so there is no reason to suppose that hybrid inviability was ever a concomitant of their divergence.

In fact, it is probable that there is no necessary relation, in allopatric populations, between hybrid inviability and evolutionary divergence at the lowest levels. When two populations are evolving in different regions, the thing of primary evolutionary importance is the adaptation of each to its own environment. If the two happen to adapt in different ways then they are said to diverge. The genetic basis of this adaptation may or may not be of a sort that leads to hybrid inviability, if the two are crossed. This divergence need not involve the development of different external characters, although if it does not, the chances of detecting it are reduced. There is no reason why adaptation should involve the development of differences that can be used conveniently by taxonomists.

We might conclude that adaptation, the development of hybrid inviability, and the development of "taxonomic characters," will be progressing at different rates in two populations undergoing evolutionary divergence.

VI. REFERENCES

Ahrenfeldt, R. H., 1952. Pairing of male *Bufo bufo* with a female *Rana temporaria* in captivity followed by infertile spawning. *Brit. J. Herpetol.* **1**, 129–131.

Allison, J. E., 1953. Growth of transplanted tissues derived from normal and overripe eggs. Dissertation, see *Biol. Abstr.* 1954, **28**, No. 6152.

Baker, A. S., 1951. A study of the expression of the burnsi gene in adult *Rana pipiens*. *J. Exptl. Zool.* **116**, 191–229.

Baltzer, F., 1940. Über erbliche letale Entwicklung und Austauschbarkeit artverschiedener Kerne bei Bastarden. *Naturwissenschaften* **12**, 177–187, 196–206.

Baltzer, F., 1950. Chimaren und Merogone bei Amphibien. *Rev. suisse zool.* **57**, Suppl. 1, 93–114.

Baltzer, F., 1952. The behavior of nuclei and cytoplasm in Amphibian interspecific crosses. *Symposia Soc. Exptl. Biol.* **6**, 230–242.

Barth, L. G., 1946. Studies on the metabolism of development. *J. Exptl. Zool.* **103**, 463–486.

Barth, L. G., and Barth, L. J., 1954. "The Energetics of Development." Columbia Univ. Press, New York.

Barth, L. G., and Jaeger, L., 1947. Phosphorylation in the frog's egg. *Physiol. Zool.* **20**, 133–146.

Biesinger, D. I., and Miller, D. F., 1952. Seasonal and hormone induced changes in the testes of *Rana pipiens*. *Ohio J. Sci.* **52**, 169–175.

Blair, A. P., 1941a. Variation, isolating mechanisms, and hybridization in certain toads. *Genetics* **26**, 398–417.

Blair, A. P., 1941b. Isolating mechanisms in tree frogs. *Proc. Natl. Acad. Sci. U.S.* **27**, 14–17.

Blair, A. P., 1946. Description of a six-year old hybrid toad. *Am. Museum Novitates* **1327**, 1–3.

Blair, A. P., 1947. Field observations on Spadefoot toad. *Copeia* **1947**, 67.

Blair, A. P., 1950. Note on Oklahoma microhylid frogs. *Copeia* **1950**, 152.

Brachet, J., 1944. Acides nucléiques et morphogénese au cour de la parthénogénèse, la polyspermie et l'hybridation chez les anoures. *Ann. soc. roy. zool. Belg.* **75**, 49–74.

Brachet, J., 1947. Biochemical and physiological interrelations between nucleus and cytoplasm during early development. *Growth* **11**, 309–324.

Brachet, J., 1949. Le rôle des nucleoprotéides dans la fécondation, la parthénogénese et le développement embryonnaire chez les Amphibiens. *Union intern. sci. biol.* **B3**, 54–70.

Brachet, J., 1952. The role of the nucleus and the cytoplasm in synthesis and morphogenesis. *Symposia Soc. Exptl. Biol.* **6**, 173–200.

Brachet, J., 1954. Constitution anormale du noyan et metabolisme de l'embryon chez les Batraciens. *Arch. biol. Liége* **65**, 1–71.

Bragg, A. N., 1939. Possible hybridization between *Bufo cognatus* and *B. w. woodhousei*. *Copeia* **1939**, 173.

Briggs, R. W., 1941. The development of abnormal growths in *Rana pipiens* embryos following delayed fertilization. *Anat. Record* **81**, 121–135.

Briggs, R. W., 1946. Effects of the growth inhibitor, hexenolactone, on frog embryos. I. Effects on diploid embryos. II. Differential effects on haploid and diploid embryos. *Growth* **10**, 45–73.

Briggs, R. W., 1947. The experimental production and development of triploid frog embryos. *J. Exptl. Zool.* **106**, 237–266.

Briggs, R. W., 1949. The influence of egg volume on the development of haploid and diploid embryos of the frog. *Rana pipiens*. *J. Exptl. Zool.* **111**, 255–294.

Briggs, R. W., 1952. An analysis of the inactivation of the frog sperm nucleus by toluidine blue. *J. Gen. Physiol.* **35**, 761–780.

Briggs, R. W., and Berrill, N. J., 1941. Transplantation experiments with an extodermal growth of frog embryos. *Growth* **5**, 273–284.

Briggs, R. W., Green, E. U., and King, T. J., 1951. An investigation of the capacity for cleavage and differentiation in *Rana pipiens* eggs lacking "functional" chromosomes. *J. Exptl. Zool.* **116**, 455–500.

Briggs, R., and King, T. J., 1952. Transplantation of living nuclei from blastula cells into enucleated frogs' eggs. *Proc. Natl. Acad. Sci. U.S.* **38**, 455–463.

Briggs, R., and King, T. J., 1953. Factors affecting the transplantability of nuclei of frog embryonic cells. *J. Exptl. Zool.* **122**, 485–506.

Bushnell, R. J., Bushnell, E. P., and Parker, M. V., 1939. A chromosome study of five members of the family Hylidae. *J. Tenn. Acad. Sci.* **14**, 209–215.

Chen-Chao-hsi, 1940. Notes on a new hybrid toad (*Bufo raddei* ♀ × *Bufo asiaticus* ♂). *Chinese J. Exptl. Biol.* **1,** 335–338.

Cukierzys, J., 1937. Die Reptilien und Lurche der Umgebung von Trohe sowie Artbastarde von *Rana arvalis* ♀ (Niels) und *Rana fusca* ♂ (Rös) im Freien. *Trav. soc. sci. ef lettres Wilno* **11,** 343–352.

Drebinger, K., 1951. Kerngifte und Lichtstrahlung. Eine studie an Froschspermien zur wirkungsanalpse der Kerngifte. *Arch. Entwicklungsmech. Organ.* **145,** 174–204.

Dürken, B., 1938. Über die Keimdrüsen und die chromosomen der Artbastarde *Rana arvalis* Nils × *Rana fusca* Rös. *Z. indukt. Abstamm.-u. Vererbungsl.* **74,** 311–353.

Eakin, R. M., 1947. Determination and regulation of polarity in the retina of Hyla regilla. *Univ. Calif. Berkeley Publs. Zool.* **51,** 245–287.

Fankhauser, G., 1945. The effects of changes in chromosome number on Amphibian development. *Quart. Rev. Biol.* **20,** 20–78.

Fankhauser, G., 1952. Nucleo-cytoplasmic relations in amphibian development. *Intern. Rev. Cytol.* **1,** 165–193.

Fedorova, Z. F., 1951. Anomalies in the development of hybrids caused by a distant cross-breeding. *Compt. rend. acad. sci. U.R.S.S.* [n.s.] **79,** 903–906.

Gallien, L., 1953. L'Hétéroploidie expérimentale chez les amphibiens. *Ann. Biol.* Paris **29,** 5–22.

Gallien, L., and Houillon, C., 1951. Table chronologique du developpement chez *Discoglossus pictus. Bull. Biol. France et Belg.* **84,** 373–375.

Green, E., 1953. Regular occurrence of the haploid number of chromosomes in mesenchymal cells of the tail tip of *Rana pipiens* tadpoles. *Nature* **172,** 766–767.

Green, E. U., and Freed, J., 1954. DNA content of nuclei in tail mesenchyme of *Rana pipiens* tadpoles. *Anat. Record* **120,** 728.

Gregg, J. R., 1948. Carbohydrate metabolism of normal and of hybrid amphibian embryos. *J. Exptl. Zool.* **109,** 119–133.

Gregg, V. R., and Puckett, W. O., 1943. A corrosive sublimate fixing solution for yolk-laden amphibian eggs. *Stain Technol.* **18,** 179–180.

Guyénot, E., and Danon, M., 1953. Chromosomes et ovocytes des Batraciens. Etude cytologique et an microscope électronique. *Rev. suisse zool.* **60,** 1–130.

Harding, D., 1949. Effect of heparin on artificial activation in the frog egg. *Proc. Soc. Exptl. Biol. Med.* **71,** 14–15.

Healy, E. A., 1952. Studies on a hybrid frog embryo. Unpublished dissertation. Columbia University.

Henshaw, P. S., 1943. Peculiar growth lesions in frogs induced by irradiation of sperm cells with X-rays. *J. Natl. Cancer Inst.* **3,** 409–418.

Hertwig, G., and Hertwig, P., 1920. Triploid Froschlarven. *Arch. mikroskop. Anat. u. Entwicklungsmech.* **94,** 34–54.

Hertwig, P., 1936. Artbastarde bei Tieren. *Handbuch der Vererbungswiss.* Lief. 21 (II,B).

Hill, H. C., and Robinson, T. W., 1941. Induced ovulation in *Rana pipiens* II. *Trans. Illinois State Acad. Sci.* **34,** 221–222.

Holtfreter, J., 1943. A study of the mechanics of gastrulation. *J. Exptl. Zool.* **94,** 261–318.

Hsu, T. C., Hsiang, W., and Liu, T. T., 1949. Colchicine induction of polyploidy in the frog, *Rana plancyi. Science Record China* **2,** 320–322.

Humphrey, R. R., Briggs, R., and Fankhauser, G., 1950. Sex differentiation in triploid *Rana pipiens* larvae and the subsequent reversal of females to males. *J. Exptl. Zool.* **115,** 399–428.

Jaeger, L., 1945. Glycogen utilization by the Amphibian gastrula in relation to invagination and induction. *J. Cellular Comp. Physiol.* **25**, 97–120.

Kawamura, T., 1939a. Artificial parthenogenesis in the frog, I. Chromosome numbers and their relation to cleavage histories. *J. Sci. Hiroshima Univ. Ser. B Div. 1*, **6**, 115–218.

Kawamura, T., 1939b. Artificial parthenogenesis in the frog. II. The sex of parthenogenetic frogs. *J. Sci. Hiroshima Univ. Ser. B Div. 1*, **7**, 1–86.

Kawamura, T., 1939c. The occurrence of triploid parthenogenetic frogs. *Zool. Magazine* **51**, 629–632.

Kawamura, T., 1940. Artificial parthenogenesis in the frog. III. The development of the gonads in triploid frogs and tadpoles. *J. Sci. Hiroshima Univ. Ser. B Div. 1*, **8**, 119–164.

Kawamura, T., 1941. Triploid frogs developed from fertilized eggs. *Proc. Imp. Acad. Tokyo* **17**, 523–526.

Kawamura, T., 1949. Further observations on diploid and triploid parthenogenetic frogs of *Rana nigromaculata. J. Sci. Hiroshima Univ. Ser. B Div. 1*, **11**, 1–5.

Kawamura, T., 1950. Studies on hybridization in amphibians. II. Interspecific hybrids in red-colored frogs. *J. Sci. Hiroshima Univ. Ser. B Div. 1*, **11**, 61–70.

Kawamura, T., 1951. The offspring of triploid males of the frog, *Rana nigromaculata. J. Sci. Hiroshima Univ. Ser. B Div. 1*, **12**, 11–20.

Kawamura, T., 1952. Triploid hybrids of *Rana japonica* Günther ♀ × Rana temporania ornativentris Werner ♂. *J. Sci. Hiroshima Univ. Ser. B Div. 1*, **13**, 129–138.

Kawamura, T., and Miyada, S., 1951. Diploid-tetraploid mosaics in the frog, *Rana nigromaculata. J. Sci. Hiroshima Univ. Ser. B Div. 1*, **12**, 21–33.

Kawamura, T., and Moriwaki, T., 1953. On a tetraploid frog, *Rana limnocharis. J. Sci. Hiroshima Univ. Ser. B. Div. 1*, **14**, 117–123.

Kawamura, T., and Tokunaga, C., 1952. The sex of triploid frogs, *Rana japonica* Günther. *J. Sci. Hiroshima Univ. Ser. B Div. 1*, **13**, 121–128.

Kemp, N. E., 1953. Synthesis of yolk in oocytes of *Rana pipiens* after induced ovulation. *J. Morphol.* **92**, 487–511.

Keppel, D. M., and Dawson, A. B., 1939. Effects of colchicine on the cleavage of the frog's egg (*Rana pipiens*). *Biol. Bull.* **76**, 153–161.

King, T. J., and Briggs, R., 1953. The transplantation of living nuclei from late gastrulae into enucleated eggs (*Rana pipiens*). *Anat. Record* **117**, 556.

King, T. J., and Briggs, R., 1954a. Transplantation of living nuclei of late gastrulae into enucleated eggs of *Rana pipiens. J. Embryol. Exptl. Morphol.* **2**, 73–80.

King, T. J., and Briggs, R., 1954b. Nuclear changes in differentiating endoderm cells as revealed by nuclear transplantation. *Anat. Record* **120**, 723–724.

Kopsch, F., 1952. "Die entwicklung des braunen Grasfrosches *Rana fusca* Roesel." Thieme, Stuttgart.

Lantz, L. A., 1947. Note (Appendix to article by Bruce and Parkes "Observations on Discoglossus pictus Orrh."). *Proc. Roy. Soc. (London)* **B134**, 52–56.

Lüscher, M., 1946. Die Entstehung polyploider Zellen durch Colchinbehandlung im Schwantz der Xenopus-Larve. *Arch. Julius Klaus-Stift. Vererbungsforch. Sozialanthropol. u. Rassenhyg.* **21**, 303–305.

Mandeville, L. C., and Spurway, H., 1949. The development of hybrids between *Rana esculenta* Linn. and *Rana ridibunda* pallas. *Brit. J. Herpetol.* **1**, 39–50.

Mazia, D., 1949. Desoxyribonucleic acid and desoxyribonuclease in development. *Growth* **13**, Suppl. 5–31.

Mezger-Freed, L., 1953. Phosphoprotein phosphatase activity in normal, haploid, and hybrid Amphibian development. *J. Cellular Comp. Physiol.* **41**, 493–517.

Montalenti, G., 1938a. L'ibridazione interspecifica degli Anfibi anuri (Suppl. Archivo Zoologico Italiano). *Attualità Zool.* **4**, 157–213.

Montalenti, G., 1938b. Il fenotipo degli ibridi di prima generazione fra *Bufo vulgaris* Laur. ♀ e *Bufo viridis* Laur ♂ *Arch. Zool. Torino* **26**, 1–39.

Moore, A. B. C., 1950. The development of reciprocal androgenetic frog hybrids. *Biol. Bull.* **99**, 88–111.

Moore, B. C., and Ryan, E. W., 1940. Chromosomes of frog eggs and embryos stained by the Feulgen method to avoid excessive staining of yolk granules. *Anat. Record* **78**, Suppl. 122.

Moore, J. A., 1941a. Developmental rate of hybrid frogs. *J. Exptl. Zool.* **86**, 405–422.

Moore, J. A., 1941b. Developmental rate of hybrids between *Rana pipiens* and *Rana sphenocephala*. *Proc. Soc. Exptl. Biol. Med.* **47**, 207–210.

Moore, J. A., 1942. An embryological and genetical study of *Rana burnsi* Weed. *Genetics* **27**, 408–416.

Moore, J. A., 1943. Corresponding genes in spotted frogs. *J. Heredity* **34**, 2–7.

Moore, J. A., 1944. Geographic variation in *Rana pipiens* Schreber of eastern North America. *Bull. Am. Museum Nat. Hist.* **82**, 345–370.

Moore, J. A., 1946a. Studies in the development of frog hybrids. I. Embryonic development in the cross *Rana pipiens* ♀ × *Rana sylvatica* ♂. *J. Exptl. Zool.* **101**, 173–220.

Moore, J. A., 1946b. Incipient intraspecific isolating mechanisms in *Rana pipiens*. *Genetics* **31**, 304–326.

Moore, J. A., 1946c. Hybridization between *Rana palustris* and different geographical forms of *Rana pipiens*. *Proc. Natl. Acad. Sci. U.S.* **32**, 209–212.

Moore, J. A., 1947a. Hybridization between *Rana pipiens* from Vermont and eastern Mexico. *Proc. Natl. Acad. Sci. U.S.* **33**, 72–75.

Moore, J. A., 1947b. Studies in the development of frog hybrids. II. Competence of the gastrula ectoderm of *Rana pipiens* ♀ × *Rana sylvatica* ♂ hybrids. *J. Exptl. Zool.* **105**, 349–370.

Moore, J. A., 1948. Studies in the development of frog hybrids. III. Inductive ability of the dorsal lip region of *Rana pipiens* ♀ × *Rana sylvatica* ♂ hybrids. *J. Exptl. Zool.* **108**, 127–154.

Moore, J. A., 1949a. Patterns of evolution in the genus Rana. *in* "Genetics, Paleontology, and Evolution" (G. L. Jepsen, G. G. Simpson, and E. Mayr, eds.). Princeton Univ. Press, New Jersey.

Moore, J. A., 1949b. Geographic variation of adaptive characters in *Rana pipiens* Schreber. *Evolution* **3**, 1–24.

Moore, J. A., 1950. Further studies on *Rana pipiens* racial hybrids. *Am. Naturalist* **84**, 247–254.

Moore, J. A., 1951. Hybridization and embryonic temperature adaptation studies of *Rana temporaria* and *Rana sylvatica*. *Proc. Natl. Acad. Sci. U.S.* **37**, 862–866.

Moore, J. A., 1954. Geographic and genetic isolation in Australian amphibia. *Am. Naturalist* **88**, 65–74.

Moore, J. A., and Moore, B. C., 1953. Studies in the development of frog hybrids. IV. Competence of gastrula ectoderm in androgenetic hybrids. *Biol. Bull.* **104**, 68–74.

Moriwaki, T., 1953. The inheritance of the dorso-median stripe in *Rana limnocharis* Wiegmann. *J. Sci. Hiroshima Univ. Ser. B Div. 1*, **14**, 159–164.

180 JOHN A. MOORE

Moriya, K., 1951. On isolating mechanisms between the two subspecies of the pond frog, *Rana nigromaculata*. *J. Sci. Hiroshima Univ. Ser. B Div. 1*, **12**, 47–56.

Moriya, K., 1952. Genetical studies of the pond frog, *Rana nigromaculata*. I. Two types of *Rana nigromaculata* nigromaculata found in Tokata district. *J. Sci. Hiroshima Univ. Ser. B Div. 1*, **13**, 189–197.

Muto, Y., 1951. Haploid-triploid mosaic toads induced by heat treatment of the unfertilized eggs. *J. Sci. Hiroshima Univ. Ser. B Div. 1*, **12**, 39–46.

Muto, Y., 1952. Production of triploid toads, *Bufo vulgaris formosus* (Boulenger), by a temperature-shock on fertilized eggs. *J. Sci. Hiroshima Univ. Ser. B Div. 1*, **13**, 163–171.

Nadamitsu, S., 1953. Ovulation *in vitro* in several species of amphibians. *J. Sci. Hiroshima Univ. Ser. B Div. 1*, **14**, 151–157.

Neill, W. T., 1949. Hybrid toads in Georgia. *Herpetologica* **5**, 30–32.

Orton, G. L., 1951. An example of interspecific mating in toads. *Copeia* **1951**, 78.

Parmenter, C. L., 1933. Haploid, diploid, triploid, and tetraploid chromosome numbers, and their origin in parthenogenetically developed larvae and frogs of *Rana pipiens* and *R. palustris*. *J. Exptl. Zool.* **66**, 409–453.

Parmenter, C. L., 1940. Chromosome numbers in *Rana fusca* parthenogenetically developed from eggs with known polar body and cleavage histories. *J. Morphol.* **66**, 241–260.

Parmenter, C. L., 1952. Diploid virgin frog eggs; a possible origin of diploid parthenogenetically developed frog larvae without delay in cleavage and of triploid larvae developed from fertilized eggs. *J. Morphol.* **90**, 243–262.

Perri, T., 1946. Sull' ibridazione tra *"Bufo viridis"* e *"Bufo vulgaris,"* Esperienze di trapianto tra ibridi e normali. *Atti accad. nazl. Lincei, rend. Classe sci. fis. mat. e nat.* **1**, 995–1000.

Perri, T., 1949. Sull' ibridazione tra *"Bufo viridis"* e *"Bufo vulgaris."* *Atti accad. nazl. Lincei, rend. Classe Sci. fis. mat. e nat.* **6**, 255–259.

Pickens, A. L., 1927. Intermediate between *Bufo fowleri* and *B. americanus*. *Copeia* No. **162**, 25–26.

Pollister, A. W., and Moore, J. A., 1937. Tables for the normal development of *Rana sylvatica*. *Anat. Record* **68**, 489–496.

Ponse, R., 1941. La proportion sexuelle dans la descendance issue des oeufs produits par l'organe de Bidder de Crapauds femelles. *Rev. suisse zool.* **48**, 541–544.

Porter, K. R., 1939. Androgenetic development of the egg of *Rana pipiens*. *Biol. Bull.* **77**, 233–257.

Porter, K. R., 1941a. Diploid and androgenetic haploid hybridization between two forms of *Rana pipiens* Schreber. *Biol. Bull.* **80**, 238–264.

Porter, K. R., 1941b. Developmental variations resulting from the androgenetic hybridization of four forms of *Rana pipiens*. *Science* **93**, 439.

Porter, K. R., 1942. Developmental variation resulting from various associations of frog cytoplasms and nuclei. *Trans. N. Y. Acad. Sci.* **4**, 213–217.

Power, J. H., 1926. Note on the occurrence of hybrid anura at Lobatsi, Bechuanaland Protectorate. *Proc. Zool. Soc. London*, pp. 777–778.

Robinson, T. W., and Hill, H. C., 1940. Induced ovulation in *Rana pipiens*. *Trans. Illinois State Acad. Sci.* **33**, 223–224.

Rollason, G. S., 1949. X-radiation of eggs of *Rana pipiens* at various maturation stages. *Biol. Bull.* **97**, 169–186.

Rostand, J., 1943. Essai d'inoculation de noyaux embryonnaires dans l'oeuf vierge de grenouille. *Rev. Sci.* **81**, 454–456.

Rostand, J., 1951a. Sur un cas de gynogenèse, spontané ou provoquée chez *Bufo bufo*. *Compt. rend. soc. biol.* **145**, 341–342.

Rostand, J., 1951b. Parthénogénese expérimentale chez le Xenope (*Xenopus laevis*). *Compt. rend. soc. biol.* **145**, 1453–1454.

Rugh, R., 1934. Induced ovulation and artificial fertilization in the frog. *Biol. Bull.* **66**, 22–29.

Rugh, R., 1935a. Pituitary-induced sexual reactions in the Anura. *Biol. Bull.* **68**, 74–81.

Rugh, R., 1935b. Ovulation in the frog. I. Pituitary relations in induced ovulation. II. Follicular rupture to fertilization. *J. Exptl. Zool.* **71**, 149–193.

Rugh, R., 1937. A quantitative analysis of the pituitary-ovulation relation in the frog (*Rana pipiens*). *Physiol. Zool.* **10**, 84–100.

Rugh, R., 1939. Developmental effects resulting from exposure to X-rays. I. Effect on the embryo of irradiation of frog sperm. *Proc. Am. Phil. Soc.* **81**, 447–471.

Rugh, R., 1948. Experimental embryology. "A Manual of Techniques and Procedures." Burgess Publishing, Minneapolis.

Rugh, R., 1954. The effect of ionizing radiations on amphibian development. *J. Cellular Comp. Physiol.* **43**, Suppl. 1, 39–76.

Rugh, R., and Exner, F., 1940. Developmental effects resulting from exposure to X-rays. II. Development of leopard frog eggs activated by bullfrog sperm. *Proc. Am. Phil. Soc.* **83**, 607–619.

Rugh, R., and Railey, C., 1948. The polar bodies of the frog, *Rana pipiens*. *J. Exptl. Zool.* **108**, 471–483.

Ryan, F. W., and Grant, R., 1940. The stimulus for maturation and for ovulation of the frog's egg. *Physiol. Zool.* **13**, 383–390.

Samartino, G. T., and Rugh, R., 1945. Frog ovulation *in vitro*. *J. Exptl. Zool.* **98**, 153–159.

Sambuichi, H., 1952. Androgenetic hybrids between two subspecies of the pond frog, *Rana nigromaculata*. *J. Sci. Hiroshima Univ. Ser. B Div. 1*, **13**, 185–188.

Sato, M., 1952. The sex of triploid frogs, *Rana limnocharis*. *J. Sci. Hiroshima Univ. Ser. B Div. 1*, **13**, 155–161.

Schmidt, K. P., 1953. A check list of North American amphibians and reptiles. American Society of Ichthyologists and Herpetologists.

Shaver, J. R., 1949. The role of cytoplasmic granules in artificial parthenogenesis. *J. Cyto-embryol. Belgo-néerland. Gand.*, pp. 61–66.

Shaver, J. R., 1953. Studies on the initiation of cleavage in the frog egg. *J. Exptl. Zool.* **122**, 169–192.

Shumway, W., 1940. Stages in the normal development of *Rana pipiens*. I. External form. *Anat. Record* **78**, 139–147.

Shumway, W., 1942. Stages in the normal development of *Rana pipiens*. II. Identification of the stages from sectioned material. *Anat. Record* **83**, 309–315.

Slater, D. W., and Dornfeld, E. J., 1939. A triple stain for amphibian embryos. *Stain Technol.* **14**, 103–104.

Spurway, H., 1953. Genetics of specific and subspecific differences in European Newts, *Symposia Soc. Exptl. Biol.* **7**, 200–237.

Storm, R., 1952. Interspecific mating behavior in *Rana aurora* and *Rana catesbeiana*. *Herpetologica* **8**, 108.

Sze, L. C., 1953. Respiration of the parts of the hybrid gastrula *Rana pipiens* × *R. sylvatica*. *Science* **117**, 479–480.

Taylor, A. C., and Kollros, J. J., 1946. Stages in the normal development of *Rana pipiens* larvae. *Anat. Record* **94**, 7–24.

Tchou-Su, 1948a. Etudes cytologique et Experimentale sur la maturation artificielle osmotique *in vitro* sur l'oeuf d'anoures. *Acta zool. Taiwan.* **1** (1), 1–66.

Tchou-Su, 1948b. Maturation imparfaite *in vitro* sur les oeufs intra-ovariens de Crapaud (*Bufo bufo asiaticus*). *Science Record China* **2**, 206–209.

Tchou-Su, 1948c. Maturation parfaite *in vitro* sur l'oeuf intraovarien de Crapaud (*Bufo bufo asiaticus*). *Science Record China* **2**, 209–211.

Tchou-Su, 1950. Etude cytologique de la parthénogénèse experimentale osmotique sur l'oeuf intra-ovarien maturé *in vitro* chez le Crapaud (*Bufo bufo asiaticus*). *Chinese J. Exptl. Biol.* **3** (1), 1–40.

Tchou-Su, and Chen-Chao Hsi, 1942. Fertilization of artificially ovulated premature eggs of Bufo. *Science Record China* **1**, 203–208.

Thomas, R., Steinert, M., Gothié, S., and Brachet, J., 1952. Le spécificite biologique des acides désoxyribonucleiques de diverses espéces animales. *Experientia* **8**, 18.

Ting, H. P., 1939. A study of the reciprocal hybrids of two species of frogs, *Rana nigromaculata* and *Rana plancyi*. *Peking Nat. Hist. Bull.* **13**, 181–190.

Ting, H. P., 1948. A study of the two-year old hybrids of *Rana nigromaculata* and *Rana plancyi* with notes on a backcross experiment. *Lingnan Sci. J.* **22**, 115–119.

Ting, H. P., 1950. An aceto-carmine squash technique for amphibian chromosomes. *Stain Technol.* **25**, 127–128.

Ting, H. P., 1951. Diploid, androgenetic, and gynogenetic haploid development in anuran hybridization. *J. Exptl. Zool.* **116**, 21–57.

Ting, H. P., and Price, J. W., 1950. Spade-foot toad sperm as an activating agent in producing gynogenetic haploid embryos from Rana and Pseudacris eggs. *Science* **112**, 595–596.

Tokunaga, C., 1949. Albino frogs produced by artificial parthenogenesis. *J. Heredity* **40**, 279–281.

Volpe, E. P., 1952. Physiological evidence for natural hybridization of *Bufo americanus* and *Bufo fowleri*. *Evolution* **6**, 393–406.

Volpe, E. P., 1954. Hybrid inviability between *Rana pipiens* from Wisconsin and Mexico. *Tulane Studies Zool.* **1**, 111–123.

Waring, H., Landgrebe, F. W., and Neill, R. M., 1941. Ovulation and oviposition in Anura. *J. Exptl. Biol.* **18**, 11–25.

Weisz, P., 1945. The normal stages in the development of the South African clawed toad, *Xenopus laevis*. *Anat. Record* **93**, 161–169.

Wickbom, T., 1945. Cytological studies on dipnoi, urodela, anura, and emys. *Hereditas* **31**, 241–246.

Wickbom, T., 1949a. Further cytological studies on anura and urodela. *Hereditas* **35**, 33–48.

Wickbom, T., 1949b. A new list of chromosome numbers in anura. *Hereditas* **35**, 242–245.

Witschi, E., 1952. Overripeness of the egg as a cause of twinning and tetratogenesis: A review. *Cancer Research* **12**, 763–786.

Wittek, M., 1952. La vitellogénèse chez les Amphibiens. *Arch. Biol. Liége* **63**, 133–197.

Wright, P. A., 1950. Time relationships in frog ovulation. *J. Exptl. Zool.* **114**, 465–474.

Zimmerman, L., and Rugh, R., 1941. Effect of age on the development of the egg of the leopard frog, *Rana pipiens*. *J. Morphol.* **68**, 329–345.

Zorzoli, A., and Rugh, R., 1941. Parthenogenetic stimulation of aged Anuran eggs. *Proc. Soc. Exptl. Biol. Med.* **47**, 166–167.

Recent Genetics of the Domestic Rabbit

PAUL B. SAWIN

Roscoe B. Jackson Memorial Laboratory, Hamilton Station, Bar Harbor, Maine

I. INTRODUCTION

As an experimental animal, the rabbit occupies a position somewhere between the relatively large and slow breeding domestic animals, dogs and primates on the one hand, and the relatively small and rapidly breeding rodents on the other. Its size, rate of maturity, prolificacy, and feeding habits are such as to permit statistically satisfactory samples without excessive cost, and it possesses a number of unique species characteristics which have made it a most useful animal in various fields of biological investigation. For example, the serologist first found that its large and relatively exposed ear veins and its size provide ready access to adequate blood and serum samples, thus making it valuable in immunological

183

investigations. About the same time the physiologist, and later the embryologist, found that its dependence upon the copulatory stimulus for ovulation provided an easy way of timing their experimental material in studies of the physiology of reproduction and of development. As a species, it also manifests certain fundamental endocrine as well as other physiological characteristics and patterns of growth and development which, as in man, appear somewhat associated with resistance and susceptibility to various constitutional diseases. Thus, economically and biologically, it not only provides satisfactory genetic material, but it fills needs not supplied by other species. Although, in the same lapse of time since the establishment of genetics as a science, nothing like the number of genes or chromosomal linkage groups have been observed in the rabbit as compared with other laboratory species, substantial progress has still been made, and a number of genetically determined conditions such as ataxia, Pelger, the achondroplasias, tuberculosis resistance or susceptibility, etc., in the rabbit are making notable contributions to analogous human conditions. Appreciation of the importance of the genetic background in the attack upon the constitutional diseases is undoubtedly in a considerable degree responsible for directing the attention of investigators away from the purely theoretical genetic problems such as coat color, body size, and other external and relatively normal characteristics which first attracted mammalian geneticists and were so important in establishing basic principles. In recent years efforts have become focused upon the genetics of internal morphological and physiological variations, many of which are abnormal and a serious handicap, if not lethal, but which contribute information upon the original or fundamental effects provided by the gene. Eventually, these may make their biggest contribution to theoretical genetics and to preventive rather than corrective medicine.

Because of the mass of material to be covered, and the fact that genetic studies of the rabbit have been so ably reviewed by Castle (1930, 1940), this discussion can, in general, be confined to work subsequent to this period. However, it is both undesirable and impossible to treat it entirely independently because so much recent progress is dependent upon those early studies pioneered by Castle which led to now well-established principles, particularly those of chromosomal architecture and quantitative inheritance. Hence, reference will be made in some cases to those studies in the earlier period which either are particularly pertinent or which will preserve continuity of thought for the reader.

II. Hair Color

Published genetic studies of mutations affecting pigmentation have not been extensive in the period under review. There have been reports of several possible somatic changes, one reverse mutation, several studies of pigmentation itself, and one of a new modifying gene.

Two new black-blue mosaic rabbits have been described, one by Pickard (1936) and one by Smith (1944). In neither case were mosaic young obtained from breeding these animals, although 144 colored young were obtained from the first (a male) and seven from the second (a female). Both, as in Castle's original mosaic case, appear to involve heterozygotes of the dilution or d locus and are in rabbits manifesting the recessive Dutch white-spotting phenotype. Whether these mosaics are the result of a somatic mutation of the d locus as suggested by Smith, or perhaps influenced by its association with the Dutch-spotting as noted by Castle, are interesting speculations. The d locus is not the only one which has been involved in mosaic production, however. Pickard (1929) has described a mosaic involving the b (black-brown) and l (short-hair-angora) loci.

Marchlewski (1934) has observed what appear to be two cases of reverse mutation from one of the chinchilla genes (probably c^{ch2}) to full color. The first, a castorrex, arose from purebred chinchilla rex parents. Crossed with chinchilla or albino females it gave a 1:1 ratio of full color agoutis and chinchillas, demonstrating its constitution to be Cc^{ch2}. In another closely related line, the F_2 progeny from a cross of chinchilla rex by white (cc) angora contained two full yellows. Mating one of these with normal-haired pure chinchillas or to triple recessive chinchilla males also gave a 1:1 ratio of full colored and chinchillas. Because reverse mutations are usually rare, the fact that (as Marchlewski points out) both of these cases occurred from related animals, and in a population of less than 500, suggests that these observations may be of further significance. Since the C gene in the rabbit has mutated at least 5 times, this observation may indicate that, at least under certain circumstances, it is a relatively unstable locus.

The distribution of pigment in the various types of hair and body regions as affected in various color gene combinations has been shown in tabular form by Hadjidimitroff (1933). Angora and rex show much the same pigment distribution, but greater or lesser hair growth alters proportionally the amount of pigment a given portion of the hair shows.

Inhibition of pigment formation in the Himalayan rabbit has been found by Voloss-Mialhe (1950) to result from either elevation of cutaneous temperature or from sympathectomy. The effect of sympathectomy is in part due to its thermogenic effect, but sympathectomy itself causes inhibition of normal melanogenesis. The temperature effect is in line with the earlier studies which dealt with the effects of cold, which increases pigmentation.

The author has noted segregation of a "darkening modifier" in race X, a synthesized subline of Castle's small race. It is manifest in *aaeeBB* combinations by more intense black pigmentation in those areas which in this genotype usually show non-agouti black (see Fig. 1). It is similarly manifest in *aaeebb* and *aaeebbc^{ch2}c^{ch2}* combinations, and when combined

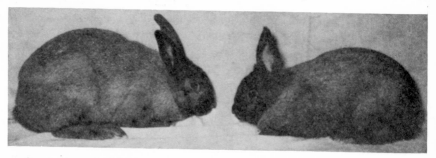

Fig. 1. Normal rabbit of constitution *aaeeBB* (right) and one of same constitution possessing also the "darkening modifier." The difference in ear size between the homozygous normal (*dwdw*) and the heterozygous dwarf (*Dwdw*) is also shown in this picture.

with *AE* or *AE^dE* or *AE^de* produces comparable intensification of black. The darkening modifier appears to be incompletely dominant over its absence, indicated by intermediate shades in heterozygotes (see Table 1).

III. HAIR MORPHOLOGY

Several new mutations affecting the structure of the hair have been reported, and the effects of modifying influences upon the rex and angora genes have been noted.

a. *Furless* (*f*). This simple recessive gene, discovered earlier by Hammond, the inheritance of which has been described by Castle (1933), has been subjected to histological examination at several pertinent ages by Drapeau (1933). She observed the extensive absence of under hair to be due to a premature keratinization which affects first the sebaceous glands, then the inner epithelial sheath. The final effect is an abnormal channel which causes an erratic escape, especially of regenerating hairs, into the surrounding tissue rather than to the surface. The hair then atrophies, frequently with an inflammatory condition in the areolar tissue. Apparently there is no check on the growth from the bulb or root. Other elements of the skin show the same excessive keratinization. The furless gene has been shown by Hammond to be independent in its inheritance of the *a*, *b*, *d*, *e*, *En*, *r^1*, *r^2*, and *v* genes (see Table 1).

b. *Naked* (*n*). David (1932) examined one of Kislovsky's (1928) "naked" rabbits, which in many ways resembles furless. In this case,

TABLE 1

Known Mutated Genes of the Rabbit and Their Associations in the Chromosomes

Linkage† group	Alleles	Phenotype	References
IV	A, a^t, a	Gray, black and tan, black	Castle, 1930, 1940
	Ac, ac	Normal, lethal achondroplasia*	Pearce and Brown, 1945a
V	An, an	A antigen vs. α-agglutinin	Sawin, Griffith, and Stuart, 1944
VI	As, as	Atropinesterase present in blood serum, no enzyme	Sawin and Glick, 1943
I ?	Ax, ax	Normal, sublethal ataxia*	Sawin, Anders, and Johnson, 1942
I	B, b	Black, brown (chocolate)	Castle, 1930, 1940
V	Br, br	Normal feet, brachydactyly	Greene, 1935; Greene and Saxton, 1939; Inman, 1941; Castle and Sawin, 1941
	Bu, bu	Normal, buphthalmous, or hydrophthalmus	Nachtsheim, 1940; Castle, 1940
I	$C, c^{ch3}, c^{ch2}, c^{ch1}, c^h, c$	Fully colored, chinchilla³, chinchilla², chinchilla¹, Himalayan, complete albino	Sawin, 1932
	D, d	Intense, dilute	Castle, 1940
	Da, da	Dachs-viable achondroplasia, normal	Crary and Sawin, 1952
II	Du, du^d, du^w	Unspotted, dark Dutch, white Dutch	Castle, 1940
IV	Dw, dw	Dwarf,* normal size	Castle, 1940; Greene, 1940
VI	E^d, E, e^i, e	Steel (with A), gray (with A), Japanese, yellow	Castle, 1940
II	En, en	English (spotted), unspotted	Castle, 1940
VII ?	Ep, ep	Normal, epilepsy or audiogenic seizures (see text)	Nachtsheim, 1938; Castle, 1940
V	F, f	Normal, furless	Castle, 1933; Castle and Sawin, 1941
	H^1, H^2, H^0	Hemagglutinogen 1 in blood Hemagglutinogen 2 in blood No hemagglutinogen in blood	Castle and Keeler, 1933 Keeler and Castle, 1933
II	L, l	Hair length normal, long-haired angora	Castle, 1940
	Lx, lx	Normal, luxate	DaRosa, 1945
	Mc, mc	Normal, lethal muscle contracture*	
	N, n	Normal, naked	Kislovsky, 1928
	O, o	Normal, osteopetrosis*	Pearce and Brown, 1948
	P, p	Pelger,* normal	Nachtsheim, 1950

TABLE 1. *(Continued)*

Linkage† group	Alleles	Phenotype	References
III	R^1, r^1	Hair length normal, short-haired (rex¹)	Castle and Nachtsheim, 1933
III	R^2, r^2	Hair length normal, short-haired (rex²)	Castle and Nachtsheim, 1933
	R^3, r^3	Hair length normal, short-haired (rex²)	Castle and Nachtsheim, 1933; Castle, 1940
	S, s	Normal coat, satin coat	Castle and Law, 1936
	Sp, sp	Normal, spastic paralysis*	Nachtsheim, 1938
	Sy, sy	Normal, syringomyely*	Nachtsheim, 1938
	T, t	Normal, shaking palsy (tremor)*	Nachtsheim, 1938
	V, v	Self-colored, self-white (eyes blue)	Castle, 1930, 1940
IV	W, w	Normal agouti (normal band), wide banded agouti	Sawin, 1934; Wilson and Dudley, 1946
	Wa, wa	Normal, hair waved	Pickard, 1941
	Wh, wh	Wirehair, normal	Pearce, unpubl.
	Wu, wu	Normal hair, wuzzy	(See text)
I	Y, y	White fat, yellow fat	Castle, 1940; Wilson and Dudley, 1946

*Lethal. † See Section X.

however, the skin was unusually thin, the epidermis was normal, except that the stratum granulosum was less distinct. Most striking, however, is the fact that the follicles were much reduced in number, and the erector pili muscles either lacking or rudimentary. Also, the hair and sebaceous glands of the head were apparently normal except for epithelial pearls. Since in all of these points Drapeau and David are at variance, it seems probable that furless and naked are not due to the same gene.

c. *Satin* (s). Discovered by W. A. Huey of Pendleton, Indiana, in 1930, satin has been found by Castle and Law (1936) to be characterized by thin cell walls and thin cell layers of cuticulum and cortex in which the medulla cells are compacted together into a stratified structure continuous with the cortex. The cuticulum, being less conspicuous, presents a smoother surface, making the hair colors more brilliant.

d. *Waved* (wa). The autosomal recessive mutation, waved, is manifested only in rex rabbits, although it can be transmitted by angoras. It is not linked with either blue (d) or brown (b). Waved young frequently molt so rapidly as to become temporarily naked (Pickard, 1941).

e. *Wuzzy* (wu). A new mutation, "wuzzy," was discovered in 1953 in a New Zealand white race in California by John W. Meyer (see Fig. 2).

The hair as it grows appears to mat in tufts in a very characteristic fashion which is quite different from that of the long-haired angora. In our laboratory, it has been crossed with normal-haired animals, and the resulting normal hybrids have produced 21 backcross and 3 F_2 young. Although the number of progeny is still too small for statistical significance, it would appear to be a simple recessive having segregated in both populations, 10 being wuzzies in the larger group.

FIG. 2. Wuzzy.

Several investigators have reported further observations of the long-haired or angora rabbit, whose hair length is primarily determined by the angora gene l.

f. "*Woolly*" (*long-haired*). "Woolly" and normal-haired rabbits and their hybrids, derived from New Zealand White rabbits, were studied and compared with the angora rabbit, a breed of the genotype ll developed by selection for desired fiber quality (Hardy and Markley, 1944). In fiber length, number of medullary cells, cross-sectional diameters, and ratio of guard to wool hairs, the hybrids are intermediate in hair length between short and long haired coats. The angora has a longer fiber with a lesser diameter.

Crary and Sawin (1953) have further shown that the total weight of wool produced by the angora also tends to be intermediate in hybrids and that, although there is no indication of an influence of heterosis upon either wool yield or rate of growth, molt is initiated later and is of shorter duration in hybrids of all ages.

Pickard (1929a) has found no significant effect of sex upon hair growth in the angora.

g. *Wirehair* (*Wh*). The incompletely dominant gene, wirehair, was obtained from Dr. Louise Pearce of the Rockefeller Institute (Fig. 3). Characteristically, it seems to have a relatively large proportion of guard to wool hairs and, at birth, its skin has the same shiny appearance as the

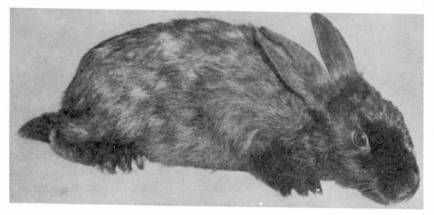

FIG. 3. Wirehair.

furless rabbit, due to tardy hair growth. Whether it is an allele of furless or an entirely independent mutation is still unknown. Hybrids are intermediate with respect to these characteristics.

IV. MORPHOLOGICAL CHARACTERS

Some morphological variations in the rabbit appear to manifest a simple Mendelian behavior with 100% penetrance and high expressivity. Others, particularly the internal variations, have incomplete dominance and a quantitative range of expression indicative of polygenic inheritance. In the first category are certain skeletal variations including luxation of the hip, internal hydrocephalus, brachydactyly, achondroplasia (described in Section IX), and possibly oxycephaly. There are also two eye characters, cataract and buphthalmus. In most of these cases, however, altered genetic background seems to affect either expressivity or penetrance or both.

1. *Single Gene Variations*

a. *Congenital luxation* (*lx*). DaRosa (1945) has described congenital luxation of the hip in chinchilla rabbits with blue eyes, which appears to be due to a simple recessive autosomal sublethal gene, sometimes behaving as a partial dominant. Affected animals are normal at birth but, when 2–4 months old, they begin to show subluxation of one or both hips due to incomplete development of the acetabulum and head of the femur.

b. *Brachydactyly* (*br*). This is described by Greene (1935) as a simple recessive, producing a series of deformities ranging from brachydactyly to acheiropodia, and closely resembling well-known human affections. Embryologically, the first abnormal change is a dilation of blood vessels in affected limb buds, which is followed by edema, hemorrhage, and necrosis of the parts involved (Greene and Saxton, 1939). Inman (1941) observed endothelial injury as early as the twelfth day of gestation. Sloughing subsequently occurred, the lesion healed, and the character was usually completely expressed by the twenty-fifth day of fetal life. Abnormalities of the ear and tail may occur in association with, or independently of, malformations of the limbs, and the expression is variable (Greene and Saxton, 1939). In this laboratory, two normal animals from brachydactyl parents (*brbr*) have been observed which produced only brachydactyl offspring, and were evidently normal overlaps.

c. *Thoraco-gastroshisis*. The cleft of thoracic and abdominal walls known as thoraco-gastroshisis has occurred eight times in four matings from two generations of Lurie's C line in a total of 38 progeny, which is a very close approach to the ratio expected from a simple Mendelian recessive segregating from hybrid parents. Unfortunately, the stock was bred for other technical purposes and was lost.

d. *Cataract*. Several types of opacity of the lens have been observed in rabbits. Nachtsheim (1940) reports one type which is manifest as early as 5 weeks and which he interprets as a recessive. It has also occurred sporadically in race X (derived from Castle's small size race), a total of 12 cases in a period of 3 years.

e. *Buphthalmus* or *hydrophthalmus* (*bu*). In the condition, buphthalmus or hydrophthalmus, the eye becomes enlarged and distended with fluid; the cornea is opaque and there is loss of vision. It occurs with some frequency in this country among New Zealand White rabbits, but rarely with sufficient frequency as to indicate a simple Mendelian inheritance. Although here it is rarely seen in pigmented animals, Nachtsheim (1940) reports it as a simple recessive manifested in colored rabbits.

f. *Tooth anomalies*. Malocclusion of the teeth and other anomalies are as well known in the rabbit as in man and other animals. For discussion of them and for further reference the reader may be referred to Nachtsheim (1938b). One such anomalie, the failure of the small second incisor teeth in the upper jaw, appears to be transmitted as a simple dominant (symbol I2). Most of them, however, are either much more complex in inheritance or are also influenced by environmental factors.

2. Polygenic Variations—Skeletal Patterns

a. *Ribs and vertebrae.* Sawin (1937) in a preliminary study of homoeotic variation in the axial skeleton observed that an extra or thirteenth pair of ribs and extra presacral vertebra, in certain races of rabbits, could be explained by neither a simple nor a multifactorial Mendelian interpretation, although the major influence upon them was genetically and developmentally induced. In a later study (1945), it was found that, when successive generations were bred from a cross of a race of rabbits having a posterior displacement of both thoraco-lumbar and lumbo-sacral borders (extra ribs and presacral vertebrae) in 95% of cases, with two races having a minimal but different average number of displacements at these borders, these displacements tended to be transmitted simultaneously and in similar amounts. It was thought at that time that a single incompletely dominant gene substitution was adequate to explain the major difference between the races, but that other genetic influences were responsible for minor differences in the "minimal" races as well as for differences in dominance and in relative incidence and expression of displacement in succeeding generations. Relationship of these influences to normal growth processes, generally, and to specific regions, was discussed and attention was called to the fact that the real effect of the gene could not be induction of any one specific extra unit (rib or vertebrae), but that it had a much broader distribution over all units of the lumbar and parts of the thoracic and sacral regions.

This idea was tested further in a new series of crosses using races manifesting differences in penetrance and expression at the thoraco-lumbar and lumbo-sacral borders (Sawin and Hull, 1946). In this study differences were evaluated on the basis of the relative antero-posterior level, and the magnitude of the lumbar region measured in terms of vertebral number. Three of these races, which differed in position and magnitude of the lumbar region, manifested distinctly different dominant genetic influences, and, when crossed, produced F_1's which were intermediate with respect to position and magnitude. In the F_2's and backcross generations the recovery of parental lumbar types, and of new types unlike either parental race, was considered evidence of segregation. However, the intermediate nature of the F_1, F_2 and backcross populations was reminiscent of quantitative studies of adult body size. Hence, it was concluded that the position of these borders and the magnitude of the area involved in any individual or race, as in body size, is dependent upon the combination of a number of genes, each of which has its relatively specific region of influence. At least some of these influences are independent of adult body size, and possible association with primary and secondary growth gradients was pointed out. Further discussion of studies of the genetics of such growth processes is to be found in a later section.

b. *Ventral spinous processes, sternebrae, and rib ossification.* The same inadequacy of a monofactorial interpretation and the same tendency toward intermediateness, characteristic of the quantitative or polygenic type of inheritance, has been found in connection (1) with the ventral spinous processes which are found on the vertebrae at or just posterior to the thoraco-lumbar border (Sawin, 1946), (2) with the number, size, and relationships of the sternebrae (Peck and Sawin, 1950), and (3) with the rate of ossification of the ribs (Hull, 1947).

In the quantitative study of the sternebrae, certain crosses are particularly illuminating because they not only show the same tendencies for genetically unlike races to manifest an intermediateness of pattern in the hybrids and in successive backcross generations, but they also demonstrate both positive and negative complementary action. In one cross between races III and V, two races are involved whose sternebrae are quantitatively about the same length, and which have only six sternebrae. But, when these two races are crossed, the F_1 progeny have an average greater length of sternebrae, as well as an extra or seventh sternebra, and these differences are primarily in the posterior region of the sternum. In the backcrosses and F_2, there is a tendency to return to the parental race pattern. In another cross, involving races IIc $\times$ X, the opposite situation is found. Both races have again about the same length of sternum and in this case both have the extra sternebra. In the F_1 the sternebrae are significantly shorter and the extra unit is almost completely lost. In this cross the results are almost the exact opposite of the III $\times$ V cross, the greater length and extra unit tending to be restored in the later generations. Obviously size and number of sternebrae are genetic, and equally obvious is the fact that the influences in these races are very different. The interpretation also will be discussed in section X in relation to regional growth differences.

3. *Polygenic Variations—Vascular Patterns and Other Variations of Soft Tissues*

a. *Vena cava.* A similar situation to that in the skeleton has been found in at least three cases with respect to vascular patterns. McNutt and Sawin (1943) observed 29 distinct variations from the normal vena cava which were traceable to persistent irregularities in the portions of the embryonic postcardinal, supracardinal, and cardinal collateral systems for which a single-factor interpretation of inheritance was impossible, but the manner of inheritance was discussed in relation to differential growth.

b. *Ilio-lumbar arteries and aorta.* A parallel situation was observed by Sawin and Nace (1948) with respect to the origin of the ilio-lumbar arteries and the bifurcation of the aorta. In this case, the variation is of particular interest because of the effect of the genetic background on the expression of asymmetry.

In the majority of the animals these paired vessels rise asymmetrically, with the left vessel being the more anterior. In all populations, both symmetrical and asymmetrical individuals and reversed asymmetrics always occur, and these tend to fall into frequency distributions in which the modal group shifts from one side to the other, in proportion to the type of mating from which the offspring are derived. Thus it seems difficult to think of the variation as being determined by a single or simple gene substitution, involving merely the matter of dextrality or sinistrality. Nor is a multiple factor interpretation adequate, since the nature and amount of variation observed in the parental races, F_1, F_2, and backcrosses does not entirely compare with that commonly recognized as evidence of such inheritance. Whether they are primarily determined by the location of a particular point of origin of the vessels in the two sides, or by modified expression originating later from such a point of origin, is a moot question. There seems to be no more indication that the structural differences in the two sides necessarily represent corresponding specific genetic differences, than in the case of the well known torsion and displacements of the digestive tube and viscera; however, because of the manner in which the antero-posterior level of these vessels, as well as the asymmetry, are associated with other variations (skeletal) in these same races, all of which are transmitted in the same general way, a common genetic background is suggested.

c. *Aortic arch patterns.* The relation of 16 different patterns of vessels arising from the aortic arch (most of which have been observed in man) to localized growth areas have been discussed by Sawin and Edmonds (1949) in the light of 3000 observations in the same races as above.

Of particular significance is the presence or absence of the so-called innominate and brachiocephalic arteries, both of which may or may not occur from species to species in mammals, and may or may not occur in man and rabbit. Race III tends to lack the brachiocephalic artery in a high proportion of cases. Race X has both vessels and race V tends to lack the innominate. Thus races III and V represent deficiencies at two different antero-posterior levels. Matings within and between these races show little indication of dominance and segregation of single gene effects specific to these two vascular changes, although there is a tendency for matings of either of the deficiencies to breed true, and for the normal type possessing both vessels to produce the entire range of variation. However, the same strong tendency exists for hybrids between the several racial types to be intermediate, and for the backcross populations to return to the grandparental distributions which are found in connection with the skeletal variations described above. There is also evidence of production of combination types in F_2.

d. *Gall bladder*. Variations in size and shape of this organ have been observed by Sawin and Crary (1951). Although crosses between unlike parental races have not been made, the range of variation is such that the same sort of genetic transmission for this variation, as for those described above, may be anticipated.

e. *Oxycephaly*. Genetic factors affecting differential growth have also been noted in the skull (Greene, 1932, 1933). Among some 500 skulls of different breeds several distinct types have been observed with respect to shape of the "dome" and "ridges." These seem to be hereditary, since they respond to inbreeding and selection. They appear to trace to irregularities in displacement and divisions of primary ossification centers which, in turn, result in differences in size and shape of individual bones, in suture pattern, and in the angle of bony union at the bregma. Greene considers them as recessive to the normal condition, and indicates that they can be recombined to form new types as well as being recovered in the original parental type.

f. *Skull form*. Suchalla (1943) has studied the sagittal skull outline and 27 different measurements of the skulls of small and large sized races (represented by Hermelin and lopped-eared English Giant rabbits) and of subsequent F_1, F_2, and backcross generations of crosses between them. In brief, the outstanding results are that the F_1 combines the high nasal arch of the giant race with the relatively high fronto-parietal arch of the Hermelin, and these tend to segregate in the F_2. Backcrosses of the F_1 to the Hermelin tend to return to Hermelin-like skulls and backcrosses to the English tend to return to their grandparental type. Suchalla rightly concludes that the inheritance is complex, probably polygenic.

Whether the variation described by Greene is a single gene difference with certain specific modifiers or whether, as in Suchalla's work, the inheritance is more likely polygenic, is not entirely clear. To my knowledge, variations of this type have never occurred in our races.

Hu and Greene (1935) have described a recessive lethal mutation in the rabbit also affecting the skull and is apparently the result of over activity of the pituitary gland which also affects the thyroid function.

g. *Earless*. Rabbits in which one or both ears, or some fraction thereof, are missing are occasionally reported by rabbit breeders. In the writer's

30 years experience, only three authentic cases of this character have been observed in approximately 62,000 animals. These were all born in the same inbred race X descended from Castle's small race and each was observed within less than 18 hours of birth, at which time there was no evidence of postnatal mutilation. Hence, they may be considered as truly congenital. Although the first, ♂ ×974, born in July 1946, was used extensively and many of his progeny were sib-mated, the recovery of only two affected offspring indicates either a low penetrance or the existence of several genes necessary to its manifestation. Since the brachydactyl gene (*br*), which, in the proper genetic combination, can also produce ear and tail deficiencies, has never been bred into this stock, and no evidence of limb defects of this nature have ever been observed, it is unlikely that these cases are an expression of this gene.

In summary of the morphological variations described, inheritance seems clearly to be of at least two distinct kinds. On the one hand, a certain number of qualitative variations, including hydrocephaly, brachydactyly, the achondroplasias, and possibly the eye and ear defects, are transmitted by single major gene differences. These, however, are relatively rare as compared with the wide range of internal morphological variations occurring in the skeletal, vascular, glandular, and perhaps in all of the other systems, Some of these at first seem to be qualitative variations, but they usually lend themselves to quantitative methods, and, when so studied, thus far have manifested the same tendencies to intermediateness in the F_1, and to return to parental types in the backcrosses, which have characterized the quantitative studies of body size and length made by Castle. These variations will be referred to later in the section on body growth, section IX.

V. PHYSIOLOGICAL CHARACTERS

a. *Osteopetrosis* (*o*). This disease is characterized by abnormal bone and tooth development, retardation of growth, anemia, and progressive cachexia. It is recognizable at birth, soon after which it is invariably fatal. The results of X-ray, hematologic, and chemical studies show a close resemblance to those of the severe juvenile form of human osteopetrosis (Pearce, 1948). The outstanding skeletal abnormalities include the persistence of spongy bone, failure of development of the marrow cavity, and greatly reduced hemopoietic tissue (Pearce, 1950a). Histologically, the characteristics are those of progressive anemia, including extramedullary foci of hemopoietic tissue, lymphoid hyperplasia, and occurrence of hemosiderin in liver, spleen, and lymph nodes. There was some indication of parathyroid involvement and effects of other endocrine glands including thyroid, adrenals (both cortex and medulla), and pituitary (Pearce, 1950b). As indicated by Pearce and Brown (1948), osteo-petrosis is a simple recessive, lethal and not sex-linked. Rabbits which are heterozygous (*Oo*) are identified only by appropriate breeding tests.

b. *Atropinesterase* (*As*). Levy and Michel (1938) first recognized the presence of an enzyme in rabbit serum capable of destroying atropine, which seemed to be hereditary. In studies of the properties of the enzyme in the serums of certain rabbits capable of hydrolyzing atropine, Glick (1940) and Glick and Glaubach (1941) also became aware of this fact. Extensive population studies by Sawin and Glick (1943) have demonstrated that the presence of the enzyme atropinesterase, which is capable of hydrolyzing atropine, is determined by a single gene dominant to its absence and borne in the same chromosome as the gene *E* for extension of black pigment in the coat. Homozygotes produce the enzyme more effectively than heterozygotes, The gene induced enzyme also appears to destroy monoacetyl-morphine. It is not present at birth but appears first at about one month of age and tends to occur in a higher percentage of females and in greater concentration in females than in males.

VI. Mutations of the Nervous System, Neuromuscular Disorders, and Differences in Behavior Patterns

1. *Single Gene Variations of the Nervous System*

The rabbit, like man and the mouse, seems to be particularly susceptible to disorders of the central nervous and neuro-muscular systems and most of them seem to be lethal and transmitted in a simple Mendelian manner. At least four of these have been described by Nachtsheim (1938) and co-workers in Germany.

a. *Spastic paralysis* (*sp*). The condition, spastic paralysis, may or may not be detected at birth, but, by the time the young are 10–14 days old, a stiff, paralyzed condition of the hind legs is noted. It passes through three characteristic stages (1) a rapid trembling, characteristic of the first 3 weeks, (2) a paresis of the extremities at about 4 weeks, and (3) a complete paralysis at about 3 months. The condition becomes permanent in affected individuals without affecting other body parts or interfering with growth. Mature individuals are unable to reproduce, however, because of mechanical difficulties. This condition is due to a single recessive gene.

b. *Shaking palsy* (*tremor*) (*t*). Shaking palsy is a character which becomes manifest at 10 days of age as a continuous trembling, which changes to extreme shaking movements, and finally to convulsions, which are usually fatal at about 3 months of age. Nachtsheim obtained several males in which the condition was less severe, which he was able to raise to sexual maturity, and obtained young from them by unaffected mothers. All were normal; hence, he considers it a simple recessive.

c. *Syringomyelia* (*sy*). This gene first occurred in 1927 in rex^2 rabbits in France. It is an asymmetrical spastic paralysis usually affecting only one leg. Ordinarily it attacks mature rabbits, although symptoms may appear as early as 5 months. The hips appear hollow, the gait stiff, and finally complete paresis develops. The disease is a simple recessive, no symptoms being manifest in F_1, but reappearing in the F_2. The expression is irregular depending upon the genetic milieu in which it is carried.

d. *Epilepsy or audiogenic seizures* (*ep*). Animals which are subject to epileptic-like seizures have long been known to occur occasionally in the Vienna White breed of rabbits. Both Nachtsheim and Castle observed them independently in their laboratory stocks. Affected individuals behave in every way as if normal, until they are startled by an unusual noise or quick movement of a caretaker. Then the rabbit will dash wildly around the cage until it falls in a swoon, and lies on its side seemingly dead. Presently, however, it begins to breathe naturally and gradually resumes normal behavior, the entire seizure usually lasting less than 5 minutes. Castle (1940) reports it as sporadic in occurrence, but restricted to homozygous (*vv*) individuals, and never occurring in colored individuals derived from Vienna White crosses. For this reason Nachtsheim (1938) concluded that it is due to a mutation of the Vienna White locus, and thus is one of three alleles of which V is normal, v causes the absence of pigment in the coat and a blue eye, and *ve* the blue-eyed white which is subject to seizures. Although Castle is in agreement with this interpretation, he called attention to the fact that from a cross of a Vienna White race (in which epilepsy occurred) to a colored race, an extracted Vienna White race was obtained which did not manifest the disorder, and hence concluded that, if it is a by-product of this gene, it requires a particular genetic background for expression. In our laboratory, it has occurred in a white-spotted race (resembling the Vv animal) obtained in 1948 from the Rockefeller Institute, in which the blue-eyed whites segregate, presumably the Vienna white. It frequently occurs, however, in spotted individuals and tests are now being made for evidence of linkage with the v gene. Apparatus for controlled testing has been developed by Antonitis *et al.* (1954).

e. *Ataxia* (*ax*). In 1942, Sawin, Anders, and Johnson described a disorder of the central nervous system inherited as a simple Mendelian recessive and lethal. Homozygous recessives (*axax*) are normal at birth but develop an ataxic loss of coordination, which a preliminary examination by Anders showed was due to degeneration in the vestibulo-cerebellar and ponto-cerebellar systems. Anders (1945) continued the study, demonstrating a progressive failure of motor coordination with later involvement of autonomic functions. The disorder becomes manifest about the 73rd day of life and progresses in a characteristic manner until death, 12 to 15 days later. Neuropathological lesions occur first in the vestibular and cochlear nerves and nuclei, and later in the vestibular, pontine, and cerebellar nuclei and fibers, the medial and lateral lemniscus, the facial and oculomotor nerves, and the internal capsule. Because of the effects on the cochlear and vestibular nuclei the sensory end organs of these nerves were examined, but no detectable damage was found (Anders, 1947).

This gene is proving of particular value in bioassays of drugs and chemicals reputed to have therapeutic properties for the neuromuscular disorders. Its value over similar disorders existing in other species lies principally in the time of onset, well after weaning, and the relatively usual short course (less than 30 days) of the disease.

f. *Lethal muscle contracture (mc)*. This condition appears to be well known in other domestic breeds of livestock, having been described in cattle, sheep, and swine, in all of which it is apparently a simple recessive and frequently of serious consequence to the mother at parturition. A character comparing almost identically with these has been observed in our laboratory in two races of rabbits which are entirely unrelated; one race, V (chinchilla), having been under our observation since 1928, and the other race, AC, a Dutch marked race received from the Rockefeller Institute in 1949. In both of these races it first appeared sporadically, but in 14 selected matings from known transmitters all seem to fit the same interpretation advanced for the other species. The character is variable in expression. In general, the forelimbs tend to approximate each other over the sternum or are extended parallel with the body leaving the skin of the neck taut and showing obvious signs of muscle atrophy. The hind limbs, likewise, are approximated and extended, but usually the manifestations are less severe (see Fig. 4). Unlike the other species, normal parturition appears not to be interfered with. A detailed study, when completed, will be published elsewhere. For review of literature see Nachtsheim (1939).

g. *Hydrocephalus*. This has been described as a simple recessive by Nachtsheim (1939). In an F_2 population of 58 young, there were 39 normal and 19 affected. In this case, however, it was closely associated with a dwarf condition "nan" and brachygnathia. The dwarf heterozygote was intermediate in body size.

DaRosa (1946) has also described in detail an "internal hydrocephalus" transmitted as a simple autosomal gene incompletely dominant in the heterozygote. The character is recognizable at birth by a high cranial vault, which is soft and easily depressed on palpation. Eye abnormalities apparently are secondary effects, varying from ectopia of the eyeball, through coloboma of the iris and choroid, posterior polar cataract, microphthalmus, to anophthalmia, and are unilateral or bilateral.

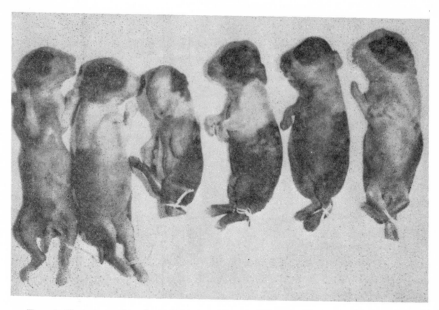

Fig. 4. Shows varying degrees of lethal muscle contracture in a litter from two transmitting parents. The first on the left is normal. The second and fourth show only slight manifestations, and the third, fifth, and sixth are severe. Varying degrees of accompanying hydrocephalus are found in this litter, which may or may not be a secondary affect of the same gene.

In our laboratory hydrocephalous individuals have occurred in various races, but in all cases they have been sporadic and no clear-cut hereditary pattern is, therefore, evident. Whether, as in mice, there are several major genes which produce this characteristic or whether there are numerous genetic and nongenetic modifying influences, is not clear at this time; hence, no symbol has been assigned.

h. *Spina bifida.* The character, spina bifida, cannot be described as clearly and definitely genetic. Yet, if the term is used as inclusive of all of the 5 types referred to by Patten (1953), there is evidence of at least a certain degree of racial susceptibility to this character. During the years 1936–54 (18 years), in the colonies of rabbits maintained by the writer first at Brown University and since 1947 at the Jackson Laboratory, there have occurred 58 such specimens, 34 of them during the past $3\frac{1}{2}$ years. Nineteen of the 34 are as nearly equally divided between two races, the AC received from the Rockefeller Institute, and race III, a New Zealand White race bred under my observation since 1934. The rest have been found scattered through the years and in various races and hybrid origins. Because every effort has been made to inbreed as closely as consistent with maintenance of a high level of production, it has not been possible to select parentage which were known transmitters of this character, but without conscious effort the proportion seems to have increased considerably over that in other races or the colony as a whole. The group of 34 includes a substantial number which would be classified as cranium bifidum. Most of these are in the present collection of anomalies in this laboratory.

2. Differences in Behavior Patterns

a. *Maternal and sex behavior*. Significant racial differences in maternal behavior have been described by Sawin and Crary (1953). One race, X, is characteristically a prepartum nest builder. In approximately 60% of parturitions, mothers of this race both build their nests and line them with hair, plucked from their bodies, from one to four days before the young are born. In race III and its subline IIIc, in contrast, approximately 60% of the parturitions are accompanied by these nesting reactions at, or shortly after birth. The nature of the nest and the amount of lining are similarly but less closely associated, and neither is associated with the time of nesting reaction. Race X nests tend to be poor, those of race III good, and of IIIc intermediate. In the light of present knowledge of these races, differences are believed in some way to be associated with differences in pituitary and sex hormone balance indicated by their relative sexual responses, the relative size of the gonads, and the number of follicles, etc., produced per ovulation. As such, they afford unique material for genetic studies of hormone balance and for studies of hormone therapy in relation to sex and maternal behavior.

b. *Timidity*. Wilson (1936) in a cross of the placid Black Beveran (Sitka) females with timid, nervous, gray males, observed that the F_1's were all timid and nervous and that the F_2's and F_3's were timid, but to a lesser degree, and concluded that timidity is dominant and due to more than one factor.

VII. SEROLOGICAL CHARACTERS

Some differences in antigen and antibody relations found in human and animal bloods appear to be species specific. Others are peculiar to individuals and have been generally ascribed by immunologists to con-

stitutional differences. Knowledge of variations of this kind, which prove
to be inherited, are important not only for their genetic value, but they
also afford a means of biological analysis and standardization comparable
to the standardization of reagents in the field of chemistry. This is par-•
ticularly important in the common laboratory animals whose blood is
used in preparation of immune serums, in numerous and varied clinical
procedures, and in many types of theoretical investigations. Concomitant
with the studies of blood groups in several species, doves, cattle, rabbit,
man, etc., it has become increasingly apparent that internal patterns,
involving associations of antigen and antibody obtainable within the
species, may be as numerous and complex as are the external patterns
of coat color, and may be influenced in the same manner by the interactions of both genetic and environmental forces. The very nature of these
variations makes this genetic analysis dependent upon precise qualitative
and quantitative methods.

Particularly when studied in relation to chromosome architecture,
the large numbers of serological variations, which appear to be identifiable
in those species which have been adequately studied, seem to offer a
tremendous challenge to those interested in fundamental gene activities.

In the rabbit, since the early studies of the blood groups by Levine
and Landsteiner (1929, 1931), who at that time postulated a great number
of agglutinogens, five have been described by Fischer (1935) and Marcussen (1936) and a sixth by Knopfmacher (1942). Normal agglutinins occur
with none of these.

Study of the genetic background of the blood groups (immune isoagglutinins) was extended by Castle and Keeler (1933), and Keeler and
Castle (1933), who showed that the inheritance of the H^1 and H^2 antigens
are transmitted by three alleles, two of which (H^1 and H^2) are dominant
over the third (H^0).

More recently, Kellner and Hedal (1953) have described a pair of
blood group factors identified by serological means which have been
designated G and g and are apparently alleles of the same locus. They
are capable of stimulating the formation of specific immune isoagglutinins
when repeatedly injected into appropriate rabbits as was the case with
H^1 and H^2. They show a close resemblance to those of the Rh-Hr system
of man.

Cohen (1954) independently has observed two antigens, A and F,
which he has compared serologically with G and g of Kellner, and finds
them the same. He is in complete accord with the manner of inheritance,
but, with a larger and more variable colony, he has also been able to find
animals which possess neither of these two antigens, which Kellner was
unable to do.

Since in none of the cases of the other H^3–H^6 antigens of previous workers was there evidence of a third allele, and since many of these rabbits are descendants in the same races in which these characters were previously studied, there is good reason to believe that Cohen's A and F and Kellner's G and g are related, if not the same, as the original H^1 and H^2 antigens of the previous workers. Cohen also has antisera for four other antigens, each of which appears to represent a single genetic locus.

With regard to the resemblance of these antigens to the Rh-Hr systems, Kellner and Hedal (1953), by matings of the proper males (homozygous GG) and females (homozygous gg), have been able to find 5 out of 10 mothers which developed specific anti-G antibodies in their serum. These prove capable of crossing the placentae into the fetal circulation of the fetuses in utero. When the mother's antibody titer was low, the fetuses were usually born alive. When it was high, they were often born dead and macerated, or, if alive, they died shortly after birth. Hydrops fetalis, necrosis of the liver, and enhanced extramedullary hematopoiesis were observed in the fetuses from immunized mothers. Nachtsheim, as early as 1946, had described a similar phenomenon, but, in the same stocks of rabbits, Heard, Hinde, and Mynors (1949) were unable to reproduce it. Although the material in the rabbit is thus probably no less complex than in man, the fact that at least two investigators have produced the same apparent phenomenon is strong indication that the same biological processes are functioning in the rabbit as in man, and thus valuable animal material is available for analysis of at least some of the perplexing questions associated with erythroblastosis fetalis.

Wheeler, Sawin, and Stuart (1939a) discovered a mutually exclusive relationship between the presence of human A antigen and a-agglutinin in the rabbit. The presence or absence of the A antigen segregates as a single Mendelian pair of contrasting characters, presence being dominant to absence.

Rabbits without these group specific a-agglutinins have in their serum (not in their red cells) the same agglutinogen which is found in human group A-cells. Rabbits which have a normal a-agglutinin in their serums are capable of producing a high-titer, immune, group-specific a-agglutinin on immunization with human A cells, but rabbits lacking these normal agglutinins (and thus carrying A-antigen) are not.

Certain rabbits possess both the A-agglutinogen and an irregular a-agglutinin in their serum, the latter usually manifesting itself only temporarily. These rabbits behave genetically like ordinary rabbits with A-antigen, but without a-agglutinin. Presence of the irregular agglutinin may likewise be genetically determined.

The serological relationships and technique used in demonstrating this character are described pictorially (Sawin, Stuart, and Wheeler, 1943). The chromosomal relationship of this gene (An), responsible for the A character, with brachydactyly (br) and furless (f) (Sawin, Griffin, and Stuart, 1944) was the first clear evidence that such blood differences could be genetically linked with a morphological character.

The ability of rabbits to produce immune specific human M-agglutinins is also probably inherited in a simple manner but the evidence is incomplete. (Wheeler, Sawin, and Stuart, 1939b.)

Culbertson (1935) has reported individual differences in response to immunization with crystallized egg albumin in Black Dutch rabbits which he believes to be genetic. Furthermore, individuals which respond poorly to egg albumin respond quite satisfactorily to a suspension of *Eberthella typhosa*. Individual differences in the formation of precipitins in the rabbit are constitutional and hereditary. The weak response is probably recessive. Rabbits with strong precipitin response must be different in their genotypes, as shown by cross-breeding experiments (Kleczkowska and Kleczkowski, 1939).

Kleczkowski has also been able to divide families of rabbits into "strong," "medium," and "weak" antibody producers with respect to human serums, and the pedigree he presents suggests the segregation of a single gene, the one homozygous allele being "strong," the other "weak," and the heterozygote intermediate.

Sang and Sobey (1954) found a strong degree of heritability in rabbits for antibody response to tobacco mosaic virus, although this virus is not a single and simple antigen, but has at least seven components. The fact that the rates of response to it vary from animal to animal suggest that, possibly, the susceptibility to the individual components may also be broken down into separate genes. They also observed that a proportion of the rabbit population showed no response to bovine plasma albumin even in massive doses, and suggest that this failure is probably due to a recessive gene or genes segregating in the population. Response to several other antigens was not affected by this "genetic block." Besides these specific differences, rabbits tested with all of the several antigens showed a significant tendency to produce related responses to different antigens, suggesting that they have a general predisposition to respond at some level to all antigenic stimuli.

Wheeler (1938) has also noted familial differences among certain races of rabbits, with respect to quantitative production of cold-hemagglutinins. Three out of seven races produced significantly higher cold-titers.

VIII. Disease Resistance

a. *Tuberculosis.* Relative resistance to both human and bovine tuberculosis in rabbits has a definite genetic background. Opie and Freund

(1937) observed that a Havana breed of rabbits was much more resistant to tuberculosis after vaccination, and resisted infection better than Chinchilla, Himalayan, Dutch, and New Zealand rabbits. Lurie, Abramson, and Heppleston (1952) have demonstrated that, if genetically susceptible and resistant rabbits simultaneously inhale from 100–2000 virulent human tubercle bacilli, resistant rabbits overcome the infection completely so that after 2–5 months the lungs are entirely free of any gross tuberculosis in 80% of individuals, whereas, in 90% of the susceptible animals, disease of varying extent often involving a greater part of the lung parenchyma, is present. By their methods not only can the time necessary for determining resistance be shortened, but the distinction between genetically resistant and susceptible animals becomes an all or none difference in a majority of individuals. Evidence was found that genetically resistant rabbits are not only able to inhibit growth of organisms inhaled, but also possess an inherent capacity to destroy them which susceptible rabbits do not possess. At the same time, as a consequence of this difference in capacity, genetically resistant rabbits tend to develop allergic sensitivity to tuberculin more rapidly than susceptible rabbits.

Lurie, Zappasodi et al. (1952) have shown that the response of rabbits to the intracutaneous innoculation of BCG, a nonvirulent mutation of the tuberculosis organism, may serve as an index of native resistance to virulent tuberculosis organisms, and is a useful and practical method of evaluation in selective breeding for disease resistance or susceptibility. The fact that this nonvirulent BCG strain of tuberculosis organisms has not caused progressive tuberculosis in any species, plus the fact that, in rabbits of the highly resistant races, allergic sensitivity and antibodies develop more rapidly than in the susceptible races, makes this method very practical and useful for this purpose. At the same time a degree of heightened resistance conferred by the BCG innoculation is superimposed upon the native resistance of the rabbit, whereas in the inherently susceptible animal this increase does not occur. Lurie (1950) has also shown that localization of the disease at the portal of entry, which is characteristic of the response of genetically resistant rabbits to tuberculosis, and its dissemination from the portal of entry, which characterizes the disease in natively susceptible rabbits, can be simulated in rabbits of the same genetic resistance to the infection, by exposing them to estrogen and chorionic gonadotrophin, respectively. The first retards the progress of tuberculosis at the port of entry, and diminishes its dissemination to the internal organs chiefly by reducing the permeability of the connective tissue. Chorionic gonadotrophin has the opposite effect enhancing the disease. Since Lurie's highly resistant race III is the same as is referred to elsewhere in this paper as a highly estrogenized race, the genetic background, with reference to the endocrine pattern, may be of prime significance in the relative resistance of this race. A similar hormone relationship has been noted by Magnuson, Rosenau, and Greenberg (1951) in connection with the effect of sex, and male sex hormones in induction of experimental syphilis. Here, however, the authors believe the effect of testosterone to be the result of interaction with other factors, presumably hormonal in nature.

Serum sensitivity. Susceptibility to rheumatic fever in man is thought by several investigators to be governed by genetic influences Wilson (1940). Uchida (1953) has indicated that, in her pedigrees, the results can be fitted to a simple Mendelian interpretation assuming an abnormal penetrance. This interpretation is not compatible with previous data, however, and she concludes that no definite mode of inheritance is yet established.

Rich and Gregory (1943) and Gregory and Rich (1946) have shown that rabbits subjected to experimental serum sickness in some cases develop lesions that in their basic characteristics resemble closely those of rheumatic carditis and rheumatic pneumonitis. Because of the difficulties in securing adequate data from human pedigrees, a demonstration that the incidence of hypersensitive cardiovascular lesions in rabbits is governed by simple and specific gene action, would supply an economical genetic tool with which to investigate the basic genetic principles involved, lend further weight to the proposition that the rheumatic state and the induced rabbit lesions have a similar etiology, and supply predictable experimental material with which to investigate other fundamental problems of clinical importance. Gregory (unpublished data) has observed considerable heterogeneity with respect to this character in a number of rabbit races. He has found two contrasting races, however, one being relatively susceptible to cardiac lesions and the other highly resistant. In work done in collaboration with the author, the difference between resistant and susceptible races of rabbits has been found to be genetic, but, as in man, it is not explainable by a single gene substitution, and intensive efforts are now being made to critically analyze the genetic background of the character in the rabbit.

b. *Spontaneous mammary tumors.* Susceptibility to spontaneous growths of this kind seems to have a genetic background, having appeared in a certain line of Belgian Hares, in a "dwarf English" line, and in hybrid descendants of the two (Greene, 1939). In the Belgians, and hybrids with predominant Belgian blood, the condition at the same stages tends to malignancy, whereas in the English, and hybrids of predominant English blood, it does not. The mechanism of inheritance, however, is not clear but contradictory, indicating that the genetic background is not of a simple Mendelian nature, or that factors other than heredity may play a decisive role in the expression of the genetic factors. Although numerous animals of unrelated lines were fostered by tumor-bearing animals and held under observation for long periods of time, no evidence was noted of a milk factor such as found in mice.

c. *Uterine adenomata*. Susceptibility to this disorder also tends to manifest influences which are genetic (Greene, 1941). Racially, the incidence varied from 0 in 41 Belgians and 10 Rex rabbits to 20% in 35 Dutch rabbits, and from 14 to 21% in hybrid populations of various kinds in which upwards of several hundred animals were maintained beyond two years of age.

IX. BODY SIZE, BODY PROPORTIONS, AND GROWTH

Problems of body growth, size, and proportion in the rabbit fall into five categories quite comparable to those recognized in man: those induced by specific genes such as Da, Dw, and ac, those of general body size, those which are regionally localized, those with specific tissue differences, which in man are recognizably a part of the muscle, bone, fat ratio, and those due to endocrine influences either genetically or environmentally induced.

1. *Specific Genes*

At least five genes in the rabbit are known to affect body size in specific ways and all are lethal or sublethal.

(1) "Pituitary" dwarf (Dw). This gene, which originated in a small-sized Polish race, was described by Greene (1940) as a simple recessive, but the difference in birth weight of homozygous and heterozygous individuals, together with more recent studies of specific organ differences (Crary and Sawin, 1949; Latimer and Sawin, 1955) indicates incomplete dominance. This gene induces effects in the pituitary and gonads which are the antithesis of those produced by the pituitary dwarf mouse. However, suppression of the gonad-stimulating hormone and certain changes in the histological elements of the pituitary, together with certain changes brought about when in genetic combination with a second abnormal dwarf type, "cretinoid," lead Greene to conclude that the primary effect is an inhibition of the secretory functions of the pituitary.

(2) *Achondroplasia* (ac). This is present at birth, characterized by size reduction, disproportion of body parts (most marked in the limbs), and an invariable lethal effect before or very shortly after birth, and has a remarkable resemblance to the disease in man, cattle, and dogs. It is inherited as a simple Mendelian recessive, showing, so far as we know, no manifestations in the heterozygous condition (Brown and Pearce, 1945).

The head tends to be disproportionately large, the limbs shortened with small shortened bones, cartilaginous in appearance and texture. The teeth are immature and cleft palate occurs in one-fourth of the cases. The heart is small, the thymus is relatively enlarged, the spleen and liver enlarged and discolored, and the stomach distended with thin, greenish mucus but no milk. Organ size in terms of net body weight is larger than those of normal newborn litter mates. Actual weights of kidneys, brain, and especially spleen and thymus are larger than their respective values in normal sibs, whereas the heart, liver, and adrenals are slightly smaller. The pituitary shows no difference. Histologically, abnormalities of the long bones are very similar to fetal chondrodystrophy in man, fowl, dog, and calf. No evidence was found which would suggest the nature of the responsible causal agent (Pearce and Brown, 1945b).

(3) *Dachs (Da)*. A second type of achondroplasia (Crary and Sawin, 1952) is viable in the homozygote, and, if the individual is not too abnormal, it will mate and conceive. It is characterized by a retardation of endochondral ossification manifested primarily in the limbs and particularly in the hip and shoulder joints, but with significant changes also in the skull, external ear, and first two vertebrae. The first detectable sign roentgenographically is the distorted scapula at birth. By six days of age, dislocation of the ossifying head of the femur can also be observed. The resulting changes during postnatal development are often so serious as to cripple the animal. A small cartilaginous papilla, arising at the base of the external auditory meatus, identifies homozygotes at birth, and a remnant of this papilla is manifest in heterozygotes in the same relative position. It was first described as a recessive, but in view of this observation it is properly regarded as an incomplete dominant.

(4) *Pelger (P)*. Another specific gene, known to have significant effects upon body size, gets its name from a closely analogous syndrome in man. Nachtsheim (1950) has described it as a simple autosomal Mendelian dominant with incomplete penetrance, which is also usually a lethal in the homozygous state. Its primary influence is upon the nuclei of leucocytes, especially the neutrophils. Secondarily, is found a typical pattern of chondrodystrophy, especially in the long bones of the extremities and in the ribs. It apparently also differs from the *Da* gene in that the distal and proximal portions of the limb are equally affected. Death results by an emphysema of the lungs developing in consequence of a fixation of the thorax (see also Harm, 1952).

(5) *Dwarf (n = nanus)*. Nachtsheim (1937) has described still another dwarf gene associated with "Leuzismus." This gene in the homozygous state induces a birth weight of 15–20 g. as compared with an average of 40 g. in normal sibs. Associated with it is marked hydrocephalus

and a shortening of the upper jaw resulting in protrusion of the lower incisor teeth. Many of these nanus dwarfs manifest exophthalmia, and dominance is incomplete.

Kröning (1939) also has described a mutation quite similar to Dw which occurred in Himalayan rabbits. Both Dw and that of Kröning differ from Nachtsheim's dwarf in a smaller birth weight and shorter life. The nanus dwarfs sometimes live to 33 days and lack the changes in the skull and teeth.

Schnecke (1941) has made further comparison of Nachtsheim's and Kröning's material and has observed an interesting interaction between rex and nanus. Homozygous rex-nanus ($rr\ nn$) die before birth but $rr\ Nn$ individuals become better able to manifest the dwarf conditions. He also calls attention to the interesting association between body weight and length of life of the dwarfs. Homozygous $dwdw$ rabbits of Greene die at or within 1–2 days after birth. Those derived from Himalayan, which are a slightly heavier breed, average about 5 days of life, and those of the "Leuzismus" type as long as 33 days. He suggests the three may be variates of the same dwarf type, but whose manifestations or expressivity is different in the several races, possibly being influenced by body weight differences.

2. General Body Size

Investigation of body size and growth prior to 1940 has been concisely summarized and discussed by Castle (1940). Hence, only certain items particularly pertinent and basic to more recent work will be mentioned here. The fact that adult body size in mammals is inherited is well recognized. In crosses between extremes in size, it follows a well recognized pattern of transmission, which is explainable in terms of multiple genes, some of which increase and some of which decrease body size and whose dominance is in general incomplete. This is true for F_1 and for backcross matings. Castle and Gregory (1931) have shown that size genes in the rabbit effect their differences by altering developmental rate. Eggs of races of genetically large body size cleave more rapidly than eggs of small-bodied races, form a large embryonic disk, and result in larger young at birth. They continue a greater growth rate to maturity. The parental influence thus exerted through the sperm and egg is shared by both parents, but Castle has shown that the total influence on body size of the offspring is slightly greater by the mother than by the father, which is thought to indicate an influence of the egg cytoplasm on developmental rate. Castle (1941) has demonstrated significant effects of certain specific color genes upon body size in mice, rabbits, and rats. In the rabbit, however, the mutations nonagouti, English, yellow, and blue are without influence on body size. Of those tested, brown seems to be the only one with such effects.

3. Regional Body Growth

One of the earliest studies first made by Castle in 1909, of regional growth was that of ear length in rabbits, the inheritance being described as blending. Later Castle and Reed (1936) renewed the study in crosses of lop-eared and ordinary short-eared rabbits and concluded that, as is the case with general body size, the evidence for inheritance of ear length, in general, supports the multiple factor or polygenic interpretation first applied by Lang. Among ordinary breeds of rabbits, ear length is closely correlated with general body size and the same tends to be true among lop-eared rabbits. However, special mutated genes in the case of pure-bred lop-eared rabbits nearly double the ear length as compared with that of ordinary rabbits of like body size. This increase, however, has not been attained by any change in shape, the ratio of length to width being nearly the same (0.56) in all breeds and at all ages between one month and maturity. Dunlop and Hammond (1937) have shown significant proportional development of parts in relation to body weight. In one or two cases, certain mutations decreasing the size of ears in relation to that of body size have also occurred, and these have been incorporated in such small-bodied and short-eared breeds as the Polish, as for example, the dwarf gene (Dw) (see Fig. 1 and also Schnecke (1941) for other examples).

An effort to isolate or define the effects of other specific genes involved in body size has been made by Sawin et al. in studies of the internal variations described in the section on morphological characters above. Although no direct single gene-morphological unit association has been observed, a relationship, however, between groups of skeletal and other units localized at specific antero-posterior levels, which together manifest accelerated growth and are genetically transmitted, has been noted (Sawin and Hull, 1946; Peck and Sawin, 1950). Differences in incidence, expressivity, and quantitative measurements of such morphological units, when studied in parental races and as being transmitted to hybrid and subsequent backcross generations, thus provide a clue to the nature, location, and size of specific regions of accelerated growth, and constitute the landmarks which define their limits.

The study of ventral spinous processes (Sawin, 1946) first demonstrated the fact that these areas of greater growth, when brought together in the same race, may enhance each other and induce extra morphological units. Study of sternebral variations (Peck and Sawin, 1950) further demonstrated this point and also showed that it could eliminate them, presumably depending upon the interrelation of the specific genetically induced growth influences involved. Here it also became apparent that these regional growth influences are not only transmitted in the same general quantitative manner as is characteristic of general body size, but that in some cases, at least those affecting general body size and those acting locally, can be distinguished from each other. This was also noted by Tanner and Sawin (1953) in quantitative studies of adult vertebrae.

That these growth processes are not only definable with respect to place (antero-posterior level), but also in time, has been demonstrated in studies of adult populations of some of these races (Sawin and Dietz, 1950, Tanner and Sawin, 1953) and also in 20 and 21 day embryos (Crary, Sawin, and Parsons, 1953). Adults, as compared with newborn young, show evidence in part that the same growth processes are manifest at birth but tend to be masked by later developmental processes, thus emphasizing the importance of longitudinal studies of growth processes, which will demonstrate their limits in time, as well as place. Embryonic studies thus far, as might be expected, being less widely separated in time from newborns, show closer similarities between populations of the same race than do the adults. But, as with the comparison of adults and newborns, they clearly indicate that growth in width of vertebrae, as compared with growth in length in parental races, at least are not controlled by quite the same localized or timed processes, although they are probably transmitted in a similar quantitative manner. Similarly, unpublished data is now available which demonstrates that the pattern of regional growth activity of even so closely associated structures as the centra and neural arches of the axial vertebral complex is not quite the same in these races. Epiphyseal union in the vertebrae, however, does seem to follow the same pattern as onset of ossification in the centra (Sawin and Dietz, 1950). With the recognition of these localized growth processes and better definition of their influence in place and time, a method of genetic analysis appears to be unfolding which should facilitate a more concrete determination of those specific gene effects controlling normal growth and development, which secondarily are responsible for many internal morphological variations.

Attention should also be directed here to several additional investigations which not only constitute further evidence of the principles just discussed but which also provide additional material with which to test them. The first of these is a similar (but longitudinal) comparison of the onset of ossification of the several components of the fore and hind limbs (Crary and Sawin, 1949) in the same races. It shows that the growth processes involved in both general body size and in one of the specific gene differences, *Dw* mentioned above, can also be differentiated specifically in the limb regions. Neither the general growth differences nor the specific Dw gene appear to influence the order of appearance of ossification centers, it being the same in the three populations studied. Time of appearance, however, is significantly different and progress of ossification, as measured by width and length of the third metacarpal or metatarsal, manifests significantly different patterns. The effect of the Dw gene is much greater than the effects of general size.

The second study is in connection with patterns of ossification induced by the Da gene (Crary and Sawin, 1952). The major effects of this gene are upon the femur, pelvis, and scapula, but a highly localized regional effect is also noted upon the atlas and axis which is of both functional and evolutionary significance, as well as being of interest through induction of localized growth in the axial skeleton. Secondarily, the influence upon these vertebrae appears to affect the shape of the skull.

Still another approach to analysis of the regionally greater growth areas is a search for evidence of their effects upon all organs at given specific antero-posterior levels. Theoretically, regional differences noted in the axial skeleton, sternum, and vascular pattern may also be expected to become manifest in others of the soft tissues and organs. That races III and X manifest striking differences in ovary and adrenal size seems easily recognizable, and these differences have been reflected in the potential as well as actual fertility and fecundity of these races (see Section XII on reproduction). Consequently, H. B. Latimer has undertaken a study of organ weights and size in relation to general body size and to the gene Dw, which is at the present time nearing completion. Effects of the Dw gene upon brain and cord size is of particular significance (Latimer and Sawin, 1955).

4. Specific Tissue Differences

Almost nothing has been done to analyze specific tissue differences in the rabbit, although the Belgian Hare, Champagne d'Argent and New Zealand rabbits provide excellent material for genetic analysis of the muscle-bone-fat ratio. The Belgian Hare combines refinement of bone with minimum fleshing quality, an extreme ectomorphic type. The Champagne manifests a refinement of bone which by X-ray is almost identical with the Belgian, but the fleshing quality is relatively the same as the New Zealand which manifests both heavy bone and fleshing. Crosses between these breeds should afford good material for the genetic analyses of these traits which are of great interest in human developmental problems.

5. Maternal Influence

Venge (1950) has made a very intensive study of maternal influence upon birth weight of rabbits based both upon normal breeding experiments and on experiments involving transplantations of fertilized ova.

His material was taken from Polish as the small size and Flemish Giant, Blue Vienna, and from crosses between them as large races. Crosses have been made reciprocally. The total variance of birth weight was separated into hereditary and environmental. The former was further separated into hereditary, in the broad sense, and cytoplasmic, and the latter, into the effects due to litter size, and intrauterine and chance influences. The effects of environmental influences upon birth weight were estimated by comparing transplanted and normal young. In the large race this variance amounted to 30–40% and was greatest in large litters. The effects of uterine environments were 33.7% of the total. In Polish these figures were 20–40% and 41.8%, respectively. On the average, reciprocal cross breeds range 33% above the normal weight due to development in a more favorable environment.

Comparison between normal large-small F_1's and transplanted small-large F_1's, or between normal small-large F_1's and transplanted large-small F_1's should indicate the cytoplasmic effect. From the results obtained, Venge concludes that there is no cytoplasmic influence on the birth weight for either of the two breeds.

By keeping the uterine (and cytoplasmic) factor constant, the variance for genetic differences between the various groups were calculated. Apparently the genetic influence is best able to express itself when the development of the fetus takes place in a comparatively limited uterine space.

In summary of this section, specificity of gene activity with respect to internal morphological units as such, in general, seems to be nonexistent at this time. Morphological units, when considered in relation to their neighbors, appear to be influenced in groups and transmitted in a quantitative manner reminiscent of polygenic inheritance. The manner in which significant racial patterns of morphological units and the regional growth areas which they define blend into each other in crosses, and then both become reestablished and form new combinations in subsequent generations, together with the variations in pattern which occur with age, all point to the need of reorientation of the genetic viewpoint with respect to this sort of variation. Whereas much of the success which Mendel achieved in his analysis of unit character inheritance was due to his, at that time, unique focus of attention upon specific hereditary units with respect to the inheritance of internal morphology, the studies of regional growth described above seem to indicate the need of a broader focus upon such groups of morphological units as may be influenced as a group and to study them and their growth and development longitudinally in time.

X. Genes and Linkage Groups

At the present time, at least 32 specific loci, having one or more alleles, have been recognized by various authors and described as shown in Table 1. Sixteen (possibly 18), or about half of these, have been found to show obvious tendencies to remain associated with genes occupying at least one, in several cases two, other loci as shown below, and the strength of those associations are indicated. The ataxic gene (ax) at present shows some (but not statistically significant) tendency to association with the c locus in chromosome I, and although Nachtsheim believes the epilepsy gene to be an allele of the v locus, the fact that this gene is not always restricted to a blue-eyed white background suggests that it may belong in the same chromosome, but not necessarily at the same locus.

Chromosome				Chromosome			
I	c	y	b	IV	a	Dw	w
	0	14.4	42.8		0	14.7	29.9
II	$duEn$	l		V	br	f	an
	01.2	14.3			0	28.3	36.8
III	r^1	r^2		VI	E	At	
	0	17.2			0	26.2	

XI. Inbreeding and Genetic Stocks

Although intensive efforts to develop inbred races of rabbits have been in progress by the author since 1930, the possibility of development of truly isogenic races is still uncertain. The reason probably is to be found in the number of lethal genes which have accumulated in the rabbit as a result of the long period of out-breeding in domestic breeds. Segregation of these lethal genes not only prunes out a substantial number of offspring relatively early in life, but also makes them susceptible to certain fatal conditions such as cystic kidneys, and respiratory and other infectious diseases. Certainly the number of easily recognizable lethals listed among the known genes of the rabbit (Table 1) would substantiate this interpretation. Our early efforts to inbreed by the accepted methods of inbreeding repeatedly resulted in decline in vigor and the necessity of accepting the results of less close inbreeding for production of the next generations. It was not until conscious effort was directed toward the study, analysis, and selection of characteristics, which in themselves or in combination make for a higher level of reproduction, that progress began to be made in insuring successive sib generations. At the present time two of our longest inbred races, X and III, have had 16 and 22 generations of close breeding in which sib-matings were made when possible, and parent-offspring, first cousins, and in some cases wider matings, were resorted to when necessary. Subsequently it has been possible at present to secure 6 consecutive sib matings with fertility, fecundity, viability, and other reproductive characters maintained well above the average.

Although from the above results the prospects of inbred rabbit races may appear discouraging to laboratory investigators, the evidence is not that inbred races of rabbits are impossible, but that emphasis must be placed (1) upon synthesis of a stock containing a maximum number of the genes essential to high reproduction, and a minimum of deleterious ones before inbreeding is initiated, and (2) once inbreeding is started, upon a program of selective inbreeding which will fix those genes in the homozygous state as rapidly as possible.

Race X, originally descended from Castle's small-sized race, has been bred so as to combine the genes, a, b, e, and c^{ch2} which are now homozygous, and the genes Dw, r^2, and s which are still segregating from heterozygous carriers. These races have been bred in this way to provide genetic tags for use in growth studies and for purposes of economy in linkage tests. Sublines of other races are perpetuating most of the genes listed in Table 1. Eight other inbred races are being maintained by Dr. M. Lurie of the Henry Phipps Institute in Philadelphia. For further discussion of the problems of development and maintenance of inbred races, the reader may be referred to Cumming and Cumming (1954).

XII. REPRODUCTION

Reproduction is a function which, under domestication and laboratory procedures in most species and breeds of livestock, seems to be difficult to maintain at its highest potential level, and especially under inbreeding often tends to deteriorate. Constant selection either consciously or unconsciously is the usual (and an essential) procedure. Few really comprehensive attempts have been made to analyze the genetic factors involved in successful or unsuccessful reproduction in any race, except as they may be of major detriment (such as specific and easily recognized lethal genes) or associated with characters of major economic importance, such as egg or milk production. Yet there is considerable evidence that there are many such factors which either by their own direct action or their interaction with other factors tend to drag down the reproductive level, thereby adversely affecting breed improvement and also growth, sex and maternal behavior patterns, disease resistance, and other medical and biological problems. In this respect the rabbit is no exception. Almost all the studies concerned with reproduction tend to be focused only upon one factor and in most cases there is no consideration of a possible genetic background or possible pliotropic effects of any other factor in the reproductive pattern as a whole. As the result of intensive efforts to develop inbred races of rabbits comparable to those existing in mice and rats, Sawin and Curran (1952) have become increasingly aware of the importance of knowledge of the complete pattern of reproduction. They have attempted to break the problem down into its component parts and to

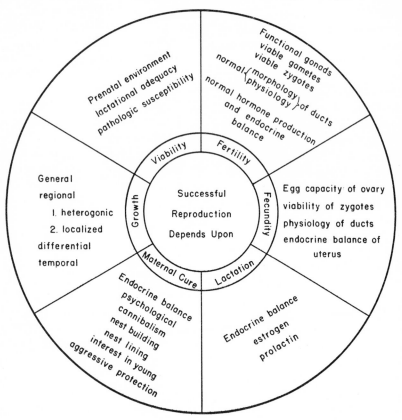

FIG. 5. Factors in reproduction (from Sawin and Curran, 1952).

consider them in relation to each other in the study of racial differences. If the reproductive value of a race is not only considered to be the number of young conceived per individual mother, but the per cent which mature and ultimately achieve production of the next generation, the factors involved may be considered under six categories, as shown in Fig. 5. Information with regard to genetic influences effective within these categories are given below.

a. *Fertility*. Contributions to the genetics of problems in fertility are of two kinds, those dealing with functions of the mother, such as ovulation and transportation of gametes, and those dealing with differential viability, motility, and other functions of the gametes themselves. Chang (1952) noted racial differences in infertility which in one race he could trace to failure to ovulate and failure in ova transportation. Others deal with differential viability and fertilization. Fröhlich and Venge (1948) noted significant individual and racial differences in semen samples, both as to volume of ejaculate and in sperm number and concentration, both of which are significant factors in successful fertilization. Sperm number seems to be correlated with body weight, as is the case with egg number (see section XII, b) and some evidence was found that sperm concentration is influenced by heterosis.

Racial differences in the sex ratio have been noted by Sawin and Gadbois (1947) which can be the result of differences in relative motility, viability, and fertilizability of the x and y sperm, which in turn could be affected by genetic influences affecting the threshold of physiological processes of the female tract. These could be strictly chemical, such as the pH of the tract; endocrine, involving production of several sex and pituitary hormones and their balance; or nutritional, being effective either through the gametes or the mother.

Several attempts have been made to alter the sex ratio by producing conditions in the genital tract more favorable to one type of sperm than to the other. These have centered principally around the acid-alkali balance. The results of methods employing a vaginal douche have not been consistent. Casida and Murphree (1942), after considering these, made a further test, treating the sperm *in vitro*, inseminating artificially, and observing the longevity of sperm in the female tract. Neither sodium bicarbonate nor lactic acid reduced the fertility greatly nor did they affect the sex ratio differentially, although motility was stopped in many cases. For other work of this nature see this reference.

b. *Fecundity*. Gregory (1932) has made a close study of potential fecundity (based upon the number of ruptured follicles) and actual fecundity (based upon litter size) in several races of rabbits. He found that the number of eggs shed at a single ovulation, and the number of young in a single birth are functions of body weight. The small Polish produce an average of 3.97 eggs, the large Flemish 12.9. Hybrids producing an average of 8 are intermediate. They tend to have a greater viability throughout the gestation period. Venge (1950) has observed the same relationships between body size and number of ova released. He also finds that the relationship is closer in the small races than in the large.

Rosahn, Greene, and Hu (1934) made a statistical analysis of litter size in 509 pregnancies involving 11 breeds, and found the population homogeneous with respect to season and mean age of mother at first mating. Variation was greater, however, between breeds than within breeds when divided according to weight; heavier breeds, as in Gregory's case, have the larger litters, a fact also noted much earlier by Castle (see 1940 reference) in his studies on size inheritance.

Chang (1952) found that whereas infertility in one race was the result of failure in ovulation and ova transportation, in another it was primarily due to embryo degeneration. In two other races both ovulation failure and ova transportation were important factors. In heterogeneous races fertility and fecundity were relatively higher than in those more closely bred. He concluded that the inheritance of these physiologic characters involves not only the amount of hormone in the blood but also the reactivity of target organs.

Hammond (1934) recognized two causes of small litter size, one resulting from the number of ova shed per ovulation. The other is the result of a recessive gene carried and transmitted by the mother, which reduces her litter size by means of fetal atrophy. It segregates in inheritance, quite in contrast to the first which is quantitative and continuously variable.

Pickard (1930) also found racial differences in litter size and similar tendencies for intermediateness in hybrids as observed by Gregory.

Wilson (1936) crossed the Sitka (Black Beveran) with wild rabbits with some difficulty, and noted small litter size in several generations and also reduced maternal behavior. This may be of considerable significance in view of the popular belief that hybridization increases fecundity.

c. *Sex and maternal behavior.* Sawin and Crary (1953) have described significant racial differences in specific maternal behavior reactions at parturition. One race builds its nests at the time the young are born. The other builds them from 1 to 4 days prepartum. Associated with this difference are other differences with respect to the quality of the nest and amount of hair that is plucked from the mother's coat to line the nest. The significance of these observations with respect to the endocrine balance of these races was discussed and has led to more extensive studies of both sex and maternal behavior as affected by hormone therapy (as yet unpublished). In brief, it may be stated at this time that race X (the prepartum nest builder) tends to be an "anestrous" race. It enjoys a distinct anestrous period during the months of December and January, and makes a rather poor response to estrogen therapy and to FSH so far as estrous behavior is concerned. Race III, the postpartum nest builder, on the other hand, tends to be sexually much more receptive at all seasons and no matter what the reproductive state. Its potential fecundity is high, perhaps too high in that the very fact that a high ovulatory rate seems frequently to result in failure to implant, or in a high incidence of fetal atrophy and resorption. As detailed information upon the pattern of reproduction has accumulated, one has become increasingly conscious of the importance of having complete knowledge of the entire pattern in order to interpret any of its parts. Sawin (1954) has studied some of these differences in relation to the age of the mother. In race X the life span of the young is longest when they are born of young mothers. In race III offspring of older mothers up to 18 months tend to be longer lived, after which there is a decline. The changes in maternal behavior, gestation, and fecundity with age, some of which are comparable with changes known to occur in thyroidectomy, seem to suggest that here the racial difference is one of endocrine balance. Because of the part which endocrine imbalance is considered to play in several of the constitutional diseases, and also in problems of human and livestock reproduction, the importance of genetic background and of endocrine balance, as measured by sex and maternal behavior, cannot be overemphasized.

d. *Artificial insemination.* The techniques of semen transportation over considerable distance, and of artificial insemination, are now being used by a number of investigators and are even of considerable practical importance in several of the domestic animals including the rabbit. More recently low-temperature storage of spermatozoa has been found practical, but species differ in their response to such technique and to the methods used. Parkes and Palge (1952) have found that, as compared with fowl and human sperm, the rabbit sperm are very sensitive. Chang and Marden (1954) have recently shown that rabbit ova also are capable of surviving aerial transport over long distances. Much is now known about the physiology and mechanics of both ova and sperm transportation inside and outside the body, and about the physiology of fertilization (Chang and Pincus, 1951), and there is appreciable evidence of individual and racial differences. It would seem that the way is now clear for important genetic studies in this field.

XIII. Concluding Remarks

As indicated above, the rabbit has been contributing valuable genetic material for the solution of a wide range of genetic, medical, and other biological problems.

The mutations discussed seem to affect almost every organ system, and the genetic background of growth and development appears to cut across several, if not all, organ systems rather than any one. Although most of these genetic mechanisms have been by no means fully exploited, their present values are both practical and theoretical. Perhaps the most significant ones are those (1) in immunology where it was first shown both that blood differences do conform to the recognized laws of inheritance affecting other characteristics, and that the inciting gene can be linked in the same chromosome with other known genes; (2) in disease resistance where, by consideration of the genetic background, forward steps have been taken in separating the phenomena of resistance and susceptibility into component genetic functions, transmitted by either the pathogenic organism or the host or both, in much the same manner as Mendel separated his unit characters of inheritance; and (3) in the studies of growth and development in which there is now considerable reason to believe that growth processes can be separated genetically in four distinct ways, those affecting growth and body size generally, those affecting it locally, either as specific genes or as gene complexes, those affecting specific tissues, and those acting more generally in time and place through the endocrine glands. Whether or not the specific action of single genes in those cases where polygenic complexes are involved can be isolated so as to demonstrate distinct limits of effect in time and place, as has been done with coat color, still remains to be demonstrated. Because these effects are visually demonstrable in many cases and can be treated quantitatively, such analysis may not be outside the realm of possibility. The fact that the regional growth differences do seem to cut across more than one organ system is also of special significance in view of the increasing evidence of the part played by endocrine imbalance, in at least certain types of constitutional disease, and to some extent also in sex, maternal, and possibly other types of behavior.

Another significant fact emerging from the regional growth studies is the manner of appearance or disappearance of specific morphological units, or of changes in their relative size, depending upon the genetically induced areas of greater or lesser growth transmitted by the parental races and the manner of their interactions. Since several morphological mutants such as the *Da* and *Dw* genes are also known to have such effects, but in different locales, material is now available for testing both the biological interaction as well as some of the pleiotropic effects. In the latter connection, the effects of the regional growth influences, first, upon the endocrine system and, secondarily, through endocrine balance upon reproduction, sex and maternal patterns, and disease are of special significance.

Pleiotropism has been discussed repeatedly in connection with analysis of specific mutations and with tissue and cell specificity, but, in the study of internal variations and their underlying growth influences, there seems to be a communion of gene influence, which transcends all organ and tissue boundaries, and still has its own rather specific regional limitations. Attention focused, on the one hand, upon the specific action of these influences themselves in reciprocal hybrids, and, on the other, on their action, as influenced by diverse maternal influences and by other genetic backgrounds such as induced by specific genes, as for example, the dwarf (*Dw*) and achondroplasia (*Da*), should offer fruitful approaches to the activities of the growth promoting genes. In all of such studies the importance of the longitudinal approach in time cannot be over emphasized.

Although analysis of the chromosomal architecture of the rabbit has not kept pace with the rate of discovery of new genes, this is partly due to the number which are lethal recessives, linkage tests for which, although not impossible, are very slow and expensive to make. One multiple recessive race is now available which facilitates this work. Others undoubtedly will be made eventually. Such races are not only valuable for linkage tests, but, as Castle demonstrated, they also may be of value both in showing their pleiotropic effects, or as tags of less obvious growth or other physiologically gene activities. They have been of particular value in the practical studies of the type of constitutional disease which they represent, and, at the same time, genetically, in the analysis of primary gene activity.

XIV. Acknowledgments

I should like to express my grateful personal appreciation to Dr. W. E. Castle, who very early recognized the value of the domestic rabbit for experimental laboratory purposes, and particularly the importance of knowledge of its genetic background. His scholarly approach and penetrating insight laid the foundation for much that is written in these pages, and his guidance, untiring efforts, and abiding interests have been a continuing source of inspiration to me, and doubtless to others, during the past 25 years.

XV. References

Anders, M. V., 1945. The histopathology of a new type of hereditary loss of coordination in the domestic rabbit. *Am. J. Anat.* **76**, 183–194.

Anders, M. V., 1947. Microscopic study of the inner ear of the ataxic rabbit. *Arch. Otolaryngol.* **46**, 335–340.

Antonitis, J. J., Crary, D. D., Sawin, P. B., and Cohen, C. Sound induced seizures in the rabbit. *J. Heredity* **45**: 279–284.

Brown, W. H., and Pearce, Louise, 1945. Hereditary achondroplasia in the rabbit. I. Physical appearance and general features. *J. Exptl. Med.* **82**, 241–260.

Casida, L. E., and Murphree, R. L., 1942. Fertility and sex ratios in the rabbit. *J. Heredity* **33**, 434–449.

Castle, W. E., 1930. "The Genetics of Domestic Rabbits." Harvard Univ. Press, Cambridge.

Castle, W. E., 1933. The furless rabbit. *J. Heredity* **24**, 81–86.

Castle, W. E., 1940. "Mammalian Genetics." Harvard Univ. Press, Cambridge.

Castle, W. E., 1941. Influence of certain color mutations on body size in mice, rats, and rabbits. *Genetics* **26**, 177–191.

222 PAUL B. SAWIN

Castle, W. E., and Gregory, P. W., 1931. The effects of breed on growth of the embryo in fowls and rabbits. *Science* **73**, 680–681.

Castle, W. E., and Keeler, C. E., 1933. Blood group inheritance in the rabbit. *Proc. Natl. Acad. Sci. U.S.* **19**, 92.

Castle, W. E., and Law, L. W., 1936. Satin, a new hair mutation of the rabbit. *J. Heredity* **27**, 235–240.

Castle, W. E., and Nachtsheim, H., 1933. Linkage interrelations of three genes for rex coat in the rabbit. *Proc. Natl. Acad. Sci. U.S.* **19**, 1006–1011.

Castle, W. E., and Reed, S. C., 1936. Studies of inheritance in lop-eared rabbits. *Genetics* **21**, 297–309.

Castle, W. E., and Sawin, P. B., 1941. Genetic linkage in the rabbit. *Proc. Nat. Acad. Sci. U.S.* **27**, 519–523.

Chang, M. C., 1952. An experimental analysis of female sterility in the rabbit. *Fertility & Sterility* **3**, 251–262.

Chang, M. C., and Marden, W. G. R., 1954. The aerial transport of fertilized mammalian ova. *J. Heredity* **45**, 75–78.

Chang, M. C., and Pincus, G., 1951. Physiology of fertilization in mammals. *Physiol. Revs.* **31**, 1–26.

Cohen, C., 1954. Blood groups in the rabbit. In press. *J. Immunol.* **74**, not printed yet.

Crary, D. D., and Sawin, P. B., 1949. Morphogenetic studies in the rabbit. VI. Genetic factors influencing the ossification pattern of the limbs. *Genetics* **34**, 508–523.

Crary, D. D., and Sawin, P. B., 1952. A second achondroplasia in the domestic rabbit. *J. Heredity* **43**, 254–259.

Crary, D. D., and Sawin, P. B., 1953. Some factors influencing the growth potential of the skin in the domestic rabbit. *J. Exptl. Zool.* **124**, 31–62.

Crary, D. D., Sawin, P. B., and Parsons, A. H., 1953. Regional growth in the axial skeleton of the rabbit. *Anat. Record* **117**, 600.

Culbertson, J. T., 1935. The relative precipitin response of various breeds of rabbits. The possibility of a genetic factor in antibody production. *Am. J. Hyg.* **22**, 190–198.

Cumming, C. N., and Cumming, E. L., 1954. Carworth Farms Quarterly Letter. New City, New York.

DaRosa, F. M., 1945. Uma Nova Mutacao, Luxacao congenita da anca, no coelho. *Rev. med. Vet. y Parasitol.* **10**, 1–23.

DaRosa, F. M., 1946. Hidrocefalia, uma nova mutacao no coelhi. *Rev. med. Vet. y Parasitol.* **11**, 1–55.

David, L. T., 1932. External expression and comparative dermal histology of hereditary hairlessness in mammals. *Z. Zellforsch. u. mikros Anat.* **14**, 616–719.

Drapeau, E. E., 1933. Histological basis of hairlessness in the rabbit. *J. Morphol.* **54**, 365–388.

Dunlop, G., and Hammond, J., 1937. The growth and proportions of the rabbit's ear in relation to body weight. *J. Genetics* **34**, 463–475.

Fischer, W., 1935. Über Blutgruppeneigenschaften beim Kaninchen. *Z. Immunitätsforsch.* **86**, 97.

Fröhlich, A., and Venge, D., 1948. Semen production in different breeds of rabbits. *Acta Agri. Suecana* **3**, 83–88.

Glick, D., 1940. Properties of tropine esterase. *J. Biol. Chem.* **134**, 617–625.

Glick, D., and Glaubach, S., 1941. The occurrence and distribution of atropine esterase, and the specificity of tropin esterases. *J. Gen. Physiol.* **25**, 197–205.

Greene, H. S. N., 1932. Hereditary variations in the skull of the rabbit. *Science* **76**, 421–422.

Greene, H. S. N., 1933. Oxycephaly and allied conditions in man and in the rabbit. *J. Exptl. Med.* **57**, 967–976.

Greene, H. S. N., 1935. Hereditary brachydactylia and associated abnormalities in the rabbit. *Science* **81**, 405–407.

Greene, H. S. N., 1939. Familial mammary tumors in the rabbit. I. Clinical history. II. Gross and microscopic pathology. III. Factors concerned in their genesis and development. *J. Exptl. Med.* **70**, 147–184.

Greene, H. S. N., 1940. A dwarf mutation in the rabbit. *J. Exptl. Med.* **71**, 839–856.

Greene, H. S. N., 1941. Uterine adenomata in the rabbit. III. Susceptibility as a function of constitutional factors. *J. Exptl. Med.* **73**, 273–292.

Greene, H. S. N., Hu, C. K., and Brown, H. B., 1934. A lethal dwarf mutation in the rabbit with stigmata of endocrine abnormality. *Science* **79**, 487–488.

Greene, H. S. N., and Saxton, J. A., 1939. Hereditary brachydactylia and allied abnormalities in the rabbit. *J. Exptl. Med.* **69**, 301–304.

Gregory, P. W., 1930. The early embryology of the rabbit. *Carnegie Inst. Wash. Publ.* **407**, 141–168.

Gregory, P. W., 1932. The potential and actual fecundity of some breeds of rabbits. *J. Exptl. Zool.* **62**, 271–285.

Gregory, J. E., and Rich, A. R., 1946. The experimental production of anaphylactic pulmonary lesions with the basic characteristics of rheumatic pneumonitis. *Bull. Johns Hopkins Hosp.* **78**, 1–12.

Hadjidimitroff, P., 1933. Die pigmentverteilung im Kaninchenhaar. *Z. Zücht. Reihe B. Tierzücht. Züchtgsbiol.* **27**, 169–324.

Hammond, J., 1934. Inheritance of fertility in rabbits. American Poultry and Rabbit Conference, Harper Adams College.

Hardy, T. M. P., and Markley, M. H., 1944. A microscopic study of coat variations in white New Zealand and angora rabbits. *J. Heredity* **35**, 183–192.

Harm, Helga, 1952. Beitrage zur Morphologie und genetik der Pelgeranomalie bei Mensch und Kaninchen. *Z. menschl. Vererbungs.-u. Konstitionslehre* **30**, 501–539.

Heard, D. H., Hinde, I. T., and Mynors, L. S., 1949. An experimental study of haemolytic disease of the newborn due to isoimmunization of pregnancy. I. An attempt to produce the syndrome in the rabbit. *J. Hyg.* **49**, 119–131.

Hu, C. K., and Greene, H. S. N., 1935. A lethal acromegalic mutation in the rabbit. *Science* **81**, 25–26.

Hull, B., 1947. Morphogenetic studies in the rabbit. IV. The inheritance of developmental patterns in rib ossification. *J. Exptl. Zool.* **105**, 173–197.

Inman, O. R., 1941. Embryology of hereditary brachydactyly in the rabbit. *Anat. Record* **79**, 483–501.

Keeler, C. E., and Castle, W. E., 1933. A further study of blood groups in the rabbit. *Proc. Natl. Acad. Sci. U.S.* **19**, 403.

Kellner, A., and Hedal, E. F., 1953. Experimental erythroblastosis fetalis in rabbits. I. Characterization of a pair of allelic blood group factors and their specific immune isoantibodies. *J. Exptl. Med.* **97**, 33–60.

Kislovsky, D. A., 1928. Naked—a recessive mutation in the rabbit. *J. Heredity* **19**, 438–439.

Kleczkowska, J., and Kleczkowski, A., 1939. Über die Vererbung der Fahigkeit zur precipitinbildung beim Kaninchen. *Z. Immunitätsforsch.* **95**, 218–226.

Knopfmacher, H. P., 1942. A study of four antigenic components of rabbit's erythrocytes. *J. Immunol.* **44**, 121–128.

Kröning, F., 1939. Ein neuer Fall von erblichem Zwergwuchs beim Kaninchen. *Biol. Zentr.* **59**, 148–160.

Latimer, H. B., and Sawin, P. B., 1955. The weight of the brain, of its parts and the weight and length of the spinal cord in the rabbit (Race X). *J. Comp. Neurol.* in press.

Levine, P., and Landsteiner, K., 1929. On immune isoagglutinins in rabbits. *J. Immunol.* **17**, 559.

Levine, P., and Landsteiner, K., 1931. On immune isoagglutinins in rabbits. *J. Immunol.* **21**, 513.

Levy, J., and E. Michel, 1938. Enzymatic hydrolysis of atropine. *Compt. rend. soc. biol.* **129**, 820–822.

Lurie, M. B., 1950. Mechanisms affecting spread of tuberculosis in animals. *Ann. N.Y. Acad. Sci.* **52**, 1074–1090.

Lurie, M. B., Abramson, S., and Heppleston, A. G., 1952. On the response of genetically resistant and susceptible rabbits to the quantitative inhalation of human type tubercle bacilli and the nature of resistance to tuberculosis. *J. Exptl. Med.* **95**, 119.

Lurie, M. B., Zappa Sodi, P. Carcona-Lynch, E., and Dannenberg, A., Jr., 1952. The response to the intracutaneous inoculation of BCG as an index of native resistance to tuberculosis. *J. Immunol.* **68**, 368–387.

Magnuson, H. J., Rosenau, B. J., and Greenberg, B. G., 1951. The effects of sex, castration and testosterone upon the susceptibility of rabbits to experimental syphilis. *Am. J. Syphilis Gonorrhea Venereal Diseases* **35**, 146–163.

Marchlewski, T., 1934. Reverse mutations in color factors in the rabbit. *J. Genet.* **29**, 153–157.

Marcussen, P. V., 1936. Ueber Gruppendifferenzierung bei Kaninchen mit besonderem Hinblick auf die Spezifität der Isoimmunsera. *Z. Immunitätsforsch.* **89**, 453–472.

McNutt, C. W., and Sawin, P. B., 1943. Hereditary variations in the vena cava inferior of the rabbit. *Am. J. Anat.* **72**, 259–287.

Nachtsheim, H., 1937. Erbpathologische untersuchungen an Kaninchen. *Z. indukt. Abstamm.-u. Verebungol.* **73**, 463.

Nachtsheim, H., 1938a. Die Genetik einiger Erbleiden des Nervensystems des Kaninchens. Vortrage auf dem Internationalen Fortbildungskurs. Gegenwarts Probleme der psychiatrisch-neurologischen Forschung. Berlin, 1938.

Nachtsheim, H., 1938b. Erbpathologie der Haustiere. Part 1: Organe des äusseren Keimblattes. Fortschritte der Erbpathologie, Rassenhygiene und ihrer Grenzgebiete. **2**, 58–104.

Nachtsheim, H., 1939. Erbleiden des Nervensystems der Säugetiere. Handbook der Erbbiologie des Menschen. Vol. 5, pp. 1–58.

Nachtsheim, H., 1940. Die Erbanlagen des Säugetierauges. Handbook der Erbbiologie des Menschen. Vol. 3, pp. 543–574.

Nachtsheim, H., 1950. The pelger-anomaly in man and rabbit. *J. Heredity* **41**, 131–137.

Opie, E. L., and Freund, J., 1937. An experimental study of protective inoculation with heat killed tubercle bacilli. *J. Exptl. Med.* **66**, 761–787.

Patten, B. M., 1953. Embryological stages in the establishing of myeloschisis with spina bifida. *Am. J. Anat.* **93**, 365–390.

Parkes, A. S., and Palge, J., 1952. *in* "The Physiology of Mammalian Germ Cells" (J. Hammond and S. J. Folley, eds.). Little Brown, Boston.

Pearce, Louise, 1948. Hereditary osteopetrosis of the rabbit. II. X-ray, hematologic, and chemical observations. *J. Exptl. Med.* **88**, 597–620.

Pearce, Louise, 1950a. Hereditary osteopetrosis of the rabbit. III. Pathologic observa‑ tions; skeletal abnormalities. *J. Exptl. Med.* **92,** 591–600.

Pearce, Louise, 1950b. Hereditary osteopetrosis of the rabbit. IV. Pathologic observa‑ tions; general features. *J. Exptl. Med.* **92,** 601–624.

Pearce, Louise, and Brown, W. H., 1945a. Hereditary achondroplasia in the rabbit. II. Pathologic aspects. *J. Exptl. Med.* **82,** 261–280.

Pearce, Louise, and Brown, W. H., 1945b. Hereditary achondroplasia in the rabbit. III. Genetic aspects; general considerations. *J. Exptl. Med.* **82,** 281–295.

Pearce, Louise, and Brown, W. H., 1948. Hereditary osteopetrosis of the rabbit. I. General features and course of disease; general aspects. *J. Exptl. Med.* **88,** 579–596.

Peck, E. D., and Sawin, P. B., 1950. Morphogenetic studies of the rabbit. VIII. Genetic variations in the sternum as determined by the interaction of general and of regionally specific growth factors. *J. Exptl. Zool.* **114,** 335–357.

Pickard, J. N., 1929a. Further studies on the wool production of angora rabbits. *Harper Adams Utility Poultry J.* **15,** 7.

Pickard, J. N., 1929b. A brown-and-black rabbit. *J. Heredity* **20,** 483.

Pickard, J. N., 1930. A preliminary study of some of the factors influencing the dura‑ tion of pregnancy and litter size in the rabbit. World Poultry Congress.

Pickard, J. N., 1936. A black-blue Dutch rabbit. *J. Genet.* **33,** 337.

Pickard, J. N., 1941. Waved—a new coat type in rabbits. *J. Genetics* **42,** 215–222.

Rich, A. R., and Gregory, J. E., 1943. Experimental evidence that lesions with the basic characteristics of rheumatic carditis can result from anaphylactic hyper‑ sensitivity. *Bull. Johns Hopkins Hosp.* **73,** 239–264.

Rosahn, P. D., Greene, H. S. N., and Hu, C. K., 1934. Hereditary variations in litter size of rabbits. *Proc. Soc. Exptl. Biol. Med.* **31,** 1214–1216.

Sang, J. H., and Sobey, W. R., 1954. The genetic control of response to antigenic stimuli. *J. Immunol.* **72,** 52–65.

Sawin, P. B., 1932. Albino allelomorphs of the rabbit with special reference to blue- eyed chinchilla and its variations. *Carnegie Inst. Wash. Publ.* **427,** 15–50.

Sawin, P. B., 1934. Linkage of "wide band" and agouti genes. *J. Heredity* **25,** 477–481.

Sawin, P. B., 1937. Preliminary studies of hereditary variation in the axial skeleton of the rabbit. *Anat. Record* **69,** 407–428.

Sawin, P. B., 1945. Morphogenetic studies of the rabbit. I. Regional specificity of hereditary factors affecting homeotic variations in the axial skeleton. *J. Exptl. Zool.* **100,** 301–329.

Sawin, P. B., 1946. Morphogenetic studies of the rabbit. III. Skeletal variations resulting from the interaction of gene determined growth forces. *Anat. Record* **96,** 183–200.

Sawin, P. B., 1954. The influence of age of mother on pattern of reproduction. *Ann. N.Y. Acad. Sci.* **57,** 564–574.

Sawin, P. B., and Crary, D. D., 1951. Morphogenetic studies of the rabbit. X. Racial variations in the gall bladder. *Anat. Record* **110,** 573–590.

Sawin, P. B. and Crary, D. D., 1953. Genetic and physiological background of repro‑ duction in the rabbit. II. Some racial differences in the pattern of maternal behavior. *Behaviour* **6,** 128–146.

Sawin, P. B., and Curran, R., 1952. Genetic and physiological background of repro‑ duction in the rabbit. I. The problem and its biological significance. *J. Exptl. Zool.* **120,** 165–202.

Sawin, P. B., and Dietz, D., 1950. Morphogenetic studies of the rabbit. IX. Masking of prenatal growth gradients in adults. "Moderne Biologie." F. W. Peters, Berlin.

Sawin, P. B., and Edmonds, H. W., 1949. Aortic arch variations in relation to regionally specific growth differences. *Anat. Record* **195,** 377–395.

Sawin, P. B., and Gadbois, D. S., 1947. Genetic influences upon the sex ratio in the rabbit. *Genetics* **32,** 287–302.

Sawin, P. B., and Glick, D., 1943. Atropinesterase, a genetically determined enzyme in the rabbit. *Proc. Natl. Acad. Sci. U.S.* **29,** 55–59.

Sawin, P. B., and Hull, I. B., 1946. Morphogenetic studies of the rabbit. II. Evidence of regionally specific hereditary factors influencing the extent of the lumbar region. *J. Morphol.* **78,** 1–26.

Sawin, P. B., and Nace, M. A. G., 1948. Inheritance of an assymetrical vascular pattern. *J. Morphol.* **82,** 331–353.

Sawin, P. B., Anders, M. V., and Johnson, R. B., 1942. "Ataxia," a hereditary nervous disorder of the rabbit. *Proc. Natl. Acad. Sci. U.S.* **28,** 123–127.

Sawin, P. B., Griffith, M. A., and Stuart, C. A., 1944. Genetic linkage of blood types in the rabbit. *Proc. Natl. Acad. Sci.* **30,** 217–221.

Sawin, P. B., Stuart, C. A., and Wheeler, K. M., 1943. Pictorial presentation of antigen and antibody relations associated with the "A" character in the rabbit. *J. Heredity* **34,** 179–186.

Schnecke, C., 1941. Zwergwuchs beim Kaninchen und seine Vererbung. *Z. menschl. Vererbungs.-u. Konstitutionslehre* **25,** 425–457.

Smith, S. E., 1944. Another case of a black-blue mosaic in the dutch rabbit. *J. Heredity* **35,** 325–326.

Suchalla, H., 1943. Variabilität und Erblickeit von Schädelmerkmalen bei Zwerg-und Riesemassen; dargestellt an Hermelin-und Widderkaninchen. *Z. morphol. u. anthropol.* **40,** 274–333.

Tanner, J. M., and Sawin, P. B., 1952. Morphogenetic studies of the rabbit. XI. Differences in the growth of the vertebral column between three inbred races of rabbits. *J. Anat.* **87,** 54–65.

Uchida, I. A., 1953. Possible genetic factors in the etiology of rheumatic fever. *Am. J. Human Genet.* **5,** 61–69.

Venge, O., 1950. Studies of the maternal influence on the birth weight in rabbits. *Acta Zool. Intern. Tidskr. Zool.* **31,** 1–148.

Voloss-Mialhe, C., 1950. Role due sympathique dans la pigmentation du lapin *Himalaya, Compt. rend. soc. biol.* **144,** 19–20.

Wheeler, K. M., 1938. Group specific agglutinins in rabbit serums for human cells. III. Cold agglutinins. *J. Immunol.* **34,** 409–427.

Wheeler, K. M., Sawin, P. B., and Stuart, C. A., 1939a. Group-specific agglutinins in rabbit serums for human cells. V. Inheritance of the A-character. *J. Immunol.* **36,** 349–359.

Wheeler, K. M., Sawin, P. B., and Stuart, C. A., 1939b. Group-specific agglutinins in rabbit serums for human cells. VI. Immune-specific M-agglutinins. *J. Immunol.* **37,** 159–167.

Wilson, M. G., 1940. Rheumatic fever, The Commonwealth Fund, New York.

Wilson, W. K., 1936. Fertility in Flemish and smaller types of rabbits. *Nature* **146,** 721–722.

Wilson, W. R., and Dudley, F. J., 1946. Fat colors and fur colors in different varieties of rabbits. *J. Genet.* **47,** 290–294.

The Origin and Evolution of Cultivated Barley

Ryuhei Takahashi

*The Ohara Institute for Agricultural Biology, University of Okayama, Kurashiki,
Okayama-ken, Japan*

I. Introduction

Barley is one of our most important food crops, grown widely over the earth from subarctic to tropic regions. It is generally believed that our remote ancestors depended on this crop more than we do now, and that it played an important role in the origin and development of neolithic culture in the Old World. Therefore, the problem of the origin of barley interests archaeologists and anthropologists, as it does agronomists and geneticists.

For a study of the origin and evolution of a cultivated plant, it is important to investigate its wild progenitor, the place where it was first brought into cultivation, and also the route of migration and the processes of its evolutionary change under cultivation. As pointed out by De

Candolle (1882) and others, this aim can be attained by integrating available information from cultural-historical investigations, namely, archaeological, anthropological, and philological studies, on the one hand, and the data obtained by biological researches, namely, comparative-morphological, biogeographical, ecological, genetic, and cytological studies, on the other.

All the varieties of barley, including the various cultivated forms and wild species allied to them, have the same number of chromosomes; they are easily crossed together, and produce completely fertile hybrids. This warns us that the ordinary cytogenetical methods used for studies of the origin of amphidiploid crop plants, such as wheat, tobacco, and cotton, cannot be applied to barley. Discovery of ancestral forms, and accumulation of important information regarding genetic and geographic differentiation of various cultivated varieties in relation to their wild relatives, may throw light on this problem. Since barley has many distinctive characters, and their genetic behavior has been thoroughly worked out, they are especially suitable for study of the evolution of the cultivated varieties. This investigation will probably afford geneticists as well as evolutionists knowledge that could hardly be expected from studies of other cultivated plants.

We owe our fundamental knowledge concerning the origin and evolution of cultivated barley to many previous investigators, especially De Candolle, Vavilov, and Schiemann. Still deeper insight into this problem was gained during the past two decades through the efforts of Freisleben, Åberg, Brücher, and others. The writer proposes to review the recent advances in this field.

II. HISTORICAL EVIDENCES

Archaeologists, philologists, and botanists have cooperated with considerable success in characterizing the kinds of barley utilized by our remote ancestors and the times and places of their cultivation. Netolitzky (1926) found a large quantity of broken grains of barley in the stomach and bowels of a mummy apparently of the Predynastic period (5,000 BC). Also, a quantity of ears, carbonized grains, and impressions of grains on vessels and bricks have been unearthed. It has thus become evident that people at that time utilized barley, along with emmer and einkorn wheats and a kind of millet, as their staple food, and possibly for brewing as well. It is noteworthy that the barley at that time was exclusively six-rowed, mostly of the dense-eared type. The six-rowed and lax-eared form, *tetrastichum*, was found among excavations from Saqqara Pyramid, which is assumed to be as much as 5,000 years old. Åberg (1950) found this specimen of barley to be much similar to the variety Manchuria that had originated perhaps in North Africa. According to Schulz (1916) and Schiemann (1951b), a naked variety of barley was grown in Egypt during the period from 3,000 to 2,000 BC. The monuments and ruins of ancient Babylon contained six-rowed and dense-eared barley and emmer wheat which had been used apparently as staple food. The same kind of barley has been discovered among remains of the neolithic and bronze ages in various parts of Europe (Schiemann, 1932).

It has generally been recognized that the cultivation of two-rowed barley began later than that of the six-rowed form. It should be noted in this connection that the identification of the two-rowed barley is difficult, unless plenty of material is available. The oldest authentic records of this variety are believed to be found among the Greek and Roman archives of about 300 BC. Two-rowed barley was rather rare until the 16th and 17th centuries in Europe, when suddenly it became rather common.

There are no records or archaeological discoveries for ancient India or China comparable to those of ancient Egypt and Mesopotamia. Hoops (1905) from his linguistic study, suspected that barley was a staple food of the Indo-Germanians before the time of the split of their country. Schulz (1912) and others are of the opinion that the six-rowed barley of the neolithic age might have been introduced into Europe by the migration of the race. According to Roxburgh, a six-rowed dense-eared variety was the only barley grown in India during the later 18th century. Chinese prehistoric remains contain tortoise-shells and bone fragments engraved with idiographs signifying barley. There are also some Chinese archives dating back to about 200 BC in which such idiographs may be found. According to Ikata (1941), it is suspected that barley was first introduced into Japan by Korean immigrants at the dawn of Japanese history. It is more than probable that the barleys cultivated in Japan were introduced several times directly from China or indirectly from Korea.

III. Possible Ancestors of Cultivated Barley

The genus *Hordeum* comprises about 25 species. According to Åberg (1940), they may be classified in the following four sections: *Stenostachys* Nevski, *Campestria* Ands., *Bulbohordeum* Nevski, and *Cerealia* Ands. The first three sections are comprised of various perennial or annual wild species, some of which are tetraploids or hexaploids presumably established by duplications of chromosome sets (Berg, 1936; Oinuma, 1952). Oinuma (1952) has found that the karyotypes of some wild diploid and tetraploid barleys, namely, *Hordeum pusillum* Nutt, *H. Gussoneanum* Parl., *H. murinum* L., and *H. nodosum* L. are of a_2 or a_3 types. These types are quite similar to those found among cultivated barley forms.

In spite of this fact, the species belonging to these three sections have very small grains. This morphological distinction indicates that their genetic constitutions are very different from that of the forms in the fourth section (see Fig. 1). Therefore, it is hard to assume that any cultivated form could have arisen from the wild species belonging to the first three sections through genetic changes while under domestication.

In the section *Cerealia* Ands. are included all of the cultivated forms and two kinds of wild barley. Åberg and Wiebe (1945) classified them in

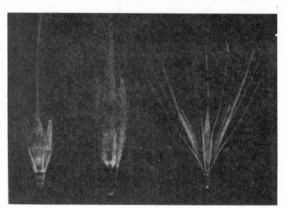

Fɪɢ. 1. Spikelet triplets of three species of the genus *Hordeum*. Left, *H. distichum;* center, *H. Spontaneum* var. *eu-spontaneum;* right, *H. murinum*.

the following five species, on the basis of brittleness of rachis and number of kernel rows on the ear:

(1) *Hordeum agriocrithon* E. Åberg   Ear brittle, six-row
(2) *H. spontaneum* C. Koch   Ear brittle, two-row
(3) *H. vulgare* L. emend. Lam.   Ear tough, six-row
(4) *H. distichum* L. emend. Lam.   Ear tough, two-row
(5) *H. irregulare* Åberg et Wiebe   Ear tough, kernel row
  irregular.

These species are winter or summer annuals, and have seven pairs of chromosomes. There is nothing suggesting physiological isolation among these species, and they may reasonably be grouped together under the single species, *H. sativum* Jess. It thus seems only natural to consider that the two wild species, *H. agriocrithon* and *H. spontaneum*, are closely related to the cultivated forms.

The wild two-rowed species, *Hordeum spontaneum*, was first described by Koch in 1848. This species is similar in many respects to some of the cultivated forms belonging to *H. distichum* L. emend. Lam., differing only in such characteristics as spontaneous disarticulation of rachises, very long and rough awns, densely haired empty glumes, and an extremely long period of dormancy of seeds. Five botanical varieties have been described by Russian investigators. Of these, the variety called *eu-spontaneum* differs from the others by its straw-colored ear and extremely long and stiff awn (Fig. 1). The remaining four varieties are rather similar in appearance but with somewhat shorter awns than *eu-spontaneum*. They are designated respectively *ischnatherum*, *bactrianum*,

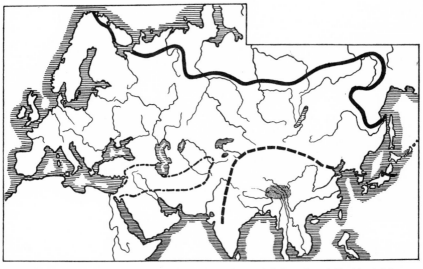

🟤 Area of *H. agriocrithon*.	◀●◀ Boundary of Oriental and Occidental types.
⊂⊃ Area of *H. spontaneum*.	◀◥ North limits of barley growing.

FIG. 2. The distribution of *Hordeum agriocrithon* and *H. spontaneum*, and the boundary between the Oriental and Occidental types of cultivated barley.

turcomanicum, and *transcaspicum*, and are distinguished from one another by yellow, gray, or black color of ear and awns. As shown in Fig. 2, the varieties of this species are found wild in regions of North Afghanistan, Iran, Iraq, the Caucasus, Asia Minor, and Arabia, with straw-colored forms the most prevalent. According to Schulz (1912) and Vavilov (1926), this species is found also in Morocco, Abyssinia, and Marmarica in northern Africa.

Six-rowed wild barley was merely a hypothetical form until the last decade, and its discovery had been long awaited by students of the origin of barleys. This expectation was realized by Åberg in 1938, when he found two kernels of covered barley in a seed sample of wheat gathered by H. Smith at Taofu, East Tibet, and confirmed them to be six-rowed barleys with brittle rachises. They were named *Hordeum agriocrithon*

E. Åberg. Stimulated by this discovery, further intensive studies on Tibetan barley were made by Freisleben (1943), Brücher and Åberg (1950), and Schiemann (1951a) and resulted in the discovery of ten or more seeds of wild six-rowed barley among seed samples of other cereals collected in central and southern Tibet. Among them, the following distinctive varieties are included: *eu-agriocrithon*, with straw-colored ears and long awns; *paradoxon*, with long-awned central row but without lateral awn on the ear; *dawoense*, with lateral awns shorter than central awns, and with purplish ear and ligule; and *eu-agriocrithon* (*nigri-agriocrithon*), a black-eared form. These findings suggest that various forms of six-rowed barleys with brittle rachises are distributed in the regions along the Himalaya mountain ranges.

There is no doubt as to the spontaneity of *Hordeum spontaneum*, as its name indicates. However, this is not the case with *H. agriocrithon*. Freisleben (1943) was of the opinion that the brittle-eared forms of *H. agriocrithon* type found in the vicinity of Lhasa, the capital of Tibet, are probably primitive cultivated varieties of barley that are still being grown for some agricultural purpose. Its spontaneity is open to question, because the original samples of kernels were all found among mixtures of seed samples of cultivated wheat or naked barley, and no one has ever seen them in the wild state. Furthermore, they seem to have less distinctive wild features than *H. spontaneum*, and are apparently closely related to the cultivated forms endemic to East Asia. Further evidence may lead to the solution of this question. New discoveries may possibly include more primitive wild forms, prototypes of the brittle forms now known.

If one wishes to show a wild plant to be a possible progenitor of the cultivated form, it is desirable to demonstrate that the latter can be readily derived from the former by a genetic mechanism known to us. The close morphological resemblance of the two wild species of barley to some of the cultivated varieties indicates similarity in their genetic constitutions. Ubisch (1919), in her study on the genetic behavior of *H. spontaneum* by means of several crosses with some varieties, confirmed that this wild barley shares 18 alleles of "normal" characters with such two-rowed, lax-eared cultivated varieties as *nutans* and *nigricans*. Åberg (1940) and Johnson and Åberg (1943) obtained similar results with *H. agriocrithon*.

IV. Phylogeny in the Light of Comparative-Morphological Studies

De Candolle was the first to study the origin of barley by means of biological methods. He considered the two-rowed wild species, *Hordeum spontaneum*, found in western Asia to be the possible ancestor from which six-rowed cultivated barley was derived before the era of ancient Egyptian civilization. Another possibility has also been suggested by him that there once existed a six-rowed wild barley which became extinct within historic time. This statement, though simple, is highly suggestive, for it relates to the old question of whether the origin of cultivated barley is monophyletic or diphyletic, pointing out at the same time the importance of the number of kernel rows.

Körnicke (1885) constructed a phylogenetical chart of the various cultivated forms of barley from *H. spontaneum* as follows:

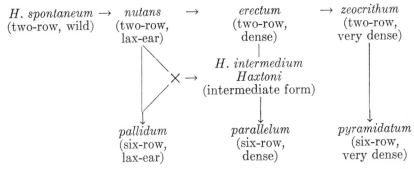

Subsequently he modified this scheme to some extent, and propounded that *H. Ithaburense* Bois. (*H. spontaneum* C. Koch) var. *ischnatherum* Cosson might be the progenitor of the six-rowed barley, because the specimen of this variety that he examined had ears the appearance of which was intermediate between those of these two forms. According to Åberg (1940), however, Cosson's original specimen has two-rowed ears, and no enlarged and awned lateral florets.

At the beginning of the present century, there appeared opinions maintaining that six-rowed barley had been derived from an unknown six-row wild prototype instead of from a two-row form. Tschermak (1914) confirmed by his crossing experiments that all the intermediate forms between two-rowed and six-rowed varieties were heterozygous; neither a six-rowed form nor an intermediate form could appear in the progeny without a six-rowed parent. He concluded that a six-rowed wild form must have existed besides *H. spontaneum*. Rimpau (1892) and Nowacki (1920) disagreed with Körnicke's view, as it is improbable that the florets once reduced would recover their fertility.

Larionow (1929) tried to derive the origin of barley from a closely related genus *Elymus*. According to him, both the two-rowed and the six-rowed cultivated barleys had originated from a common tough-rachis species of *Elymus* having three spikelets at each rachis node; the differentiation of the two varieties advanced in parallel. This view, however, was not widely accepted. From a phylogenetic study on the tribe *Hordeae*, Åberg (1940) holds that the evolution within this tribe has taken place by rudimentation of organs, and that the section *Cerealia* Ands. probably evolved from the six-rowed form through the two-rowed form to *deficiens*. The genetic behavior of the fertility of lateral florets in cultivated barley has a rather complicated feature. According to a recent study by Woodward (1949), this character pair seems to be governed by genes in a multiple allelic series: vv determines the six-rowed character, VV or V^dV^d the two-rowed character with lateral florets which are exclusively male, and V^tV^t the *deficiens* character with markedly reduced laterals which are completely sexless. V^t is incompletely dominant over V^d or V, and V^d and V are incompletely dominant over v. Consequently, it is conceivable that changes either from six-row to two-row or vice versa are equally possible. But, as some authors have pointed out, the actual change that took place in the phylogeny of barley was probably from six-row to two-row. The varieties of the *deficiens* form occupy a very limited territory, and no such species has been found among wild barleys. This fact indicates the very recent origin of this variety. Other known examples are the hooded characters (K-series) and laterally reduced awns (I- or lr-series), which are apparently due to mutation from recessive to dominant.

Schiemann (1932) published a review of the origin of cultivated barley, in which she proposed a hypothesis of her own that seems to be most adequate. According to this, the six-row types, both wild and cultivated, are older than the two-row type. Some six-row wild barley (though not known to her) might be a common ancestor of the six-row cultivated forms, as well as of two-row wild barley, *H. spontaneum*, while the two-row cultivated barley arose from *H. spontaneum* after the six-row cultivated barley. This hypothesis is based on morphological characters, and it has acquired strong support by the subsequent discovery of *H. agriocrithon*. She asserted this form to be the prototype that had been sought for a long time.

If the six-row wild barley is the most primitive type, there should be some other possibilities regarding the derivation of six-rowed and two-rowed cultivated forms from the six-rowed prototype besides that suggested by Schiemann. Åberg (1940, 1948) points out four possibilities. Of these, three possible schemata of phylogenetic development within the section *Cerealia* Ands. are as follows (Fig. 3):

(1) The six-rowed, brittle-eared forms developed into six-rowed, tough-eared forms, which in turn changed into two-rowed, tough-eared forms. The two-rowed, brittle-eared forms developed by reduction from six-rowed, brittle-eared forms, but in no way influenced the origin of

the two-rowed, tough-eared forms. This may be called monophyletic hypothesis.

(2) The six-rowed, brittle-eared forms developed into two-rowed, brittle-eared forms, which then gave rise to the two-rowed, tough-eared forms. The six-rowed, tough-eared forms were derived from the six-rowed, brittle-eared forms. (Diphyletic hypothesis)

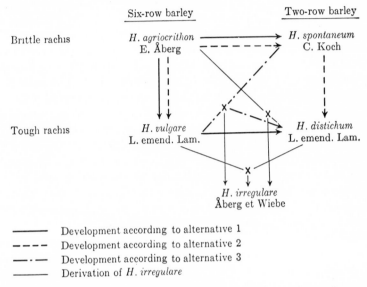

Development according to alternative 1
Development according to alternative 2
Development according to alternative 3
Derivation of *H. irregulare*

FIG. 3. Three possible schemata of phylogenetic development within *Cerealia* Ands. (Åberg, 1948).

(3) The two-rowed, tough-eared barleys arose by hybridization between the two-rowed, brittle-eared and the six-rowed, tough-eared barleys. (Diphyletic hybridization hypothesis)

It may be concluded from the foregoing review that the key to the origin of the cultivated barleys may be found if we can tell which of the three possibilities postulated above is the most probable one.

V. VAVILOV'S GENE-CENTER THEORY

The route of migration of various cultivated varieties is complicated and difficult to trace. This is especially true in crop plants that originated in remote antiquity. The difficulty is enhanced by the fact that the cultivated plants often have characters that appear similar but are genetically distinct. In spite of all these complications, there are often regularities in the geographic distribution of genes or genotypes, which suggest the origin and evolution of these plants.

Granting this possibility, Vavilov (1926 and later publications) investigated geographic distributions of a large number of varieties of important crops. He endeavored to find regions where diverse forms of each crop were concentrated. According to this hypothesis of center of origin, which had been derived from Willis (1922), the polymorphic center of a crop plant is the place of its origin. Vavilov also pointed out that the center of origin generally harbors forms having wild or dominant genes, whereas in the peripheral region there are many specialized forms with recessive characters (Vavilov, 1927).

The systematic study of barleys collected from various regions of the world has revealed two centers of diversity of the varieties. One of them is Abyssinia and Eritrea, where many varieties of covered barley are found characterized by broad empty glumes, extremely reduced lateral florets, densely haired empty glumes, and brightly colored stems with anthocyanin. Similar varieties occur in North Africa, western Asia, Europe, and perhaps also in India. Another center is southeastern Asia, including China, Tibet, and Nepal, where various kinds of naked barley, short-awned, awnless, or with hooded ears, are found.

Subsequently Vavilov altered this opinion to a considerable extent, and propounded that the chief center of the origin of *Hordeum sativum* Jess. were Abyssinia and Eritrea. China was regarded only as the center of origin of the endemic forms of awnless six-rowed barley, and the Near East as the center of origin of certain kinds of distichous cultivated barleys such as *medicum, nigricans, nutans,* etc., while the Mediteranean countries were the secondary center of forms with large grains. It was stated by him in 1940 that Chinese barley was first introduced several millennia ago from western Asia by way of India.

Orlov (1931) studied the geographic differentiation of barleys chiefly from an ecological point of view. He concluded that the cultivated barley had originated from the two centers shown by Vavilov, and that the varieties originating in the Abyssinian center never spread from there, whereas the varieties found elsewhere in the world were derived from the Asiatic center. According to Orlov, Asiatic forms are subdivided into two ecological groups, *rigidum* and *medium*, of which the former has spread through almost the whole of Asia while the latter is confined to Asia Minor. These two ecological groups are further classified into ten geographical types by differences in morphological and physiological features. Most of the varieties of barley occurring in Europe, North Africa, and Russia came from Asia Minor, and the others now distributed over northern Europe and Asia are of Central Asiatic origin and form an individual ecological type, *tenerum*.

The gene-center theory maintained by Vavilov has attracted much attention from agronomists and biologists, but was criticized from the genetic and evolutionary viewpoint by Turesson (1932), Schiemann (1939, 1951b), and Kihara (1947). These authors are of the opinion that the center of diversity should be found in the locality of development of the crop plant, where a multitude of different genotypes has been accumulated by repeated mutations and hybridizations. They admit, however, that it is questionable whether the center of development invariably coincides with the initial center of origin of the cultivated plants. Stebbins (1950) has summarized these criticisms in the following way. If the group in question is a young one, and if the selective forces of the environment, including competition with other organisms, have been operating in about the same manner throughout its evolutionary history, then the center of diversity and the primary center of origin are likely to be the same. But, if the group is old, and particularly if it has formerly existed in regions where it is no longer found, or if it has survived great alterations in the environment, secondary centers of diversity are likely to have arisen in areas which more recently have become favorable to the members of the group, and the ancestral forms may even have died out in the place of their origin. He also mentions that the center of origin suggested by Vavilov often covers a very large area, so as to make it difficult to determine the exact place of origin of the plant species, wild or cultivated.

Dobzhansky (1951) has stated that the evolutionary process which generates adaptive polymorphism, and thereby enables the species to conquer and control more and more habitats, requires time. Therefore, the longer a territory is occupied by a species the greater will tend to be the extent of polymorphism and the variability in population. There are, however, some doubts as to whether this generalization is always applicable for crop plants. Darlington and Janaki-Ammal (1945) have demonstrated on historical evidence that the center of diversity of the cultivated plant has drifted within the locality of intense cultivation of the plant. Movement enhances variation by the accumulation of variants through hybridization and selection in the course of migration. It is also probable that climatic diversity and relaxation of artificial selection as well may create diversity of forms. Therefore, it is important to examine how the center of diversity under consideration has been generated.

Abyssinia is a mountainous country and has a changeable climate; this may favor frequent occurrence of mutations and preservation of variants. Schiemann (1939, 1951b) and Freisleben (1940a,b) have asserted that Abyssinia is only a secondary center of origin of barleys, where various forms gradually accumulated. Even if it were the primary center of origin, no one would expect to find the ancestral form of barley in this geographic region where no wild relative has ever been found.

Vavilov's (1926) opinion was that *H. spontaneum* had nothing to do with the origin of cultivated barley, inasmuch as the habitat of this wild form is distant from its two centers in East Asia and Abyssinia. Later, however, the same author recognized this form to be one of the ancestral forms. At any rate, Vavilov's scheme seems to be inadequate for locating ancestral forms of cultivated plants, as pointed out by Kihara (1947).

VI. DIPHYLETIC HYPOTHESIS ON THE ORIGIN OF CULTIVATED BARLEY

In making any inference about the origin of cultivated plants, it is important that information gathered from various scientific approaches be well integrated. Åberg emphasized that neither the method of De Candolle nor that of Vavilov should be neglected, and that the compromise of both theories was especially valuable for understanding the origin of barley. It appears appropriate, therefore, to trace the course of various evolutionary changes which took place in the cultivated varieties in relation to the characteristics of the putative ancestors, *Hordeum agriocrithon* and *H. spontaneum*, especially the changes in the development of lateral florets and brittle rachises.

1. *Freisleben's Hypothesis*

Freisleben (1940a,b) investigated barley materials collected by the Deutsch-Hindukusch Expedition dispatched to southwestern Asia, mainly with regard to their variations and geographic distribution. Further studies were made on character differentiation in varieties from other parts of the world, especially those of East Asia. An important fact established by his studies was that both *H. spontaneum* and the two-rowed cultivated barley had their eastern boundary of distribution near the eastern boundary of Afghanistan, although the latter is found not only in southwestern Asia, overlapping with the former wild species, but also in Europe, North Africa, and some other regions. This suggests that the two-rowed character may have been derived from *H. spontaneum*, and also that the cultivated barley had spread gradually westward from the east. In addition to this, he found a true natural hybrid between the two-rowed wild and six-rowed cultivated forms in the Hindu Kush. These facts, as well as Åberg's discovery of *H. agriocrithon* in eastern Tibet, led him to an inference as to the origin and migration of the cultivated barley, which seems to resemble in principle the third possible scheme suggested by Åberg.

Freisleben's hypothesis is as follows:

(1) The cultivation of six-rowed wild barley of the *H. agriocrithon* type was started in eastern Inner Asia, where some primitive cultivated forms were established by selection.

(2) These cultivated forms spread eastward with their entire diversity, and also westward, though only to some extent because of barriers to migration.

(3) Entering the region of *H. spontaneum*, the cultivated forms crossed many times with the various varieties of this wild barley, and produced two-rowed and six-rowed cultivated barleys. The varieties characterized by black ear, smooth awn, or lax ear are regarded as the products of this hybridization.

(4) These forms, thus arisen, spread farther westward and southward.

2. *Presentation of Evidence in Favor of Diphyletic Origin*

Since 1940, considerable valuable information has been accumulated concerning the phylogeny of barley. The present writer has been working on this problem for more than fifteen years. The results of his studies will be elaborated later. Before giving the writer's comments on the theories about the origin of barley, some of the relevant facts will be presented.

a. *On the change from brittle to tough rachises.* The spontaneous shattering of grains due to brittleness of ear rachises is undoubtedly an adaptive character of a wild species, though useless in a cultivated form. It is quite natural for us to suppose that in a wild barley brought under cultivation this character was first taken up for improvement. The genetic behavior of brittleness versus toughness of ear rachises has been thoroughly investigated. The brittleness is practically due to the presence of two complementary genes, Bt and Bt_2, and the tough-ear condition is produced by either or both of the recessive genes allelic to Bt and Bt_2 (Ubisch, 1915, 1919; Johnson and Åberg, 1943; Takahashi and Yamamoto, 1949, 1951b, and unpublished data). There are other genes that modify the character of the rachis (Schiemann, 1921a). *Hordeum agriocrithon* and *H. spontaneum* have the same genetic constitution, $BtBtBt_2Bt_2$, while among cultivated barleys there are three kinds of genotypes, $BtBtbt_2bt_2$ or briefly type "E," $btbtBt_2Bt_2$ or type "W," and $btbtbt_2bt_2$ or type "we." Crosses between cultivated forms with tough rachises sometimes give F_1 hybrids with brittle rachises like those of the wild forms. Liebscher (1889) and many others have observed this phenomenon. Ubisch (1921) and Takahashi and Yamamoto (1949) obtained results suggesting the existence of two different lines of nonbrittle genotypes, which are distributed in entirely different geographic regions.

In the hope of obtaining more accurate knowledge about the distribution of the pertinent gene, an extensive experiment was conducted by the writer and co-workers, using about 500 varieties or strains of barley from various regions of the world. A few known varieties were selected as genotype analyzers, either type E ($BtBtbt_2bt_2$) or type W ($btbtBt_2Bt_2$).

Crosses were made with these type analyzers to obtain two kinds of F_1 hybrids, namely, $F_1(E)$ and $F_1(W)$. This has enabled us to determine the genotypic constitution of any variety, because if $F_1(W)$ is tough and $F_1(E)$ brittle the variety must be type W, if the relation is the reverse it must be type E, while a type we variety gives no brittle F_1 hybrid.

Table 1 shows the relative prevalence of these three genotypes in various regions of the world. The figures in this table may also be interpreted as the frequencies of bt and bt_2 alleles in the respective regions. Most of the varieties tested were either type E or type W, and a few were

TABLE 1

Relative Frequencies of the Nonbrittle Genes of Cultivated Barley Varieties in Various Regions of the World

Regions	Type E $(BtBtbt_2bt_2)$, %	Type W $(btbtBt_2Bt_2)$, %	Type we $(btbtbt_2bt_2)$, %	No. of varieties tested
North Japan	38	62	0	26
South Japan	96	4	0	85
North Korea	22	72	6	18
South Korea	95	5	0	62
Manchuria	33	67	0	23
China proper	100	0	0	53
India	0	100	0	12
Southwest Asia	38	62	0	13
Turkey	22	78	0	60
Russia	12	84	4	56
Europe	13	87	0	61
United States and Canada	27	69	4	26

type we. This table also shows the remarkable fact that the barleys in the "Oriental" region, namely, China proper, southern Korea (winter barley region, south of 38° lattitude), and southern Japan (south of Kwanto district, inclusive) consist with rare exceptions of type E varieties. In the remaining part of the world, what might be called the "Occidental" region, including southwestern Asia, Europe, Russia, Manchuria, northern Korea, northern Japan, and perhaps the major parts of India, the cultivated barleys include 60–80% type W, 20–40% type E, and a very few type we. Also, more than 95% of the two-rowed covered barleys grown in this region are type W, whereas of the six-rowed covered barleys 60% are type W and the remaining 40% are type E. Among the naked barleys occurring in this region, type E predominates over type W. The distribution of bt and bt_2 genes in the Oriental and Occidental regions seems to be quite similar to that of the two-rowed and six-rowed characters, both indicating the existence of two lines of descent in the cultivated barleys, which had originated in different localities and spread rather regularly as stated above.

b. *Resistance to barley mildew.* Nishikado, Takahashi, and Hiura (1951) and Hiura and Heta (1952a,c, 1954) have studied the resistance of varieties or strains of barley from various countries of the world to a physiologic race of barley mildew, *Erysiphe graminis hordei*, No. 13, which is most prevalent in southern Japan. The results, summarized in Table 2, show that almost all the varieties from China proper, southern

TABLE 2

Geographic Distribution of Different Types of Reaction of Barley Varieties to Mildew Race 13, Most Prevalent in Japan

Regions	Resistant %	Intermediate %	Susceptible %	No. of varieties tested
North Japan	40	5	55	38
South Japan	1	3	96	252
North Korea	0	24	76	21
South Korea	0	2	98	86
Manchuria	24	33	43	42
China proper	0	0	100	103
India	24	45	31	38
Southwest Asia	56	11	33	9
Turkey	39	37	24	786
Russia	36	24	40	67
Europe and United States	47	28	25	99
(*H. spontaneum*)	27	27	46	11

Korea, and Japan are with rare exceptions highly susceptible to this disease, whereas those occurring in the Occidental region contain higher proportions of resistant or medium-resistant forms, although this percentage is somewhat lower in northern Asia. It is noteworthy that the strains of *H. spontaneum* show a wide range of variation, from highly susceptible to perfectly resistant, but two strains of *H. agriocrithon* are highly susceptible. This regional differentiation of varieties in resistance to mildew race 13 is apparently similar to the differentiation between two-rowed characters as well as the differentiation between the nonbrittle *bt* and *bt₂* genes.

The relation between the host and the parasitic fungi is not a simple phenomenon. Hiura and Heta (1952b, 1953) have revealed that five dominant and two recessive alleles, either independent or closely linked, are responsible for resistance to mildew race 13, and that all the resistant varieties have at least one or more such genes. According to the same authors (1952a,c, and unpublished data), there are at least ten physiologic races of the mildew in Japan, of which race 13 is the most prevalent. The other races, though capable of infecting the same varieties as race 13, are found in restricted areas where the varieties of barley grown are chiefly resistant to race 13. This suggests that race 13 may have some ecological advantages over other races on barleys commonly grown in Japan.

Mutational changes from susceptible to resistant varieties are apparently rather rare in crop plants, or at least such mutants have never spread widely. But, as far as the parasitic fungi are concerned, it is well known that, as soon as a new resistant variety of crop plant is bred and disseminated, a new mutant race of the parasite often appears abruptly and becomes prevalent. Therefore, it is probable that, in the Oriental region, race 13 or races physiologically allied to it are more common, whereas, in the Occidental region, races of rather different physiologic nature are widely distributed.

3. *Phylogeny of Cultivated Barley on the Basis of New Evidence*

The hypothesis of monophyletic origin postulated by Åberg (1940) assumes that the six-rowed cultivated forms arose first from *H. agriocrithon*, through the genetic change from brittle rachis to tough rachis, and then, from these six-rowed cultivated forms two-rowed forms appeared through the reduction of the lateral florets. It is easy to conceive genetically that the heritable changes from six-row to two-row and from brittle to tough rachis may occur anywhere at any time. This possibility is supported by the following facts: (1) the historical evidence that the six-rowed form preceded the two-rowed form, (2) the parallelism in the series of the varieties belonging to six-row and two-row forms, and (3) the existence of some cosmopolitan varieties like *pallidum* and *coelesta*.

There are, however, some obvious difficulties in this hypothesis. First, the parallelism in the series of the varieties, mentioned above, is far from complete. As pointed out by Vavilov and Freisleben, the six-rowed barley in the Oriental region differs considerably from two-rowed forms of the Occidental region with respect to various characters. Second, the two-rowed cultivated forms resemble closely some varieties of *H. spontaneum* and have characters such as deep coloration of stem, auricle, and stem-node, large auricles, as well as abundant waxy bloom on ear and stem, which are not found in the Oriental barley. Third, it is difficult to explain by this hypothesis the origin of genes for resistance to barley mildew race 13 possessed only by Occidental barley. Fourth, the geographic regularity in the distribution of the nonbrittle genes, bt and bt_2, is hard to explain.

Hordeum spontaneum has the characters mentioned in (2) and (3) above. It is easy to explain the origin of cultivated barley from this species, based on these characters, as has been pointed out by many workers. Moreover, the marked differences in the varieties distributed in the two regions may be attributable to the phylogenetic difference of the varieties. Freisleben's hypothesis of diphyletic hybridization origin appears to be more plausible than the monophyletic theory. This does not contradict the historical evidence stated above.

It must be admitted, however, that this hypothesis assumes too simple changes from brittle rachis to tough rachis. According to this hypothesis, the genetic composition of cultivated forms of both the Oriental and Occidental regions is $BtBtbt_2bt_2$. In reality, the situation is apparently much different. In order to explain these complexities adequately, the following supposition seems to be necessary. First, the six-row cultivated forms with genotype E arose from a six-row wild barley by mutation from Bt_2 to bt_2 somewhere in East Asia and subsequently spread all over the Oriental region. There is no doubt that no mutation at the Bt locus has since taken place in the cultivated barley of this region. In the Occidental region, on the contrary, various genotypes seem to have arisen by hybridization between *H. spontaneum* or its derivatives and some six-row cultivated forms that have spread from the East. The mode of derivation was probably as follows:

Either (1) *H. spontaneum* $\xrightarrow{Bt \to bt}$ two-row type W × six-row type E;

or (2) six-row type E $\xrightarrow{Bt \to bt}$ six-row type we × *H. spontaneum;*

or (3) repeated mutations from Bt to bt in two-row and six-row segregates of the hybrid populations between six-row type E and *H. spontaneum*.

These three modes of origin may have proceeded side by side, but the second mode may be less probable on account of the scantiness of the six-row type we; the third also seems too complex to be realized.

The real situation in the Occidental region is apparently more complex, because the two-row forms are mostly type W, but about 40% of the six-row forms are type E, and only a few are type we. If hybridization between type W and type E or between type we and *H. spontaneum* had occurred, it should be expected on *a priori* grounds that types W, E, and we of the two-rowed barley as well as the six-rowed barley found in this region would occur with about equal frequencies. It is very difficult to reconcile this discrepancy. The work by Harlan and his co-workers (1940) seems to do this to some extent. These authors conducted extensive breeding experiments, using as many as 379 hybrids among 28 varieties belonging to both the six-row and two-row forms. The most notable results obtained from these experiments were that the yields of hybrid populations between the six-row and two-row varieties were far lower than those of either six-row forms × six-row forms or two-row forms × two-row forms. In the mean yields, selections from six-row × six-row were highest of all, followed by selections from two-row × two-row, and six-row selections from two-row × six-row; two-row selections from two-row × six-row were the lowest of all. Lambert and Liang (1952) indicated the possibility of obtaining high-yielding six-row forms from hybrid populations

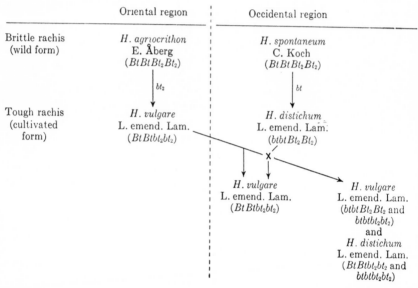

FIG. 4. Phylogeny and geographic differentiation in cultivated barleys.

between two-row and six-row varieties. These experiments definitely revealed that hybrid populations between two-row and six-row generally give two-row selections by far inferior to six-row selections. It is suspected from this that, among the various genotypes resulting from crosses between the two-row type W that originated from *H. spontaneum* and the six-row type E from the East, the two-row types E and we would eventually have disappeared, whereas the six-row type W might have been perpetuated. It is obscure, however, just what is the cause of the scarceness of varieties of six-row type we.

From the above described results a tentative conclusion, illustrated by Fig. 4, may be drawn. Namely, the first cultivation of six-row wild barley of *H. agriocrithon* type was started somewhere in East Asia, and from this original form some primitive cultivated forms differentiated by mutation from Bt_2 to bt_2. These cultivated forms and their derivatives gradually spread over various parts of the world. Thereafter, two-row cultivated forms appeared by mutation from Bt to bt from *H. spontaneum* that had been grown in southwestern Asia. These two-rowed cultivated forms were repeatedly crossed with varieties of six-rowed type E and resulted in various new two-rowed and six-rowed forms, and eventually superseded the former varieties in their range in the Occidental region.

VII. The Place of Primary Origin

1. *Karyomorphological Study*

Some earlier investigators considered Mesopotamia to be the place of origin of the ancestral cultivated barley, whereas Vavilov maintained that Abyssinia was the place. But, as stated above, it is not likely that either of these places is the original home of barley. Oinuma (1952) made a

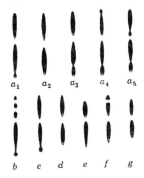

a_1 a_2 a_3 a_4 a_5

b c d e f g

Fig. 5. Karyotypes of cultivated barley (Oinuma, 1952). Upper: variation in chromosome "a." Lower: six other chromosomes.

detailed study of karyotypes of 86 barleys, including many different strains and varieties, both cultivated and wild, from various localities of the world. The seven pairs of somatic chromosomes were distinguished from one another by their length, shape, and presence or absence of trabants. The chromosomes were designated a, b, c, d, e, f, and g according to lengths. The longest, the a chromosomes, differed considerably in number and position of secondary constrictions. They were classified into five types, a_1, a_2, a_3, a_4, and a_5 (Fig. 5). The number of cultivated varieties of these respective karyotypes are listed in Table 3. Oinuma's study confirmed that both *H. agriocrithon* and *H. spontaneum* are of the a_1a_1 type. Since cultivated varieties belonging to this type are most

TABLE 3

Varietal Frequencies of Different Karyotypes in Cultivated Barley

Karyotypes	Six-row	Two-row	Total
a_1a_1	20	17	37
a_2a_2	10	21	31
a_3a_3	8	2	10
a_4a_4	0	1	1
a_5a_5	0	2	2

numerous, he concluded that evolution within the section *Cerealia* Ands. occurred in the following manner.

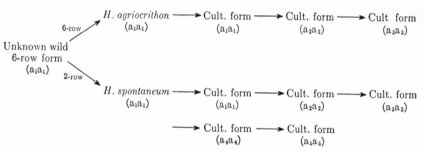

Varieties of a_1a_1, a_2a_2, and a_3a_3 types are found widely throughout the world and no relation between karyotypes and physiological or morphological characters exists. He found, however, that two Russian varieties were of type a_4a_4 and one from Lyallpur in Pakistan of type a_5a_5, and this made him believe that different karyotypes were concentrated in the Hindu Kush, where cultivated barley supposedly originated. The study of karyomorphological differentiation is still an unexplored field, and such a study might be very instructive. Further study along this line may possibly throw new light on the phylogeny of cultivated barley.

2. *Other Opinions*

Vavilov (1926) suggested that the center of origin of cultivated barley might be found in the region between Abyssinia and East Asiatic centers, while Schiemann (1932) considered it to be western Asia, perhaps around Transcaucasia. But, the situation has changed considerably since the discovery of *H. agriocrithon*. Freisleben (1940a,b) sought the home of cultivated barley within the limits of Inner Asia, and Åberg (1940, 1948) also held the same opinion. Åberg considered that *H. agriocrithon* was discovered on the easternmost part of its distribution, and that no primitive six-row wild form would be found in southwestern Asia, where a thorough exploration has been made. It should, however, be granted that all these conclusions are mere speculations.

It has been generally supposed that the two-row wild species were derived from the six-row wild form. But, as stated before, no variety of *H. agriocrithon* has ever been discovered which has more wild characteristics than does *H. spontaneum*. It is highly improbable that the former is the progenitor of the latter. Consequently, a wild, six-rowed form characterized by hairy glume, longer awns, delayed germination, and resistance to various infectious fungi is expected to be discovered. Such a discovery will contribute not only to the elucidation of phylogenetic relations within the *Cerealia* section, but also to the determination of the prototype of the cultivated barleys and their original home. Brücher believes in the possibility of such a discovery. If so, the place may be somewhere in Central Asia. It is also hoped that some archaeological discovery will confirm this supposition.

VIII. Origin of Hereditary Variations and Their Migration

The evolutionary processes in cultivated barley may be followed according to the same principles as those established by studies with other organisms. It must be admitted that evolutionary agencies such as migration, artificial and natural selection, and various kinds of isolation have been and are still operating on crop plants under human care in a manner entirely different from that in wild species. Therefore, knowledge of the evolution of crop plants should interest biologists as well. We are not in a position to deal with this problem of the evolution of cultivated barley systematically; we propose to make only fragmentary observations based on available facts.

It is almost certain that cultivated barley and its putative ancestors, *Hordeum agriocrithon* and *H. spontaneum*, possess many genes in common and only a few different genes. The differences between diverse forms of cultivated barley and their ancestors are, as stated before, wholly attributable to gene mutations that have occurred under domestication. In discussion of the origin of these genic differences, however, we are confronted with the difficult problem of whether certain genes or genotypes, found in two different localities, or distributed continuously over a wide range, represent parallel mutations or are due to migration of the same variant form from a certain original place.

It is conceivable that, since the barley plants raised in various parts of the world and especially their gametes are innumerable, many mutants of practical value, as well as a far larger number of deleterious ones, are being generated, however low their mutation rate may be, and that some of these mutations are of the same gene. We actually know some cases

of spontaneous parallel mutations. For instance, the mutant characterized by bracts on each of the outer ring of empty glumes of central spikelets was found among strains from both Afghanistan and Japan, and they
were shown to be genotypically identical. Much the same relation was found
in two subjacent hooded forms, one obtained in China and one in Japan
(see Fig. 6); an apparently similar form was discovered by Harlan in the
United States (see Takahashi *et al.*, 1953a). Certainly, we have no reason
to reject the view that the wide range of distribution of a certain phenotype may be due to parallel mutations. It is also probable that the characters of the cultivated plant have attained fixation not by a single
mutational step, but by many trials and errors.

FIG. 6. Various types of hooded spikelet. *a* and *b*: subjacent hoods of semibrachytic
and normal type; *c* and *d*: normal hood; and *e*: elevated hood.

It is also common that heritable changes are lost by accident or by
selection. Generally only a small part of the seeds harvested are sown the
next year, and farmers often eliminate ears or plants appearing like
"sports" to secure uniform growth. Moreover, all genetic changes in
autogamous plants are exposed to natural selection or competition with
other genotypes.

There is also a striking feature peculiar to cultivated plants. This is
that a variant form, however prevalent it may become in the population
of a field, has almost no chance of invading other fields of different owners.

There are many examples of excellent mutants or individuals, discovered under normal cultivation and propagated separatedly, having
gradually spread widely. It is nearly certain that this was the only way
of improvement of crops during the time preceding the introduction of
scientific breeding methods. The introduction and exchange of new or
foreign varieties are becoming more and more active. The mass migration
of semibrachytic varieties of barley of Japanese origin into South Korea,

to be mentioned later, is a good example. It is certain that the development of means of communication and exchange of agricultural knowledge has facilitated the migration of cultivated plants. Historical evidence shows, however, that even in the ancient period various crop plants were introduced repeatedly from distant places.

In short, high mutability of the genes under consideration is necessary for the fixation and increase of heritable changes, but conscious adoption and transportation by man is another important agency for the spread of variant forms of crop plants.

IX. Geographic Distribution of Genes or Genotypes of Barley in Relation to Selection

Cultivated barley is especially rich in easily distinguishable genetic variations. As far as we know, the modes of inheritance of most of these characters are rather simple (see Smith's extensive review, 1951). Discontinuous variations found chiefly in ear characters, such as adherence of lemma to caryopsis, length and forms of lemma appendages, and color of ear and grains, have usually been used as the criteria for the classification of barley varieties (Körnicke, 1885, 1908; Orlov, 1931; and others). Mansfeld (1950) after revising the descriptions of the varieties of barley published previous to his time, registered 192 botanical varieties. It must be mentioned here that these varieties described by him are not necessarily agriculturally grown ones. According to Orlov (1931), more than half of them are products of experimental fields, and only 82 varieties are being cultivated. Of these 82 varieties, 55 have been found singly in barley fields consisting of several different varieties, 12 rather rarely and 4 constantly have occurred in the fields of other varieties, and only 10 varieties are grown widely. Among these 10 varieties, *pallidum*, *nutans*, and *medicum* occupy vast cultivated areas, and the other 7 are confined to definite narrow regions. According to Willis' "age and area theory," the older the species is, the more area it will have had time to cover. The above data as applied to this theory imply that var. *pallidum*, *nutans*, and *medicum* are the oldest of all. This conclusion is plausible, because all these varieties are closely akin to the ancestral wild barleys. But, at the same time, the varieties having deep-colored ears and caryopses are probably as old as *pallidum* and *nutans*, yet they occupy only limited areas. It may thus safely be concluded that the range of distribution of species or varieties is, in the long run, determined by selective advantage or disadvantage of their genotypes, and age may act in favor of some genotypes but disfavor others.

What counts in evolution is the phenotypes that are produced by interaction of the genotypes of organisms with the environments they encounter. But, survival or death, well-being or decline, of individuals or populations in a given environment is determined, in the last analysis, by the genes they carry (Dobzhansky, 1951). As stated above, cultivated barley has many genes which manifest marked effects upon morphological and physiological characters, and consequently affect selective values of the carriers of these genes. In reality, the effect or practical value of these genetic changes constitutes the important fundamental knowledge for the praxis of barley breeding. To contribute something to this knowledge, the writer has made studies of the inheritance of these characters and the geographic distribution of the genes responsible for them. The following discussion is based on these data. For the sake of description, the data are classified into four items.

1. *Elimination of Undesirable Wild Characteristics*

As stated before, spontaneous shattering of grains makes harvesting impossible. The elimination of such a deleterious character is the first requirement for a cultivated form, and it is likely that the change from brittle to tough rachis was the first step to cultivation. It is also recognized that the nonbrittle rachis is the most important character of cultivated barley that distinguishes it from wild species.

Black, purple, red, or blue pigmentations, which may be deep or pale, in the lemma and palea and in the seed coat or aleurone layers, are not harmful in themselves. However, they spoil the commercial value of the grains by giving them an unpleasant appearance. Therefore, these characters are subject to considerable pressure from artificial selection. Black or gray color of lemmas and grains is due to deposit of a melanin-like substance and is a character produced by an allelomorphic series, B, B^{mb}, and B^g (Woodward, 1941). Cultivated varieties having black or gray chaff color are distributed in the regions from southwestern Asia to Abyssinia and also sparsely in Tibet and China. Black-eared forms of *Hordeum spontaneum* and *H. agriocrithon* have been discovered in both these regions. This coincident discovery suggests that the genes included in the cultivated forms were derived from these wild species, and that this undesirable character has persisted only in limited regions of rather primitive agriculture where little artificial selection has been practiced. This also seems to be true for purplish ear and grains, the color of which is due to anthocyanin. According to Woodward and Thieret (1953), this character is governed by the complementary genes, P and C. Cultivated forms with these genes are abundant in Tibet where a purplish form of *H. agriocrithon* var. *dawoense* has been found, extending further, though sparsely, to China proper, Korea, and Japan.

Blue color in aleurone layers of barley kernels is due to anthocyanin.

This character was proved to be governed by complementary genes, Bl and Bl_2 (Mayler and Stanford, 1942), although in the majority of crossing experiments it showed simple Mendelian segregation. Almost all wild barley forms have blue kernels, but the cultivated barleys are differentiated into forms having white kernels and those having blue kernels. It is interesting to note that the naked varieties, except those of Tibet and Mongolia, have predominantly white kernels, whereas more than half the covered varieties of the world have blue kernels, although the proportions are considerably lower in the two-row forms of Europe and in the six-row forms of Japan, Korea, and China (Takahashi and Yamamoto, 1950). The presence or absence of blue pigment matters little in covered barleys if they are used as feeds, but apparently this is not so when they are used for human consumption. Canadian traders have even taken the trouble of bleaching blue kernels for making pearl barley to be exported to England. For brewing purposes, fresh, straw-colored grains are always preferred in European countries, although American and Canadian brewers have cared little about the color. It seems probable that these human preferences have chiefly affected the geographic and varietal differentiation of the genes for blue and white aleurones.

A similar relation is observed in the case of a faint reddish pigmentation on both sides of the naked kernel, which turns to dirty brown spots in maturity. The majority of the Japanese and Korean naked varieties as well as some of the Turkish covered barleys are free of such pigment.

Why have such disagreeable wild characters persisted when their removal seems not difficult? Perhaps there is some unknown advantage for carrying these genes, and their removal might have required intensive artificial selection. Sakai and Nakayama (1953) recently proved that a paddy rice with red grains, when mixed with Japanese upland rice, showed a higher competitive ability than the latter. It has been recognized that the removal of these red-grained rice plants, and also the reduction of awn length in rice plants are the successful outcomes of rice improvement in Japan achieved during the past 80 years.

2. Fixation of New Characters Beneficial for the Cultivated Forms

Nakedness of grains, which is inherited as a simple recessive to covered grains, is undoubtedly one of the most remarkable and useful qualitative features of cultivated barley. Naked barley is distributed widely in the world, but the relative frequencies of the naked forms differ considerably in different localities. The frequency is more than 95% in Tibet and almost 50% in China, Korea, and Japan, but tends to decrease steadily towards the west, becoming low in Europe. Vavilov considered southeastern Asia to be a center of origin of naked barley, but Orlov's data (1931) showed a diversity of forms in Abyssinia. The areas of cultivation of naked barley are more or less restricted to the southern part of the winter-barley zones with warm climate (Central China, southern Korea, and Japan) and to spring-barley zones of higher latitude or altitude (Tibet, Afghanistan, Abyssinia, and the northernmost parts of Europe and Japan). This situation may be due to such common characters of naked varieties as lower winter hardiness, earliness, and higher expression of spring growth habit.

Some of the naked barleys of Oriental origin have glutinous endosperm which segregates as a simple recessive to starchy endosperm (Kashiwada, 1930, and others). A Chinese archive published in the 16th century describes this form as grown for brewing purposes. The glutinous barleys are said to have been introduced into Japan from Korea in the Tokugawa era (perhaps before the 17th century). As is general in indigenous glutinous rice, glutinous barley varieties are always characterized by purplish ear and grains.

Long and stiff awns appear quite useless in a cultivated form of barley; moreover, they are certainly harmful at the time of tillage and harvest, and especially at the time of threshing. They are to some extent useful in a wild form, however, for the protection or scattering of seeds. Therefore, any genetic change that reduces awn length or removes the harmful barbs will have selective advantage and become fixed in cultivated forms. A recessive gene, lk, for short and fine awns is rather common in southern Korea, Japan, and China, and also, though rarely, in the Hindu Kush district (Fig. 7). None has been found in western countries, however. In nearly the same regions laterally awnless forms (subsp. *intermedium* Åberg et Wiebe) are distributed. Varieties belonging to the subspecies are distinguished from each other by differential awn lengths of the main and lateral rows which, according to Syakudo (1947), are affected by at least four multiple alleles. This change possibly was inherited from *H. agriocrithon* var. *dawoense* (Takahashi, 1949; Takahashi *et al.*, 1953a) and var. *paradoxon*.

The lemma appendages sometimes show trifurcate structures or hoods, each composed of a tiny floret and two lemma wings. As seen in Fig. 6, at least three kinds of hoods may be distinguished according to the site of the hooded appendages on the lemma or awn. One of them, the subjacent hood described before, is practically valueless because of its low fertility. The other two, namely, normal hood and elevated hood, are governed by allelic genes, K and K^e, dominant and semidominant, respectively, over the long-awned condition (Takahashi *et al.*, 1953a). The normal-hooded varieties are distributed in Nepal, Tibet, and Central and North China. The elevated-hooded form is confined to some localities of Honan Province, Central China. As far as the writer knows, hooded forms in China are grown as admixtures of long-awned or short-awned forms, and have never been established as local varieties. American breeders, however, have had success in producing some excellent hooded barley varieties for feeding purposes.

Fig. 7. Variations in ear density and awn length. *a*: Long-awned lax ear of normal type *(LkLk LL UzUz)*; *b*: Short-awned dense ear of normal type *(lklk ll UzUz)*; *c*: Long-awned dense ear of semibrachytic type *(LkLk ll uzuz)*.

In spite of the practical advantages of these variations of awn, varieties having such characters are more or less confined to some limited areas of the East Asiatic region. This may be explained in part by the fact that it has often been reported that absence of awns in barley and wheat is associated not only with lowered yields but also with a tendency toward shattering. Some other unknown disadvantages may also accompany these changes.

A heritable change removing barbs from awns, briefly called "smooth awn," appears to be more useful. This character has been shown by many geneticists to be determined by a main gene r and a modifier r_2. Contrary to our expectation, the smooth-awned varieties occupy rather narrow areas. They are found only in regions including southwestern Asia, southern Russia, and a part of North Africa, although successes in breeding some promising smooth-awned varieties have recently been reported in the United States and Canada. Smooth awn markedly reduces the number of stylar branches, which to some extent results in sterility of grains and at the same time causes loose adherence of chaff to kernels. Moreover, breeding experiments have revealed the existence of close linkage of the genes with that for susceptibility to *Helminthosporium sativum*. Freisleben (1940a) inferred that the smooth-awn character must have resulted from crossings between *Hordeum spontaneum* and some six-row cultivated barleys. This assumption was based on Vavilov's observation that mutual crosses of two rough-awned forms sometimes generated smooth-awned segregates, but there is some doubt as to how far such a phenomenon is universal.

3. *Adaptive Genetic Changes*

Barley is originally a crop of the temperate zone but has differentiated into forms adapted to subarctic or high mountainous regions as well as into forms adapted to tropical plains. Among the numerous genetic changes that have permitted adaptation to these extreme habitats, those affecting reactions to temperature and day length may be the most important. Barleys are generally sown in the fall or spring. Spring barleys are always capable of heading out under high-temperature and long-day conditions, and possess a high grade of spring habit. On the other hand, varieties sown in the fall in northern districts should have winter habit in order to prevent ear formation without exposure to low temperature or short photoperiod and thereby overwinter safely. Farther south, in places with warmer winter climate, we meet with intermediate forms, and in the subtropical zone again find pure spring-habit varieties. It has been shown that varieties of wheat and barley distributed in different parts of the world have physiological properties adapted to the respective ecological regions, as stated above (Kakizaki and Suzuki, 1937; Wada and Akihama, 1934). Takahashi and his coworkers (1943, 1951c, 1953b, 1954, and unpublished data) have made genic analyses of spring varieties of various origins under more or less artificially controlled conditions. The results indicated that two kinds of dominant genes, A and C, and one recessive gene, b, were each responsible for spring habit, and these spring genes were always epistatic to winter genes. Moreover, one of the dominant genes A and the recessive gene b, involved in the different varieties tested, were all identical. It was also known that differences in the grade of the spring habit among different varieties, or the grade of low-temperature requirement for removal of the winter nature, were attributable to the different multiple alleles of the spring gene, A, of which the respective varieties possessed. Geographic distribution of spring varieties with different genotypic constitutions are shown in Table 4.

TABLE 4

Geographic Distribution of Spring Barleys of Different Genotypes

Origin of varieties	AA bb CC	AA bb cc	aa bb cc	AA BB cc*
Europe & U.S.A.	5	5		2
Russia		2		
Manchuria		1		
North Korea		3		
India		1		1
Formosa		1		1
China proper & South Korea				4†
Japan				
exotic		4	2	
endemic				7

* Each of the genes, A, b, and C is responsible for spring habit. All the winter barley varieties tested had the genic constitution of $aa\ BB\ cc$.

† Inclusive of a wild six-rowed barley, $H.\ agriocrithon$.

Although data hitherto obtained are far from being complete, the following supposition may be warranted. The six-rowed wild barley obtained from East Tibet is of the spring type and has the same genotypic constitution regarding this character as the spring barleys prevalent in southern Japan and Korea. It is conceivable, therefore, that spring as well as winter barleys in the Oriental region have been differentiated from such spring forms. The situation is somewhat different for the barleys found in the Occidental region, where spring barleys are predominant, and extending to the farthest north. It is interesting to note that the spring barleys found there have at least one recessive spring gene, b, besides one or two dominant spring genes. Therefore, it is not impossible that spring varieties that originated by mutation somewhere in the Occidental region contributed to the distribution in that region, although we are still uncertain as to the physiological effect of these composite genotypes, and also as to the relation of these spring barleys with *Hordeum spontaneum*, which includes many varieties of winter type and, according to Vavilov, some of spring type as well.

Changes in environmental conditions necessitate different adaptive genotypes. A good example of this may be found in phenological and genetical studies on Japanese and Korean barleys made by the writer (Takahashi, 1942, 1951; Takahashi and Yamamoto, 1951a). The Japanese and Korean barleys can be classified in two varietal groups, the normal and "uzu" or semibrachytic types. The semibrachytic habit has been proved to be due to a gene uz, simple recessive to normal. The gene has a remarkable pleiotropic effect, reducing the length of various plant parts without influencing their breadth (Fig. 7). A geographical survey of the distribution of four varietal groups, namely, normal covered, normal naked, semibrachytic covered, and semibrachytic naked found in Japan and Korea gave an interesting result. As seen in Fig. 8, the semi-brachytic form occupies about 80% of the whole barley acreage in Japan, though confined to the central and southwestern parts of the country which have warm and milder winters, whereas the remaining parts of the country, having rather severe climates, are sown with the normal type. A similar ecological distribution of these genotypes may be found in Korea where the semibrachytic barleys are confined to the southern coastal region, which amounts to about one-third of the entire barley area of the country.

Thus, semibrachytic barley is better adapted to the climatic and cultural conditions of southern Japan and Korea than normal-type barley. This is primarily because the short, thick plant form tolerates heavy manuring even under rainy and warm climatic conditions, and because the short awns, compact ears, and round plump grains are characteristics preferred by the Japanese farmers. This form has been spreading rapidly in Japan during recent years through work of the extension service. It was introduced into Korea in 1910 when Korea was annexed to Japan, but no special attention was given to it until recently, when the government began to recommend growing barley on the lowlands after the rice crop and also on the uplands following the cotton crop. Extreme adaptability to a specialized environment may impair or endanger the normal physiology of the organism in a different environment. Semibrachytic barley seems to be inferior to the normal varieties under rather severe climatic conditions.

As stated before, dense-eared barleys of both six-row and two-row types have been grown rather widely since the remote past. According to Raum (1930), the dense types outyield the lax varieties under favorable conditions, but the reverse is true under unfavorable conditions. The dense-eared forms commonly have short, firm stems, and hence are less liable to lodging. Genetic studies have shown that many different genes are responsible for this character. Takezaki (1927) and Takahashi *et al.*

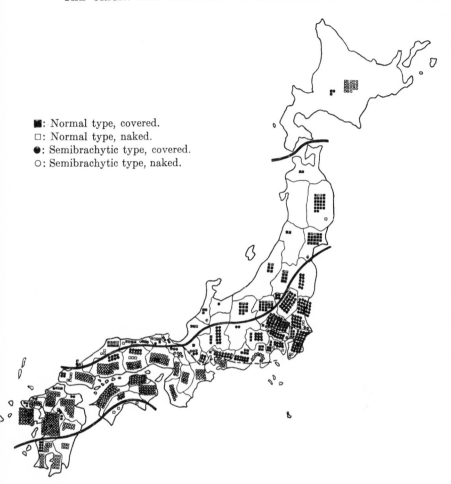

Fig. 8. Geographic distribution of normal and semibrachytic habit types in Japan.

(1953a) showed by numerous crosses that Japanese dense-eared forms commonly include a recessive gene, l, which is linked with lk for short awn and n for naked grain. The barleys having this gene are rather commonly found in China and Korea, and the gene is probably endemic to the Oriental region.

4. *Other Genetic Changes*

Various organs and their morphological variations may or may not be adaptive, and they may be good or bad for agronomic purposes. The rachilla in barley is markedly reduced to a tiny rod-shaped organ, and a hereditary variation in hairs on the rachilla surface is very likely to be an adaptively neutral character. It has been shown that two distinct types of hairs, long-straight and short-forked, are governed by a pair of genes, Ss, with the long-haired condition dominant. It is, therefore, interesting to know that, whereas all the varieties of the Oriental region and only a part of the Occidental varieties possess long-haired rachillas; a large number of varieties having short-haired rachillas are found in the Occidental region. Furthermore, it has also been observed that within the Occidental region the short-haired condition is met with more frequently in six-row forms (60% or more) than in two-row forms (20–30%) (Takahashi, 1947). A plausible explanation for such a regular distribution of genetic changes is very difficult, unless we assume that some certain successful varieties carrying the short-haired rachilla gene, or strains that arose by hybridization with such varieties, have had many opportunities to spread over the Occidental region. It is very probable, at least for barleys in Japan, that the varieties with short-haired rachilla resulted from hybridization with varieties of foreign origin.

Hairy or nonhairy condition of the basal leaf-sheath may also be a character having little relation to adaptation or to practical importance. But, we can find a geographic regularity in the distribution of the genes $HsHs$ for hairy versus $hshs$ for hairless condition of leaf-sheath. With a few exceptions the naked barleys are hairless. In the covered varieties, on the other hand, the relative frequency of hairy varieties is highest in southern Japan, reaching about 85% and decreases to about 50% in southern Korea and China proper. Westward from there it becomes far lower; and in Europe, Russia, and the northern parts of East Asia the spring barleys with hairless sheath are predominant, although about one-half of the winter barleys found there are hairy (Takahashi et al., 1948). Causal analysis of the "dimorph-ratio cline" is apparently a difficult task. However, as Huber (1932) suggested, the prevalence of spring barleys with hairless sheath in the Occidental region may be explained, though only in part, by the close linkage relation between a recessive spring gene b and the hairless-sheath gene hs.

Forms with wide, large, empty glumes, instead of normal linear, lanceolate ones, are occasionally found among the cultivated barleys. Among them, at least three distinct types are distinguishable. The varieties found in Afghanistan and Turkey rarely possess wide glumes as large as the outer palea. This character was shown to be simple recessive to normal narrow glume. The other two types are the "macrolepis," in which all the empty glumes are broad but short-awned, and the "heterolepis," in which only the outermost glumes on each lateral floret are broad. These are likely to be of hybrid origin, although the causative genetic process remains to be worked out (Schiemann, 1921b).

It should be granted that we have dealt only with genetic changes that produce marked effects, chiefly on morphological characters. Naturally, the results stated above are unsatisfactory for a thorough understanding of geographic differentiation in the cultivated barleys. Orlov (1931) and Vavilov (1940) showed that special ecotypes adapted for particular regions are differentiated in various regions of the world. It is true that each of the diverse cultivated varieties must have been selected for adaptation to natural and artificial circumstances in the respective regions. The genetic properties, as well as the ecological, physiological, or morphological characteristics recognizable among these ecotypes or varieties, imply many problems to be solved by future studies. These problems are all-important for a comprehension of the evolution of crop plants and also for breeding praxis.

X. Geographic Regularities in Gene Distribution in Barley

The majority of the genes responsible for the characters found in various forms of cultivated barleys must have been inherited immediately from wild progenitors, perhaps *Hordeum agriocrithon* and *H. spontaneum;* but some genes have undoubtedly arisen under cultivation in different occasions and places, independently and one after another. Naturally, therefore, the geographic distribution of characters or genes is seemingly haphazard; some occupy extremely wide areas without any interruption, some are scattered in patches, and others are confined more or less to limited territories, overlapping one another or occurring independently. In spite of this, we can point out the following geographic regularities in their distribution.

(1) The "normal" characters which are generally common to both the wild progenitors, and genetically dominant, are very prevalent everywhere in the world. The following characters may be listed in this category: covered grain (N), lax ear (L), long awn (Lk, k), blue aleurone (Bl), narrow, empty glume (E), rough awn (R), teeth on lemma veins (G), normal habit of growth (Uz), long-haired rachilla (S), etc.

(2) On the contrary, the numerous characters which have probably been generated under cultivation, along with a few characters which may have derived from wild barleys, are found in more or less limited territories. Moreover, there are some that occur in different places. The general distribution of these characters or genes is shown in Table 5.

It is apparent from Table 5 that the genetic changes which took place in the barleys of the Oriental region are quite different from those found in the barleys of the Occidental region; and a certain character of a variety often indicates not only its original habitat but also other characters which it possesses.

The fate of a gene or a genotype is determined by selection pressures operating upon it and also by its ability to compete with other genotypes in the wide sense. In other words, a gene may be favored over others if the genotype carrying the gene is endowed with high adaptability to the

TABLE 5

Geographic Distribution of Various Characters or Genes of Systematic and Agronomic Importance in Cultivated Barley

Characters	Genes	Abyssinia	Europe	Russia	Manchuria	North Korea	Turkey	Southwest Asia	India	Nepal and Tibet	China proper	South Korea	South Japan
Two-row	V, V^d	+	+	+			+	+					
Resistance to mildew race 13	Ml, ml	+	+	+	+	+	+	+	+				
Nonbrittle rachis	bt	+	+	+	+	+	+	+	+				
Short-haired rachilla	s	+	+	+	+	+	+	+					
Smooth awn	r	+	+	+			+	+					
Wide glume	e, etc.	+		±			+	±	±				
Spring habit	(b)		+	+	+	+			+				
Deficiens	V^t	+		+									
Irregular	?	+											
Purple chaff	P									+	+	+	±
Reduced lateral awns	$I = lr$						±		±	+	+	+	+
Short, fine awn	lk							+		+	+	+	+
Hooded	K, K^e									+	+		
Glutinous	wx										+?	±	±
Semibrachytic	uz											+	+
Six-row	v	+	+	+	+	+	+	+	+	+	+	+	+
Nonbrittle rachis	bt_2	+	+	+	+	+	+	+	+	+	+	+	+
Black chaff	B, E^g	+		+	+		+			+	+		
Naked grain	n	+	+	+		+	+	+	+	+	+	+	+
White aleurone	bl	+	+	+	+	+	+	+	+	+	+	+	+
Dense ear	l, etc.	+	+	+			+	+	+	+	+	+	+
Anthocyaninless	rp		±				+	±				+	+
Toothless on lemma veins	g		+	+				+			±	±	

ecological niche wherein the mutant has been generated or introduced, or if some other economical merits are present. If there are only a few or no genotypes of superior quality, the new genotype will possibly invade the niche. In this sense, we can infer that forms such as var. *pallidum* or var. *nutans*, which came into existence in the remote past, might have without difficulty explored new or unoccupied areas step by step. But, if the new habitat is already occupied by a more or less adaptive form, this will refuse invasion by the new genotype. Also, it is probable that the distribution of a new type becomes more and more difficult with the advancement of varietal differentiation resulting from intensified artificial and natural selection, unless genotypic reconstruction is brought about by hybridization or by further mutational changes. Each character listed in Table 5 must have occurred within the limits of its distribution, and the genotype, having useful genes, must have been given a chance to become practical and enlarge its habitats. But, owing to its limited adaptability and to defects that accompanied the mutational change, the genotype might have failed in different ecological or economical environments. It is more than probable that, if parallel mutations had occurred in different genotypes in different places, the gene could have conquered a wider area.

Phylogenetic differences among barley forms distributed in the Oriental and Occidental regions have been inferred from the morphological differentiation of characters, such as number of rows, nonbrittle rachis, and resistance to a certain mildew race. Distribution of some wild characters seems to be well-explained in relation to the wild progenitors. It is further recognized that the barleys of both regions differ in many characters which have probably arisen by mutation under domestication. The latter situation may have resulted chiefly from geographic isolation and in part from phylogenetic differences. It is generally accepted that isolated groups usually become genetically different. Matsuo (1952) and Oka (1953) have shown that the cultivated rice plants that are distributed in different regions of East Asia have been differentiated into two or three subspecies or the like.

It seems to be appropriate here to discuss the boundary of distribution between the Oriental and Occidental barleys. The existence of such a line has been suggested by Vavilov (1926) and Freisleben (1940b), and the writer has shown it in Fig 2. It should be admitted, however, that the line is doubtful in many respects. Vavilov considered India as a whole as belonging to the Occidental region, whereas Freisleben, on the basis of the distribution of two-row forms, excluded India from the Occidental region. Some facts in favor of Vavilov's view have been found by the writer, but they are still not conclusive and require further studies. In the Far East the line is apparently somewhat closer to the actual state. The line seems to be in accord with the southern limits of distribution of spring barley in the Asiatic Continent. Manchuria may have been occupied, though sparsely, by Oriental forms, but Russian barleys have gradually become predominant by virtue of higher adaptability since the time of the construction of the East Chinese Railway by the Russians, and these forms have expanded also into northern Korea. But, probably owing to ecological differences, this spring barley could not enter the winter-barley regions of North China and South Korea occupied by the Oriental forms. The situation in Japan is somewhat complicated. Immigrants to Hokkaido and Saghalein endeavored to grow various spring forms there, and finally succeeded in selecting adaptive naked barleys from southern Japan and covered forms of European and Russian origin. Foreign barley varieties were also introduced into Tohoku district, where some of the winter forms have become more dominant than the endemic forms. These and other foreign varieties, however, failed to enter the regions south of Tohoku because of their inferiority to endemic forms.

The boundary in the remaining parts of the world is not yet clear, but if Vavilov's opinion is correct, geographic barriers such as the high mountain ranges and deserts of Outer Mongolia, Sinkiang, and Tibet, as well as some ecological conditions, may have precluded or limited the migration and growth of barley.

The above statement indicates the existence of ecological or geographic isolation between barley forms of the Oriental and Occidental regions, which might have resulted in their genetic differentiation. It is conceivable, however, that, since the isolation is not so rigid, and since active interchanges of varieties will take place between both regions, as well as frequent crossings with foreign varieties (in order to recombine useful genes lacking in the endemic forms), these processes will gradually make the differences indistinct in the future. In fact, some signs of this are observable in Japanese barley.

XI. ACKNOWLEDGMENTS

The writer wishes to express his appreciation to Dr. Taku Komai, National Institute of Genetics, for his encouragement and also for his revision of the manuscript.

XII. REFERENCES

Åberg, E., 1938. *Hordeum agriocrithon*, a wild six-rowed barley. *Ann. Agr. Coll. Sweden* **6**, 159–216.

Åberg, E., 1940. The taxonomy and phylogeny of *Hordeum* L. sect. *Cerealia* Ands., with special reference to Thibetan barleys. *Symbolae Botan. Upsalienses* **4**(2), 1–156.

Åberg, E., 1948. Cereals and peas from eastern Tibet and their importance for the knowledge of the origin of cultivated plants. *Ann. Agr. Coll. Sweden* **15**, 235–250.

Åberg, E., 1950. Barley and wheat from the Saqqara pyramid in Egypt. *Ann. Agr. Coll. Sweden* **17**, 59–63.

Åberg, E., and Wiebe, G. A., 1945. Irregular barley, *Hordeum irregulare*, sp. nov. *J. Wash. Acad. Sci.* **35**, 161–164.

Berg, K. H., 1936. Autotetraploidie bei *Hordeum bulbosum* L. *Züchter* **8**(6), 151–158.

Brücher, H., and Åberg, E., 1950. Die Primitivgersten des Hochlandes von Tibet, ihre Bedeutung für die Züchtung und das Verständnis des Ursprungs und der Klassifizierung der Gersten. *Ann. Agr. Coll. Sweden* **17**, 247–319.

Darlington, C. D., and Janaki-Ammal, E. K., 1945. "Chromosome Atlas of Cultivated Plants," p. 397. Allen & Unwin, London.

De Candolle, A., 1882. "Origin of Cultivated Plants," p. 468. Paul, Trench, Trübner. London (translated and published in 1909).

Dobzhansky, T., 1951. "Genetics and the Origin of Species," 3rd rev. ed., p. 364. Columbia Univ. Press, New York.

Freisleben, R., 1940a. Die Gersten der deutschen Hindukusch Expedition 1935. *Kühn-Arch.* **54**, 295–368.

Freisleben, R., 1940b. Die phylogenetische Bedeutung asiatischer Gersten. *Züchter* **12**, 257–272.

Freisleben, R., 1943. Ein neuer Fund von *Hordeum agriocrithon* Åberg. *Züchter* **16**, 49–63.

Harlan, H. V., Martini, M. L., and Stevens, H., 1940. A study of methods in barley breeding. *Tech. Bull. U.S. Dept. Agr.* **720**, 25.

Hiura, U., and Heta, H., 1952a. Studies on the disease resistance of barley varieties, II. *Nōgaku Kenkyū* **40**, 89–95 (in Japanese).

Hiura, U., and Heta, H., 1952b. Studies on the disease resistance of barley varieties, III. *Nōgaku Kenkyū* **40**, 96–102 (in Japanese).

Hiura, U., and Heta, H., 1952c. Studies on the disease resistance of barley varieties, IV. *Nōgaku Kenkyū*, **40**, 127–130 (in Japanese).

Hiura, U., and Heta, H., 1953. Studies on the disease resistance of barley. A preliminary. *Nōgaku Kenkyū* **41**, 59–68 (in Japanese).

Hiura, U., and Heta, H., 1954. Studies on the disease resistance of barley, V. *Nōgaku Kenkyū* **41**, 145–156 (in Japanese).

Hoops, J., 1905. "Waldbäume und Kulturpblanzen," p. 280.

Huber, A., 1932. Ueber den Wintertypus der Gerste. *Z. Zücht. Reihe A.* **17**, 217–227.

Ikata, S., 1941. Wheat and barley of ancient Japan, with special reference to their origin. *Nōgyō Keizai Kenkyū* **17**(4), 78–101 (in Japanese).

Johnson, I. J., and Åberg, E., 1943. The inheritance of brittle rachis in barley. *J. Am. Soc. Agr.* **35**, 101–106.

Kakizaki, Y., and Suzuki, S., 1937. Physiologic studies on the earing of wheat plants. *Rept. Agr. Expt. Sta. Japan* **3**(1), 4–92 (in Japanese).

Kashiwada, S., 1930. On the glutinous vs. non-glutinous characters and their inheritance in barley. *Proc. Crop Sci. Soc. Japan* **2**, 193–194 (in Japanese).

Kihara, H., 1947. "Ancestors of Wheat Plants," p. 122. Sōgensha, Tokyo (in Japanese).

Körnicke, F., 1885. "Arten und Varietäten des Getreides," p. 470. Paul Parey, Berlin.

Körnicke, F., 1908. Die Entstehung und das Verhalten neuer Getreidevarietäten. *Arch. Biontol. Berlin* **2**, 393–437.

Lambert, J. W., and Liang, T. J., 1952. Studies of various characters of six-rowed segregates from crosses between two-rowed and six-rowed barleys. *Agron. J.* **44**, 364–369.

Larionow, D., 1929. Zur Frage über den phylogenetischen Zusammenhang zwischen zweizeiliger und vierzeiliger Gerste (*Hordeum sativum distichum* L. und *H. vulgare polystichum* Doll.). *Angew. Botan.* **11**, 274–284.

Liebscher, G., 1889. Die Erscheinungen der Vererbung bei einen Kreuzungsprodukt zweier Varietäten von *Hordeum sativum*. *Jena. Z. Naturw.* **23**, 215.

Mansfeld, R., 1950. Das Morphologische System der Saatgerste. *Züchter* **20**, 8–24.

Matsuo, T., 1952. Genecological studies on cultivated rice. *Bull. Natl. Inst. Agr. Sci. Ser. D.* No. 3, p. 111 (Japanese with English summary).

Mayler, J. L., and Stanford, E. H., 1942. Color inheritance in barley. *J. Am. Soc. Agr* **34**, 427–436.

Netolitzky, F., 1926. Beziehungen zwischen Getreidearten und Menschenrassen. *Fortschr. Landwirtsch.* **1**, 26–29.

Nishikado, Y., Takahashi, R., and Hiura, U., 1951. Studies on the disease resistance in barley, I. *Ber. Ohara Inst. landwirtsch. Forsch. Kurashiki, Japan* **9**(4), 411–423.

Nowacki, A., 1920. "Anleitung zum Getreidebau," p. 243. Paul Parey, Berlin.

Oinuma, T., 1952. Karyomorphology of cereals. *Biol. J. Okayama Univ.* **1**, 12–71.

Oka, H., 1953. Phylogenetic differentiation of the cultivated rice plant, I. *Japan. J. Breed.* **3**(2), 33–43 (Japanese with English summary).

Orlov, A. A., 1931. The most important agronomical and botanical forms of barley studied on the background of the collection of barleys in the possession of the Institute of Plant Industry and the principal varieties of spring barley in U.S.S.R. *Bull. Appl. Botany Genet. Plant Breeding U.S.S.R.* **27**(2), 329–381 (Russian with English summary).

Raum, H., 1930. Vergleichende morphologische Sortenstudien an Getreide. *Z. Zücht. Reihe A.* **15**, 309–344.

Rimpau, W., 1892. Die genetische Entwicklung der verschiedenen Formen unserer Saatgerste. *Landwirtsch. Jahrb.* **21**, 699–702.

Sakai, K., and Nakayama, H., 1953. Genetical competition between upland rice and paddy rice bearing red seeds. *Japan J. Breed.* **3**(1), 60 (in Japanese).

Schiemann, E., 1921a. Genetische Studien an Gerste, I. *Z. indukt. Abstamm.-u. Vererbungsl.* **26**, 109–143.

Schiemann, E., 1921b. Genetische Studien an Gerste, II. *Z. indukt. Abstamm.-u. Vererbungsl.* **27**, 104–133.

Schiemann, E., 1932. Entstehung der Kulturpflanzen. *Handbuch Vererbungsw.* **3**, p. 377.

Schiemann, E., 1939. Neue Probleme der Gerstenphylogenie. *Züchter* **12**, 145–147.

Schiemann, E., 1951a. Neue Gerstenformen aus Ost-Tibet und ein weiterer Fund von *Hordeum agriocrithon* Åberg. *Ber. deut. botan. Ges.* **64**, 57–69.

Schiemann, E., 1951b. New results on the history of cultivated cereals. *Heredity* **5**(3), 305–320.

Schulz, A., 1912. Die Geschichte der Saatgerste. *Z. Naturw.* **83**, 197–233.

Schulz, A., 1916. Ueber die nackte und beschalte Saatgerste der alten Aegypter. *Ber. deut. botan. Ges.* **34**, 607–619.

Smith, L., 1951. Cytology and genetics of barley. *Botan. Rev.* **17** (1,3,5), 1–51, 133–202, 285–355.

Stebbins, G. L., Jr., 1950. "Variation and evolution in plants," p. 643. Columbia Univ. Press, New York.

Syakudo, K., 1947. Inheritance of the awn length and the quantitative function of the causal genes in their length determination in barley. Mimeographed (Japanese with English summary).

Takahashi, R., 1942. Studies on the classification and the geographic distribution of the Japanese barley varieties, I. *Ber. Ohara Inst. landwirtsch, Forsch. Kurashiki, Japan* **9**(1), 71–90.

Takahashi, R., 1943. Studies on the classification and the geographic distribution of the Japanese barley varieties, II. *Nōgaku Kenkyū* **35**, 25–30 (in Japanese).

Takahashi, R., 1947. Studies on the classification and the geographic distribution of the Japanese barley varieties, VI. *Nōgaku Kenkyū* **37**, 132–136 (in Japanese).

Takahashi, R., 1949. Studies on the classification and geographic distribution of the barley varieties, IX. *Nōgaku Kenkyū* **38**, 77–80 (in Japanese).

Takahashi, R., 1951. Studies on the classification and the geographic distribution of the Japanese barley varieties, II. *Ber. Ohara Inst. landwirtsch. Forsch. Kurashiki, Japan* **9**(4), 383–398.

Takahashi, R., and Yamamoto, J., 1949. Studies on the classification and the geographic distribution of barley varieties, VIII. *Nōgaku Kenkyū* **38**, 41–43 (in Japanese).

Takahashi, R., and Yamamoto, J., 1950. Studies on the classification and the geographic distribution of the Japanese barley varieties, XII. *Nōgaku Kenkyū* **39**, 25–32 (in Japanese).

Takahashi, R., and Yamamoto, J., 1951a. Studies on the classification and the geographic distribution of the Japanese barley varieties, III. *Ber. Ohara Inst. landwirtsch. Forsch. Kurashiki, Japan* **9**(4), 399–410.

Takahashi, R., and Yamamoto, J., 1951b. Studies on the classification and the geographic distribution of barley varieties, XV. *Nōgaku Kenkyū* **39**, 81–90 (in Japanese).

Takahashi, R., and Yamamoto, J., 1951c. Physiology and genetics of ear emergency in barley and wheat, I. *Nōgaku Kenkyū* **40**, 13–24 (in Japanese).

Takahashi, R., Yamamoto, J., and Itano, Y., 1948. Studies on the classification and the geographic distribution of the Japanese barley varieties, VII. *Nōgaku Kenkyū* **38**, 5–10 (in Japanese).

Takahashi, R., Yamamoto, J., Yasuda, S., and Itano, Y., 1953a. Inheritance and linkage studies in barley. *Ber. Ohara Inst. landwirtsch. Forsch. Kurashiki, Japan* **10**(1), 29–52.

Takahashi, R., Yasuda, S., Yamamoto, J., and Shiojiri, I., 1953b. Physiology and genetics of ear emergency in barley and wheat, II. *Nōgaku Kenkyū* **40**, 157–168 (in Japanese).

Takahashi, R., Yasuda, S., Yamamoto, J., and Shiojiri, I., 1954. Physiology and genetics of ear emergency in barley and wheat, III. *Nōgaku Kenkyū* **41**, 87–96 (in Japanese).

Takezaki, Y., 1927. The inheritance of the ear length and awn length in barley, with special reference to their analysis and the determination of their qualifying value. *Z. indukt. Abstamm.-u. Vererbungsl. Suppl.* **2**, 1447–1454.

Tschermak, E., 1914. Die Verwerkung der Bastardierung für phylogenetische Fragen in der Getreidegruppe. *Z. Zücht.* **2**, 291–312.

Turesson, G., 1932. Die Genenzentrum theorie und das Entwicklungszentrum der Pflanzenart. *Kl. Fysiograf. Sällsk. Lund Förhandl.* **2**(6), 1–11.

Ubisch, G., 1915. Analyse eines Falles von Bastardatavismus und Faktorenkoppelung bei Gerste. *Z. indukt. Abstamm.-u. Vererbungsl.* **16**, 226–237.

Ubisch, G., 1919. Beitrag zu einer Faktorenanalyse von Gerste, II. *Z. indukt. Abstamm.-u. Vererbungsl.* **20**, 65–117.

Ubisch, G., 1921. Beitrag zu einer Faktorenanalyse von Gerste, III. *Z. indukt. Abstamm.-u. Vererbungsl.* **25**, 198–210.

Vavilov, N. I., 1926. Studies on the origin of cultivated plants. *Bull. Appl. Botany Gen. Plant Breeding U.S.S.R.* **16**(2), 1–248 (Russian with English summary).

Vavilov, N. I., 1927. Geographical regularities in the distribution of the genes of cultivated plants. *Bull. Appl. Botany Genet. Plant Breeding U.S.S.R.* **17**(3), 411–428.

Vavilov, N. I., 1935. "Botanical-Geographic Principle of Selection." United Publishing House, Moscow, U.S.S.R. (translated in U.S.A.).

Vavilov, N. I., 1940. The new systematics of cultivated plants. *in* "The New Systematics" (Huxley), pp. 549–566. Oxford Univ. Press, London.

Vavilov, N. I., and Bukinich, D. D., 1929. Agricultural Afghanistan. *Bull. Appl. Botany Genet. Plant Breeding U.S.S.R. Suppl.* **33**, 1–610.

Wada, E., and Akihama, K., 1934. Varietal differences in the expression of spring habit in wheat in relation to their geographic distribution, and its significance to breeding. *Proc. Crop Sci. Soc. Japan* **6**, 428–434 (in Japanese).

Willis, J. C., 1922. "Age and Area." Cambridge Univ. Press, London.

Woodward, R. W., 1941. Inheritance of a melanin-like pigment in the glumes and caryopses of barley. *J. Agr. Research* **63**(1), 21–28.

Woodward, R. W., 1949. The inheritance of fertility in the lateral florets of the four barley groups. *J. Am. Soc. Agr.* **41**, 317–322.

Woodward, R. W., and Thieret, J. W., 1953. A genetic study of complementary genes for purple lemma, palea, and pericarp in barley (*Hordeum vulgare* L.). *Agron. J.* **45**, 182–185.

Author Index to Volume VII

A

Åberg, E., 228–235, 238, 239, 242, 244, 246, 252, 262, 263
Abraham, E. P., 5, 6, 40, 42
Abramson, S., 205, 224
Ahrenfeldt, R. H., 146, 175
Akiba, T., 10, 34, 40
Akihama, K., 254, 266
Alexander, D. C., 35, 45
Alexander, H. E., 12, 40
Allison, J. E., 148, 175
Anders, M. V., 187, 198, 199, 221, 226
Antonitis, J. J., 198, 221
Armitage, P., 30, 40
Astaurov, B. L., 48, 52, 56, 57, 59, 60, 88
Atwood, K. C., 28, 29, 32, 40
Auerbach, C., 39, 43
Avery, O. T., 12, 40

B

Baker, A. S., 152, 175
Baltzer, F., 140, 175
Baron, A. L., 5
Barth, L. G., 145, 168, 169, 175, 176
Barth, L. J., 168, 169, 176
Basden, E. B., 51, 52, 56, 63, 86
Bauer, H., 124, 125, 132
Beadle, G. W., 96, 98, 132, 138
Beale, G. H., 14, 16, 26, 40
Beermann, W., 125, 132
Bellamy, W. D., 11, 40
Belser, N. O., 28, 35, 45
Berg, K. H., 229, 263
Berger, H., 30, 41
Berrie, G. K., 118, 132
Berrill, N. J., 148, 176
Bertani, G., 11, 36, 38, 41, 42
Betz-Bareau, M., 10, 42
Biesinger, D. I., 148, 176
Bigger, J. W., 18, 41

Biometry Department, University College, London, 62, 79, 86
Bird, M. J., 62, 86, 99, 135
Blair, A. P., 141–144, 146, 150, 172, 173, 176
Blumenheim, U., 114, 137
Boche, R. D., 49, 88
Bohnhoff, M., 6, 36, 44
Bondi, A., 28, 41
Bornschein, H., 31, 41
Boyd, M. M. M., 62, 86
Brachet, J., 140, 146, 167, 169, 170, 176, 182
Bragg, A. N., 173, 176
Braun, W., 27, 29, 36, 41, 42
Briggs, R., 148, 154, 156–158, 160–162, 164, 167, 176–178
Briggs, R. W., 145, 153, 154, 158–161, 163, 171, 172, 176
Brncic, D., 100, 109, 122, 123, 132, 133
Brown, C. H., 13, 41
Brown, H. B., 223
Brown, W. H., 187, 197, 207, 208, 221, 225
Brücher, H., 228, 232, 263
Brunetto, A., 86
Bryson, V., 1, 3, 5, 7, 9, 11, 17, 20–25, 27, 32, 33, 36–39, 41–45
Bukinich, D. D., 266
Burchenal, J. H., 39, 41
Burla, H., 50–52, 55–57, 59, 60, 63, 64, 84, 86–88, 94, 100, 120, 122, 123, 130, 132–134
Bushnell, E. P., 149, 176
Bushnell, R. J., 149, 176
Buzzati-Traverso, Adriano A., 47, 49, 50, 56, 57, 60–63, 65–72, 74, 87

C

Cain, A. J., 50, 87
Carcona-Lynch, E., 205, 224
Carpenter, R. R., Jr., 20, 42

Subject Index to Volume VII

A

Abnormalities in domestic rabbit, 191, 195, 196, 200, 201, 208
  in Salientia, 151, 153, 154, 157, 159, 161, 165, 166
Achromosomal embryos in Salientia, 159, 160, 165
Adaptation in Barley, 254–257, 260–262
Aerobacter aerogenes, 28, 30
Alleles in domestic rabbit, 187, 188, 213
Amphibia, chromosomes, 149
  gametes, 139, 149
Androgenesis in Salientia, 140, 152, 156, 159, 165
Androgenetic haploids in Salientia, 156, 157, 159, 170, 171
Androgenetic hybrids in Salientia, 157–159, 165, 167, 168
Antibiotics in microbial drug resistance, 1, 6, 11, 16, 19, 23, 24, 28, 37–39

B

Bacillus cereus, 28
  megaterium, 3, 22, 25
Bacitracin, sensitivity to, in microorganisms, 4
Barley,
  adaptation, 254, 255, 256, 257, 260, 261, 262
  cerealia, 229, 234, 235, 246, 247
  characters, 228, 235, 238, 240, 242, 249–256, 258, 259–261
  chromosomes, 228
  environment, 237, 249, 250, 256, 261
  evolution, 227, 228, 234, 235, 237, 238, 246, 247, 249, 259
  gene distribution, geographical, 259, 260
  geographic differentiation, 228, 236, 240, 241, 244, 259
  geographic distribution, 236, 238, 249, 250, 255, 256, 257
  hybridization, 228, 237, 239, 243, 258, 261

migration, 227, 228, 237–239, 247, 249
  mildew resistance, 241, 242, 261
  mutations, 237, 242, 243, 245, 247, 248, 260, 261
  origin, 227–229, 232–239, 242, 243, 245, 251
  tetrastichum, 228
  variation, 237, 245, 247, 249, 251, 253, 257, 258
  wild species, 227–234, 238, 239, 250, 251, 261
Behavior in domestic rabbit, 201, 215, 218–220
Body growth in domestic rabbit, 210–213, 219, 220
Body size, abnormal, in domestic rabbit, 207–209
Body size, general, in domestic rabbit, 209

C

Caudata, embryology, 140
  hybridization, 139, 140
Cell permeability in drug resistance, 16
Chemical treatment of sperm in Salientia, 152–154, 156, 159, 160, 165
Chloramphenicol, sensitivity to, in microorganisms, 4
Chlortetracycline, sensitivity to, in microorganisms, 4
Chromosomal aberrations in Drosophila, 96, 99, 100, 118
Chromosomal variants in Diptera, 124, 125, 127
  in Drosophila, 96, 99, 100, 119, 120, 123
Chromosome combinations in Urodele hybrids, 140
Chromosomes in Amphibia, 149
  in Barley, 228
  in domestic rabbit, 187, 188, 202, 214, 220, 221
  in *Drosophila obscura*, 48, 54–57, 59–62, 73–75, 78, 79, 82, 84
  in Salientia, 141, 152, 153, 156–161, 165, 166, 167, 171

Cumulative Subject Index to Volumes I–VI

A

Achaete gene, **3** 85, 88, 90, 91, 104
Achondroplasia, cattle, **1** 223
Achromatium oxaliferum, cell structure of, **3** 6, 21
Acmaea, species maintenance, **2** 213–214
Acrididae, cytology, **4** 275, 277, 280–286, 288, 293, 297–302, 308, 320–321, 323–324
distribution, **4** 301–302, 305–310, 317
Adenine, synthesis of, Neurospora, **3** 36
Adenofibroma, rat, **2** 101
Aegilops, **2** 240, 243–245, 247–253
allopolyploidy, **1** 414, 417–418, 420
genetics of, **2** 264
genome homologies, **2** 243–245, 253
haploidy, **2** 252
hybrids, **2** 247–250
Aesculus, allopolyploidy, **1** 417
Agamogony, definition of, **3** 193
Agglutination, in cattle, **1** 153–155
in doves, **1** 141–153
in man, **1** 135–141; **6** 184, 185, 210, 211
Aging, Protozoa, **1** 325, 339
Agnatha, chromosomes, **4** 165
Agnathia, cattle, **1** 223–224
Agropyron, **2** 240, 245–251
allopolyploidy, **1** 415, 422
genome homologies, **2** 245–247
hybrids, **2** 245–249
"Alba" frequency in Colias, **6** 428–433, 446
"Alba" gene in Colias, see Colias
Albinism, **1** 220
in mouse, **4** 8
Alcaptonuria, biochemical genetics, **3** 33
Aleurodids, parthenogenesis in, **3** 198, 199, 201, 203, 206, 208, 209, 220
Alfalfa, genetics of, **1** 7, 40–47
Alleles, frequencies in human populations, see Human populations
multiple, see Multiple allelism

Allelic series in Neurospora, see Neurospora
Allium, allopolyploidy, **1** 417–418
autopolyploidy, **1** 407, 411
chromosomes, **2** 284–286, 289, 298
Allopolyploids, see also Amphidiploids, **1** 403–405, 411–427, 432–440; **2** 240–243, 247, 250
Allosynapsis, **1** 412
Allosyndesis, **1** 412–413, 432
Allyl isothiocyanate, as mutagen, **2** 322
Alpha-Radiations, **2** 272–273, 292–293, 303, 319–320, 326
Amaurotic idiocy, juvenile, **2** 71, 93
α-Aminoadipic acid, from lysine, **3** 51
p-Aminobenzoic acid, in Neurospora, **3** 53–55
Aminobutyric acid in Neurospora, **3** 49
Amphibia, chromosomes, **4** 167–177
Amphidiploid, see also Allopolyploids
in cotton, **4** 252–253, 255, 264
in Crespis, **1** 87
in Triticinae, **2** 241–242, 245, 249–250
with reference to evolution, **4** 250, 264
Amphimixis, human populations, **2** 69–71
Amphiploids, see Allopolyploids, amphidiploids
Amylase in silkworm, **5** 107, 108, 109
activity, **5** 108
Anas, species maintenance, **2** 223
Anastomosis in Aspergillus, **5** 142, 146, 177, 183, 219
Androgenesis, definition of, **3** 194
Andropadus, sibling species, **2** 226
Andropogon furcatus, mass selection in, **1** 5
Anemia, embryonic, in mouse, **4** 11–13
macrocytic, **4** 12–13
siderocytic, in flexed, **4** 11–12, 36
Aneuploidy, wheat, **2** 241
Angiosperms, incompatibility, **6** 235, 237, 277, 281
Anilocra, interference in, **3** 141

temperature mutants, **3** 35–37, 63
tetrad data, **6** 2–10, 12, 21, 22, 24, 27, 68, 69, 78–85
tetrad segregation, **6** 2, 14, 81, 82
threonine synthesis in, **3** 46–49
translocations, **6** 25, 29, 33
tryptophanless strain, **3** 38
tryptophan synthesis in, **3** 43–46
two-point crosses, **6** 62–69
Neurospora crassa, see Neurospora
Neurospora sitophila, thiamine synthesis in, **3** 55
Neurospora tetrasperma, chromosomes of, **3** 35
Neutrons, induction of mutation, **2** 272–273, 288–293, 296–299, 303–304, 318–320
Nicotiana, maternal inheritance, **2** 20–21
mutation, **2** 310
plasmon action, **2** 56
polyploidy, **1** 412, 414, 416–418, 422, 424
sterility, **2** 24
virus resistance, **2** 53
Nicotinic acid, in Neurospora, **3** 43–46
in silkworm, **5** 121, 122, 124–126, 129
Night blindness, cattle, **1** 227
Nightingale, speciation, **2** 215
Nitrogen mustard, as mutagen, **3** 38, 39
Nocomis, species maintenance, **2** 220
Nondisjunction in silkworm, **5** 241, 294, 295, 300, 302
Notch locus, Drosophila, **3** 107
Notch-type phenotype, Drosophila, **3** 79, 82–84, 86, 102
Notropis, species maintenance, **2** 220
Nuclear dimorphism, Protozoa, **1** 269–295
Nuclear element, observation of in bacteria, **3** 4, 5, 12–14, 16–18
Nuclear genes in Epilobium, see Epilobium
Nuclear structures in *E. coli*, **3** 15, 18
Nucleic acid, effect of radiations on, **2** 274, 297

O

Odonata, kinetochore structure, **2** 137
Oenothera, genetical symbols, **2** 3

genome changes, **2** 44–48
plastid inheritance, **2** 17–19, 49–52
position effect, **3** 73, 107–109
reciprocal differences in hybrids, **2** 16–19, 23, 31, 44–48, 55
Oligogenes, **1** 386
Open-pollinated corn, **3** 167, 172, 173, 175, 177, 185
Opuntia, **2** 214
Orchard grass, **1** 22–26
hybrids, **1**, 22–24
polyploidy, **1** 406, 408
sterility, **2** 24, 52
Ornithine, synthesis in chick, **3** 43
Ornithine cycle, in Neurospora, **3** 41, 42
Orthoptera, abnormalities, **4** 290, 310, 319–320, 325
chiasma, **4** 284–289, 293, 295, 300, 310, 312, 317–318, 321–322
chromosome number, **4** 269–279, 293, 299, 301–302, 304–309, 317–319, 321–325
chromosomes, **3** 212, 213, 216, 228, 229; **4** 270–316
crossing-over, **4** 289, 295, 300, 319, 322–323
cytology, **4** 269–278, 289–304, 317
euchromatin, see Euchromatin
evolution, see Evolution
genetics, **4** 321–325
heterochromatin, see Heterochromatin
hybrids, **4** 299, 325
intersexuality, **4** 299
meiosis, **4** 281–290, 292–293, 295, 297–298, 300, 309, 312, 315–316, 318, 320–321, 325
parthenogenesis, **3** 207, 210, 211, 214, 225, 226; **4** 271, 273, 299, 316–321
polyploidy, **4** 287
sex chromosomes, **4** 292–298
spermatogenesis, **4** 284, 286–288, 290, 312, 316, 322
taxonomy, **4** 268, 269, 271, 278, 296, 301, 303–304
translocations, see Translocations
Oryza sativa, mapping data, **3** 134
Osmotic pressure, cells, **2** 30–31, 39, 49
Ostracods, parthenogenetic polyploidy, **3** 228
Oxycoccus, polyploidy, **1** 411